A STRATIGRAPHICAL
INDEX OF CONODONTS

BRITISH MICROPALAEONTOLOGICAL SOCIETY SERIES

This series, published for the British Micropalaeontological Society, will gather together knowledge for a particular faunal group for specialist and non-specialist geologists alike. The scope of the series has been broadened to include the common elements of the fauna, whether index or long-ranging species, and to convey a broad impression of the fauna and allow the reader to identify common species as well as those of restricted stratigraphical range.

The synthesis of knowledge presented in the series will reveal its strengths and prove its usefulness to the practising micropalaeontologist, and those teaching and learning the subject. By identifying some of the gaps in the knowledge, the series will, it is believed, promote and stimulate further active research and investigation.

STRATIGRAPHICAL ATLAS OF FOSSIL FORAMINIFERA
Editors: D. G. JENKINS, The Open University, and J. W. MURRAY, Professor of Geology, University of Exeter
MICROFOSSILS FROM RECENT AND FOSSIL SHELF SEAS
Editors: J. W. NEALE, Professor of Micropalaeontology, University of Hull, and M. D. BRASIER, Lecturer in Geology, University of Hull
FOSSIL AND RECENT OSTRACODS
Editors: R. H. BATE, British Museum of Natural History, London, E. ROBINSON, Department of Geology, University College London, and L. SHEPPARD, British Museum of Natural History, London
A STRATIGRAPHICAL INDEX OF CALCAREOUS NANNOFOSSILS
Editor: A. R. LORD, Department of Geology, University College London
A STRATIGRAPHICAL INDEX OF CONODONTS
Editors: A. C. HIGGINS, Department of Geology, University of Sheffield, and R. L. AUSTEN, Department of Geology, University of Southampton
PALAEOBIOLOGY OF CONODONTS
Editor: R. J. ALDRIDGE, Department of Geology, University of Nottingham
CONODONTS: Investigative Techniques and Applications
Editor: R. L. AUSTIN, Department of Geology, University of Southampton

ELLIS HORWOOD SERIES IN GEOLOGY

Editors: D. T. DONOVAN, Professor of Geology, University College London and J. W. MURRAY, Professor of Geology, University of Exeter

This series aims to build up a library of books on geology which will include student texts and also more advanced works of interest to professional geologists and to industry. The series will include translations of important books recently published in Europe, and also books specially commissioned.

A GUIDE TO CLASSIFICATION IN GEOLOGY
J. W. MURRAY, Professor of Geology, University of Exeter
THE CENOZOIC ERA: Tertiary and Quaternary
C. POMEROL, Professor, University of Paris VI.
Translated by D. W. HUMPHRIES, Department of Geology, University of Sheffield, and E. E. HUMPHRIES, Edited by Professors D. CURRY and D. T. DONOVAN, University College London
INTRODUCTION TO PALAEOBIOLOGY: GENERAL PALAEONTOLOGY
B. ZIEGLER, Professor of Geology and Palaeontology, University of Stuttgart, and Director of the State Museum for Natural Science, Stuttgart.
FAULT AND FOLD TECTONICS
W. JAROSZEWSKI, Department of Geology, University of Warsaw
RADIOACTIVITY IN GEOLOGY
E. M. DURRANCE, Department of Geology, University of Exeter

A STRATIGRAPHICAL
INDEX OF CONODONTS

Editors:

A. C. HIGGINS, B.Sc., Ph.D., D.Sc.
Chief Paleontologist
Geological Survey of Canada, Calgary

and

R. L. AUSTIN, B.Sc., Ph.D.
Senior Lecturer, University of Southampton

AB

Published by
ELLIS HORWOOD LIMITED
Publishers · Chichester

for

THE BRITISH MICROPALAEONTOLOGICAL SOCIETY

First published in 1985 by
ELLIS HORWOOD LIMITED
Market Cross House, Cooper Street, Chichester,
West Sussex, PO19 1EB

The publisher's colophon is reproduced from James Gillison's drawing of the ancient Market Cross, Chichester

Distributors:

Australia, New Zealand, South-east Asia:
Jacaranda-Wiley Ltd., Jacaranda Press,
JOHN WILEY & SONS INC.
GPO Box 859, Brisbane, Queensland 4001, Australia

Canada:
JOHN WILEY & SONS CANADA LIMITED
·22 Worcester Road, Rexdale, Ontario, Canada

Europe, Africa:
JOHN WILEY & SONS LIMITED
Baffins Lane, Chichester, West Sussex, England

North and South America and the rest of the world:
Halsted Press: a division of
JOHN WILEY & SONS
605 Third Avenue, New York, NY 10158, USA

© **1985 British Micropalaeontological Society/
Ellis Horwood Limited**

British Library Cataloguing in Publication Data
A stratigraphical index of conodonts. –
(Ellis Horwood series in geology)
1. Conodonts 2. Paleontology – Great Britain
I. Higgins, A. C. II. Austin, R. L.
III. British Micropalaeontological Society
562'.2'.0941 QE899

Library of Congress Card No. 85–16351

ISBN 0–85312–641–0 (Ellis Horwood Limited)
ISBN 0–470–20232–7 (Halsted Press)

Typeset by Ellis Horwood Limited
Printed in Great Britain by Butler & Tanner, Somerset

Contents

Contributors

Richard J. Aldridge,
Department of Geology, University of Nottingham, University Park, Nottingham NG7 2RD, England.

Ronald L. Austin,
Department of Geology, The University, Southampton SO9 5NH, England

Robert P. Barnes,
British Geological Survey, Murchison House, West Mains Road, Edinburgh EH9 3LA, Scotland.

Stig M. Bergström,
Department of Geology and Mineralogy, The Ohio State University, 125 S. Oval Mall, Columbus, OH 43210, U.S.A.

Martin D. Brasier,
Department of Geology, University of Hull, Cottingham Road, Hull HU6 7RX, England.

Christine Castle,
40, Downend Road, Kingswood, Bristol BS15 1SE, England.

Michael Drummond,
Paleoservices Ltd., Unit 15, Paramount Industrial Estate, Sandown Road, Watford WD2 4XA, England.

Alan C. Higgins,
Institute of Sedimentary and Petroleum Geology, Geological Survey of Canada, 3303– 33rd St., N.W. Calgary, Alta T2L 2A7, Canada.

William T. Kirchgasser,
Department of Geological Sciences, The State University College at Potsdam, Potsdam, New York 13676, U.S.A.

Michael J. Orchard,
Geological Survey of Canada, 100 West Pender, Vancouver, V6B 1R8, Canada.
Adrian W. A. Rushton,
British Geological Survey, Nicker Hill, Keyworth, Nottingham, NG12 5GG, England
Peter M. Sadler,
Department of Earth Sciences, University of California, Riverside, CA 92521, U.S.A.
Norman M. Savage,
Department of Geology, University of Oregon, Eugene, OR 97403, U.S.A.
E. Brian Selwood,
Department of Geology, The University, North Park Road, Exeter EX4 4QE, England
George D. Sevastopulo,
Department of Geology, Trinity College, Dublin 2, Ireland.
Ian J. Stewart,
B.P. Petroleum Development Ltd., Farburn Industrial Estate, Dyce, Aberdeen AB2 0PB, Scotland.
Andrew Swift,
Department of Geology, University of Nottingham, University Park, Nottingham NG7 2RD, England.
W. John Varker,
Department of Earth Sciences, The University, Leeds LS2 9JT, England.

Preface

The number of members within the Conodont Group of the British Micropalaeontological Society has always been small, and formal meetings of the Group have seldom been held. Nevertheless, the senior members of the Group have kept in mind one of the original aims of the Society which was to summarize the microfaunal sequence of the British area bearing in mind that many of the internationally recognized stratotype sections are within the area covered by the Society. The visit of the Pander Society of Conodont Workers to Britain in 1985 as ECOS IV provided the incentive for this volume and in 1982 planning of the project commenced.

The intention was to involve all persons engaged in the study of conodonts in Britain and thus to further a second aim of the Society, namely to encourage collective projects. Perusal of this volume will reveal many gaps in the conodont record of the British area reflecting, in part, the small number of researchers and, in part, the lack of suitable host-rocks in many British sections, particularly in type areas. To have pinpointed these gaps, in the hope that new researchers and maybe new techniques will fill them, represents a good measure of progress. At the same time, many records of conodont occurrences in the area have gone unnoticed, even by specialists, because they were reported in local journals or were merely a brief reference in a large volume or in a memoir. The contributors to this volume have attempted to record the occurrence of these in an attempt to fill some of the gaps.

The format of this volume largely follows that of the first volume in the Special Publication Series of the British Micropalaeontological Society. The information in each chapter has been provided within a uniform format, but each chapter is distinctive in reflecting both the variation in amount of information available and the emphasis of the individual contributors. However, it has not always been possible to produce complete uniformity within and between chapters. The most obvious discrepancies concern the variations in the illustrations of specimens. Some are scanning electron microscopy photographs, others are optical photographs, and a few are reproductions of original photographs. The variations in magnification are often intentional. Biostratigraphically, the intention is to illustrate the ranges of diagnostic and characteristic species, and to summarize the zones recognized in the British area. Occasionally, for completeness, internationally important zonal forms either not represented or not yet recognized in Britain are included either in the text or on the range charts. Species are illustrated and briefly diagnosed in the plates and plate explanations respectively.

The volume is aimed at both the specialist and non-specialist. We have endeavoured not to include new taxa. Detailed descriptions and illustrations of most species are to be found in the *Catalogue of Conodonts*. The revised *Treatise on Invertebrate Paleontology* volume on conodonts together with the specialist conodont symposia volumes provide additional detailed information and references. Within this volume are to be found many new records of British conodonts. The extensive bibliographies bring together for the first time the diverse literature on previously known records.

In view of both the historic and the continuing importance of the Palaeozoic sections in Britain, it is appropriate that the British Micropalaeontological Society should produce this volume. The importance is further emphasized by the place occupied by conodonts as one of the foremost microfaunal groups present in Palaeozoic rocks of value in applied micropalaeontology. Although they are less well known than some other Palaeozoic groups in Britain, published work on British conodonts has made important contributions to both stratigraphy and palaeontology. It is anticipated that this volume will maintain the tradition.

A large portion of the information contained in this volume has resulted from research supported by government grants often in the form of studentships awarded by the Department of Scientific and Industrial Research and by the National Environment Research Council. The facilities offered by each contributor's department is also much appreciated. We also thank those individuals who have provided copyright clearance. Photographs of specimens bearing registration numbers of the British Geological Survey are reproduced by permission of the Director, British Geological Survey: Crown Copyright reserved. We also acknowledge previously published material covered by copyright, which has been made available thanks to the Trustees of the British Museum (Natural History) and by the Palaeontological Association. The National Coal Board is thanked for permission to publish results from their borehole cores. D. B. Smith and J. Pattison (British Geological Survey) kindly provided borehole samples and stratigraphic information. A number of individuals have offered advice and assistance. We wish to thank in particular Professor D. L. Dineley and Professor M. R. House. D. Moore has provided much information and assisted with editing. We also thank B. Thornbury, K. Campbell, P. Jackson, M. Keeley, Rio Fin Ex and Ennex Ltd. for providing specimens. We thank S. M. Black who kindly provided the original photograph of the specimen illustrated on the front cover. Clerical assistance has been provided by J. Angell, F. Bradbury, M. Cornforth, B. Vanlier and J. Wilkinson. The photographic skills of D. Jones, J. Jones, P. Krauss and B. Marsh are much appreciated as also is the cartographic work of A. Dunkley and T. Oliveric. Our thanks also go to each contributor and to the encouragement of officers of the British Micropalaeontological Society. The Editors also sincerely thank James Gillison and the staff of Ellis Horwood Ltd. for their constant advice during the production of this volume.

A. C. Higgins and R. L. Austin

1

Introduction

R. L. Austin and A. C. Higgins

Conodonts were first recorded by Christian Pander (1856) whose monograph on Silurian fossil fish from Eastern Europe included illustrations of denticulate tooth-like structures called conodonts. It was not until Ulrich and Bassler (1926) demonstrated their biostratigraphic usefulness some 70 years later that systematic attention was paid to these fossilized curiosities. Even so, they have not come to prominence until the last two decades, aided by landmark publications such as the textbook written by Lindström (1964), the four volume catalogue of conodonts (Ziegler, 1973, 1975, 1977, 1981) and a volume of the *Treatise on Invertebrate Paleontology* (Moore, 1962; Clark *et al.* 1981a). In addition, six special symposia volumes (Sweet and Bergström, 1971; Lindström and Ziegler, 1972; Rhodes, 1973; Barnes, 1976; Martinsson and Bengtson, 1983; Clark, 1984) have been published. Many of these publications owe their being to the presence of the Pander Society, an informal society of those interested in conodonts.

1.1 EXTRACTION TECHNIQUES

One of the reasons for the usefulness of conodonts is their resistance to both mechanical and chemical attack. This also means that they are prone to reworking from older into younger sediments but this does not usually present major problems. Most conodonts are recovered as isolated elements after rock samples, usually carbonates, have been digested in acetic, formic or monochloric acid. The sieved insolubles are dried and the heavy residue is separated from the light fraction either by ultrasonic separation (Dow, 1960, 1965) or more usually by the use of heavy liquids such as bromoform or tetrabromoethane. The techniques have been described by Collinson (1963) and Higgins and Spinner (1969). The dangers have been pointed out by Hauf and Airey (1980).

1.2 MORPHOLOGY

(a) External morphology

Individual conodonts range in size from 0.2 to 5 mm; they are denticulate and composed of calcium phosphate with a mineral composition close to apatite. They range from the late Pre-Cambrian to late Triassic in age. Their colour varies from amber to black, becoming transparent with increasing heat.

Shape patterns fall into three main groups: coniform elements which are like cones (cones); ramiform elements which are blade-like with two or more processes (blades); pectiniform elements which have a blade and a platform (platforms). Pectiniform and ramiform elements can develop from the coniform type, and transitional forms can be seen in early Ordovician rocks. In the pectiniform and ramiform elements it is the basal point which is more strongly modified, expanding into branches, lobes and ledges that may carry denticulate patterns on their upper faces. On Lower Ordovician pectiniform elements having three processes, each process has a row of denticles which begins at one of the edges of the cusp. In these forms the cusp is still high, sharp and slender. More evolved conodonts of the pectiniform type have a relatively low cusp and the denticles of the anterior process are fused to form a blade. The posterior process may either form a continuation of the blade or expand into a platform with ridge and denticle patterns. The third or lateral process is reduced in many stocks, but appears again and again in the course of later evolution. This homeomorphic tendency is a recurrent feature of conodont evolution and indicates a strong correlation between form and function.

The ramiform elements can have one to four denticle rows beginning at the base of the cusp, and in more evolved forms at least one denticle row continues as a long slender process. The cusp is thin, high and pointed, and several of the denticles may also be quite prominent. One process, commonly the posterior one, is usually longer than the cusp and other denticles. The denticles may rise thin and erect at 90° from this bar or be reclined at various angles. In ramiforms with more than one prominent process, the arch formed by each pair of processes may be quite sharp and the denticles of different processes point in different directions. The space between the processes may be occupied by the basal filling, when present. This applies to the earliest pectiniform (platform), conodonts as well as to all the ramiforms.

The descriptive terms applicable to these elements are illustrated in Figs. 1.1. and 1.2. (For further discussion see Sweet, in Clark *et al.*, 1981).

Fig. 1.1 – Types of conodont element based on Sweet, 1981. (a) Geniculate coniform element where the posterior margin of cusp joins the upper edge of base to enclose an acute angle. (b) Non-geniculate coniform element where there is a smooth transition from the posterior cusp margin to the upper basal edge. In lateral view the posterior margin and upper basal edge form a straight or smoothly arcuate line. (c) Alate ramiform. A bilaterally symmetrical element that lacks an anterior process, but has a posterior process and a lateral process on each side of the cusp. (d) Tertiopedate ramiform. Asymmetric element with a posterior process and a lateral process on each side of the cusp; the posterior process is commonly long and denticulate. (e) Digyrate ramiform. Bilaterally asymmetric element with short adenticulate process and longer denticulate inner and outer-lateral processes, the distal extremities of which commonly twist in opposite directions. (f) Bipennate ramiform. An element with an anterior and a posterior process; the posterior process is commonly longer than the anterior process, which may also be curved or deflected towards one side and may even be adenticulate. (g) Dolabrate ramiform. An element consisting of a cusp and a posterior process; this element is commonly pick-shaped in lateral view. (h) Multiramate ramiform. An element with more than four basic processes. (i) Quadriramate ramiform. An element with anterior and posterior processes and a lateral process on either side of the midplane. (j) Planate pectiniform. An element with conspicuous lateral ledges, brims or platforms flanking one or more of its processes and with an attachment surface on its undersurface distinguished by a zone of recessive basal margin, which at least partially surrounds a basal pit that has groove-like extensions beneath at least the primary process. (k) Scaphate pectiniform. A laterally elaborate element with an underside marked by a capacious, commonly cup-like basal cavity. (l) Carminate pectiniform. An element with two primary processes which are anterior and posterior and a longitudinal axis that is straight, or essentially so in lateral view. (m) Angulate pectiniform. An arched element with two primary processes which are anterior and posterior. (n) Segminate pectiniform. An element with only one primary process which is anterior. (o) Pastinate pectiniform. An element with three primary processes which are anterior, posterior and lateral.

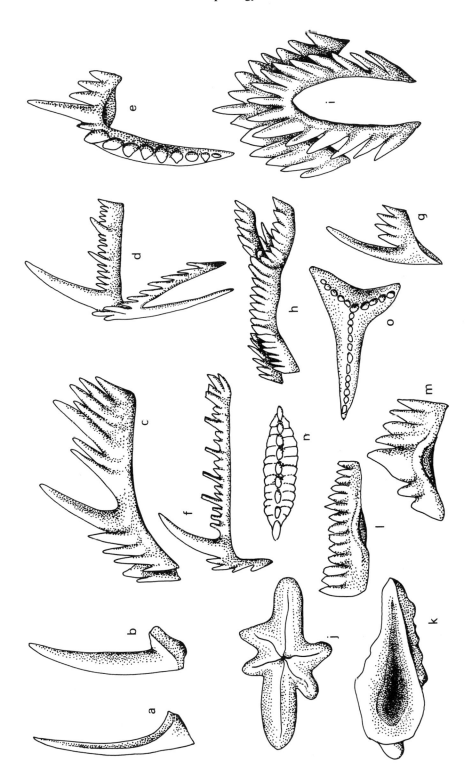

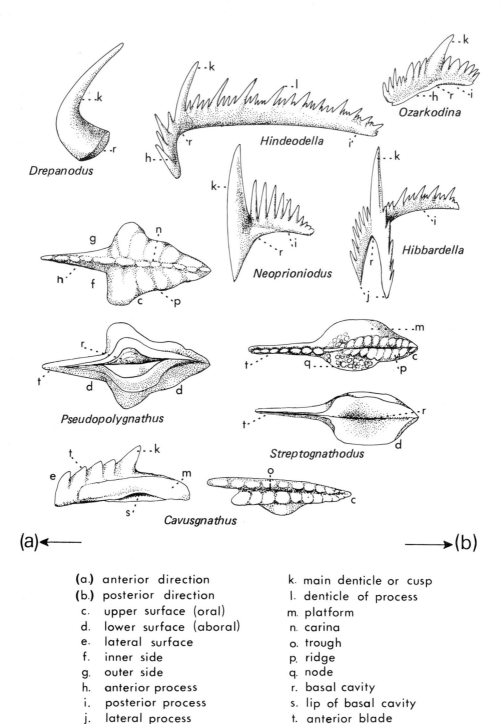

(a)⟵   ⟶(b)

(a.) anterior direction   k. main denticle or cusp
(b.) posterior direction   l. denticle of process
  c. upper surface (oral)   m. platform
  d. lower surface (aboral)   n. carina
  e. lateral surface   o. trough
  f. inner side   p. ridge
  g. outer side   q. node
  h. anterior process   r. basal cavity
  i. posterior process   s. lip of basal cavity
  j. lateral process   t. anterior blade

Fig. 1.2 – Morphological terms and orientation used to describe conodont elements.

(b) Internal morphology

Recent studies on the internal structure of conodonts have led to a better understanding of the
fundamental structure of the elements and their
evolutionary relationships. Some early conodonts
are entirely hyaline in structure but the majority
are both hyaline and include white matter. The
composition of the white matter is unknown and
whereas the hyaline material is amber and trans-
lucent the white matter is opaque in transmitted
light. It may well be that the white matter is
simply structureless hyaline matter. The white
matter is concentrated in the denticles, particularly in the main denticle situated above the basal
cavity.

Conodonts have growth lamellae added in an
outward sequence like the growth layers of wood
but, in the white matter, lamellae are not observed.
This destruction occurred during growth since the
outermost and hence youngest layer is always
hyaline. The white matter may also be recrystal-
lized. The conodont lamellae terminate at the base
of the unit, inside the basal cavity and surrounding
the basal cavity on the lower face of the base; the
edges of successive lamellae appear as concentric
lines surrounding the oldest lamella, which is
wrapped about the tip of the basal cavity. In
many conodonts, and probably originally occurring
in all, the cavity is filled by a basal plate which is
of a broadly similar composition to the conodont
but often different in colour. The internal structure of the basal plate is' the same as that of the
conodont and the growth lamellae are continuous
from one to the other.

It is possible to recognize three distinct groups
based on the ultrastructure (Bengtson, 1976).

Protoconodonts are the most ancient group
and comprise simple cones with deep basal cavities
built of hyaline phosphates with abundant organic
matter. Growth was initiated at the top with
younger lamellae added by internal secretion
in successive layers towards the base. There is no
division into conodont proper and basal plate.

Paraconodonts are mainly simple cones built
of hyaline phosphates with somewhat less organic
matter. A concentric growth centre at the tip is

added to by relatively few thick lamellae, growing
in a basal direction. The lamellae may barely
overlap on the upper and lower edges, leaving a
deep and often wide basal cavity. No basal plates
are known. The number of growth lamellae is
small compared with euconodonts and the lamellae
are thicker.

Euconodonts consist of a conodont proper
and a basal plate. Both are constructed of lamellae,
but in the former they are added orally whilst in
the latter they are added aborally. The lamellae
of the basal plate and of the conodont proper
appear to have been laid down simultaneously.

(c) Surface ornamentation

The application of electron microscopy Lindström and Ziegler (1981a) not only has greatly
improved the illustration of conodont elements
but also has made visible the different kinds of
micro-ornament first observed by Ziegler (1970).
Such micro-ornamentation is only seen in well preserved material where it takes the form of striations, reticulate patterns of ridges, furrows and
denticles which are of use in taxonomic problems.
Lindström and Ziegler (1971) described six types
of primary micro-ornamentation in the Pandero-
dontacae and this was applied to the Prioniodontidae by Lindström *et al.* (1972). The Pandero-
dontidae has been discussed by Barnes *et al.*
(1970) and the Acanthodontidae by Barnes and
Slack (1975).

The six types of primary micro-ornament
have been summarized by Lindström and Ziegler
(1971) and include the following.

Smooth surfaces occur in localized areas on
all element types. They usually occur in coniform
types on anterior and posterior margins and on the
apices. In pectiniform types of elements, such areas
occur between denticles and adjacent to the carina.

Fine striations composed of crystallites
aligned parallel to each other and commonly to
the length axis of the unit are a common structure
on many elements and are also concentrated in
certain areas. They are less than 0.7 μm in width.

Coarse striations greater than 0.7 μm occur
in coniform elements as a common and more continuous feature, and Barnes and Slack (1975)

concluded that they have an internal counterpart which they termed radial lamellae. Pectiniform and ramiform elements commonly have coarse lamellae on the denticles, often converging towards the apex of each denticle. Coarse denticle striations are also formed by crystallites.

Basal wrinkles occur in a 50–100 μm zone around the basal margin. They have only been observed in *Panderodus* where wrinkles 1–2 μm wide form bundles.

Longitudinal furrows are known only in some Panderodontacea where they occur as a furrow extending the entire length of the unit on its inner side penetrating to the basal cavity. Lindström and Ziegler (1971) suggested that the furrow could have functioned for the insertion of muscles.

Microdenticles and dental pits: microdenticles occur along the posterior margins of the Prionio-dontacae; dental pits occur both on the posterior edge of proximal denticles in ramiform elements and on the nodes of some pectiniform elements.

1.3 NATURAL ASSEMBLAGES OF ELEMENTS

Occasionally, groups of conodonts are found to-gether on bedding surfaces. These conodont assemblages are the remnants of part of or all the original conodont apparatus and are known from rocks of the Cambrian (Landing, 1977; Miller and Rushton, 1973), Ordovician (Barnes, 1967; Aldridge, 1982), Silurian (Rexroad and Nicoll, 1964; Pollock, 1969), Devonian (Mash-kova, 1972; Lange, 1968), Carboniferous (Austin and Rhodes, 1969; Rhodes and Austin, 1981, in press; Schmidt, 1934, 1950; Scott, 1934, 1942, 1973; Dubois, 1943; Rhodes, 1952, 1953a, 1953b, 1962; Schmidt and Müller, 1964; Higgins, 1975, 1981a) and Permian Systems (Behnken, 1975). These assemblages include bedding plane associa-tions which are thought to have suffered little post-mortem disturbance, coprolitic assemblages which may or may not be remnants of a single animal and fused clusters (usually of a single element) which are found in acid residues. Assem-blages of different ages vary in form. Those of Cambrian age consist entirely of simple cones arranged systematically in an arc, whereas younger assemblages have ramiform elements, coniform and

pectiniform elements or ramiform and pectiniform elements (see Rhodes and Austin, 1981, for further discussion).

The best-known assemblages, from the Carb-oniferous System, clearly show the bilateral symmetry of the more advanced apparatus and the mirror image nature of elements on both sides of the apparatus. However, not all paired elements are mirror images and it seems probable that many elements were strongly asymmetric. Lane (1969) has defined a number of classes of symmetry.

As natural assemblages are rare, the last two decades have seen many attempts to reconstruct the apparatus from discrete element analyses. The resulting multielement species thus constructed now form the basis of the classification of cono-donts in most parts of the Palaeozoic Era and Triassic System.

Reconstruction of apparatuses may be achieved in many ways. Component elements of an appara-tus often have similar denticulations, fluorescences, colours, sizes and stratigraphic ranges. Computer analysis of such similarities together with evidence of association provided by assemblage and fused cluster associations will indicate element affinity. Except for the natural assemblages, actual numbers of elements in an apparatus are difficult to deter-mine but even this problem may be resolved by X-ray analysis of the containing rock.

The recognition of conodont apparatuses involves taxonomic criteria and judgements, including the fundamental assumption that discrete elements were originally associated, and the acceptance of models of such associations and agreed criteria for their reconstruction and descrip-tion. Few contemporary conodont workers would doubt these basic assumptions, but there is dis-agreement on some aspects of the criteria involved in the recognition of the original assemblages and varying degrees of uncertainty concerning the most appropriate models and their description. All the evidence from apparatus reconstruction suggests that the number of major skeletal patterns may have been small. Several attempts have been made to classify apparatuses according to such patterns, or on the basis of distinctive features or structures shared by all the elements in apparatuses of a given plan (Rhodes, 1962; Klapper and Philip, 1971; Baesemann, 1973; Jeppsson, 1971, 1972; Sweet and Bergström, 1972. Lindström, 1973).

As it may be premature to suggest a classification of apparatuses or a nomenclature for them, a purely descriptive approach has been advocated by Sweet (1981), which is genetically non-committal. It was suggested that conodont skeletal apparatuses, however reconstructed or interpreted, be described simply, depending on whether they are composed of respectively one, two, three, four, five, six or seven morphologically distinct element types and termed unimembrate or multimembrate, the latter being subdivided into sub-categories.

Although there are problems of subjectivity with any classificatory scheme, it should be pointed out that there is no intended implication that all apparatuses of a given category are alike in element construction. The intention is only to convey the information that the apparatus is (or is thought to be) composed of a certain number of different element types. It should also be emphasized that the descriptive terminology refers only to the number of morphologically distinct types of element and not to the number of discrete elements.

Perhaps more important than a scheme for describing the element type composition of skeletal apparatuses is a means of identifying and naming homologous, or supposedly homologous, positions within the apparatus. Various methods of doing this have been advocated (Klapper and Philip, 1971; Jeppsson, 1969, 1971; Sweet and Bergström, 1972) but there is little uniformity in the notations suggested and none of the notational systems suggested has been widely adopted.

It is recognized that, although a number of different types of conodont apparatus existed, nevertheless many had a similar structural plan. In the revised edition of the *Treatise on Invertebrate Paleontology* volume on conodonts a scheme was suggested (Sweet, 1981) for identifying and naming homologous positions within the apparatus. Since many apparatuses have six element types, the seximembrate plan may be used to demonstrate the scheme of locational notation (Fig. 1.3). Components of seximembrate apparatuses can be separated into three principal categories which

are designated P, M and S. P positions are occupied by pectiniform or specialized ramiform elements, and characteristically there are two types of them which are designated Pa and Pb. M positions are typically occupied by arched pick-shaped dolabrate elements in one group and by bipennate, digyrate or coniform elements in another large group. Elements occupying the three major positions in the S category form a symmetry transition series. Elements occupying the three major positions in the Sa position are characteristically alate, Sb is occupied by digyrate or tertiopedate elements and the Sc position is occupied by dolobrate elements, commonly with a long posterior process and a laterally recurved anterior process. In septimembrate assemblages the Sd position is occupied by quadriramate elements.

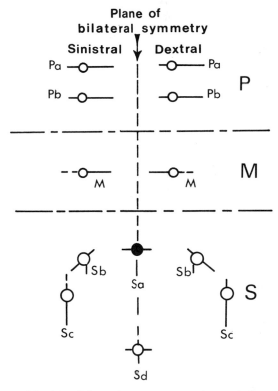

Fig. 1.3 – Schematic arrangement and suggested notation for elements in a seximembrate apparatus (modified after Sweet, 1981). The position Sd is included for a few septimembrate apparatuses.

1.4 THE FUNCTION OF CONODONTS

The position of conodonts in the body of an organism may have been external, or internal. If external, they could have been used for defence. This is unlikely since conodonts would easily break. They are unlike spines of other groups in terms of morphology and composition. Alternatively, if external, they could have functioned for chewing food. Again this is unlikely since teeth show signs of abrasion whereas conodonts do not. When teeth break off, they cannot be repaired, but conodonts can rejuvenate broken parts, which indicates that they were in life surrounded by tissue. If they were internal structures then they could have functioned as internal supports as proposed by Hass (1941) on the evidence that conodonts were surrounded by soft tissue, as an internal supporting structure for a food-gathering organ (Lindström, 1973, 1974), or as an internal device for filtering plankton as suggested by Halstead (1968) and Hitchings and Ramsay (1978). Bengston (1976) believed that conodonts were external elements and used for grasping, holding or mastication. Conway Morris (1980) disagreed.

1.5 ZOOLOGICAL AFFINITIES OF CONODONTS

More than 100 papers have addressed the problem of the origin of conodonts. Rhodes (1954) and Müller (1981) have listed the postulated affinities of conodonts ranging from coelenterates, aschelminthes, gnathostomulids, molluscs, annelids, arthropods, tentaculids, chaetognaths, chordates and even plants. The criteria used to indicate affinities can be broadly grouped into the following categories.

(a) Mineral and chemical composition

Pietzner et al. (1968) arrived at the following composition of conodonts, without basal filling, by X-ray spectral analysis: $Ca_5Na_{0.14}(PO_4)_{3.01}$-$(CO_3)_{0.16}F_{0.73}(H_2O)_{0.85}$ which they regarded as corresponding to carbonate apatite, francolite. Element distribution is not evenly spread throughout the basal plate; conodont fluorine decreases from the margin of the basal plate towards the conodont and yttrium, which is present in greater concentrations in the basal plate, is concentrated along its margin. Organic constituents are largely unknown although Armstrong and Tarlo (1966) identified amino-acids in conodonts.

Carbonate apatite occurs in the hard parts of many fossil groups, such as brachiopods, conularids, hyolithelminthids, annelids, arthropods and vertebrates. The presence of amino-acids similar to those in vertebrates led Halstead (1968) to suggest affinities with protovertebrates.

(b) Gross morphology of individual elements

Gross similarities between conodonts and structures in many distantly related groups have led to many theories concerning their origin. These include structures as diverse as gastropod radulae (Loomis, 1936), copulatory spicules of nematodes (Denham, 1944), scolecodonts (Zittel and Rohon, 1886) and carapace spines of the crustacean *Limulus* (Harley, 1861). Gross shape depends to a high degree on the function of the structure and all the above comparisons do not stand up to investigation when other features such as chemical composition or environment are considered.

(c) Apparatus structure

A number of workers have attempted comparisons of the total apparatus with similar structures in known organisms. Schmidt (1934, 1950) compared the Carboniferous conodont assemblages with the teeth, mandibles and branchial structure of placoderms. Demanet (1939) compared them with the branchial arch of *Coelacanthus*. Lindström (1964) proposed that the conodont apparatus was part of a tentacled ciliated food-gathering apparatus resembling a lophophore. The apparatus was covered with soft tissue and the conodonts embedded in the tissue could be raised to act as a deterrent to predators. Since the conodonts were covered in tissue, broken parts could be regenerated easily. Examples of cusp regeneration, whilst not common, occur in everyone's collections.

(d) Histology

Gross (1954) noted that conodonts grew centrifugally. They are not homologous with the enamel of teeth since enamel grows by the addition of one lamella on the inside of another. Dentine of teeth also differs from conodonts in possessing dentinal tubes. Endoskeletal bone has a central cavity which is lacking in conodonts. Nevertheless, Gross was impressed by the similarity in composition between conodonts and vertebrate bone.

(e) Soft parts

Since 1973 a number of fossil finds of exceptional importance have been made in which conodonts have been found in close association with soft-bodied organisms.

Melton and Scott (1973) published an account of an animal from the Bear Gulch Formation of Montana, of late Mississippian age, which contained conodonts within it and which they referred to a new subphylum Conodontochordata. This find was important in that it referred to an animal 60–70 cm long which was either the host to the conodonts or a predator of conodont animals. The latter seems more likely than the former in view of the large number and mixed nature of the conodonts when compared with known assemblages.

The Middle Cambrian Burgess Shale yielded the next important discovery with the appearance of a specimen referred to a new taxon *Odontogriphus omalus* described by Conway Morris (1976). This poorly preserved fossil has impressions and moulds of possible coniform conodonts. The structure that they were associated with was interpreted as a lophophore by Conway Morris and compared with similar structures in the phyla Brachiopoda, Phoronida and Bryozoa.

The third discovery, was of an animal from the Lower Carboniferous rocks of Scotland (Briggs *et al.,* 1983). This specimen is 40.5 mm long and mostly less than 1.8 mm across, with a worm-like body and fins at the posterior end. The trunk appears to be 'segmented' and its posterior part bears posteriorly sloping fin rays; a small ray-supported caudal fin appears to be separated from a large anteriorly expanded fin by a gap. The conodonts occur in the poorly preserved head region which has a pair of semicircular lobes, anterior to the conodonts, with what may represent a lumen between them leading to a mouth. The conodonts clearly correspond to a natural assemblage consisting of paired elements arranged in subparallel fashion. The assemblage is multimembrate with a pectiniform element of cavusgnathoid type identified by Aldridge as *Clydagnathus* cf. *cavusformis* (Rhodes *et al.,* 1969). The arrangement of the elements is opposite to that supported by many researchers (e.g. Rhodes and Austin, 1981), in that the pectiniform element is to the posterior. This animal does not provide an obvious solution to the problem of conodont affinities but serves to emphasize the uniqueness of these structures. Hence, Briggs *et al.* place the animal in the Phylum Conodonta.

1.6 CLASSIFICATION OF CONODONTS

It is not surprising that classification of conodonts is problematical. Historically, generic and specific names were applied to individual single elements based on the variation in shape. This was the system originally adopted by Pander. Hinde (1879) describing a conodont assemblage applied a generic name to the complete collection of conodonts present in the assemblage. Different assemblages subsequently were given generic names. Thus developed the so-called dual system of nomenclature for conodonts, based either on the form morphology of single elements or on the multielement nature of the associations present in assemblages.

Assemblages contain conodonts of a variety of shapes. Often conodonts of similar form are present in more than one assemblage. Further the individual elements of an assemblage have often been recognized by different generic names since they were first described as isolated single elements.

Slowly the dual taxonomy is being suppressed. Generic names are now applied to multielement associations as apparatuses of the different genera are reconstructed. The name applied to the apparatus is the name applied to the component which was first described, often in terms of form taxonomy.

In the revised edition of the *Treatise of Invertebrate Paleontology* conodonts were given a new and independent status — Conodonta. Differentiation into two major orders was based on chemical differences and ultrastructure. Grouping of similar apparatus reconstructions was the basis for recognition of 11 superfamilies. Distinctive apparatus and element compositions were diagnostic for 47 families of some 180 different genera. This replaces the suprageneric classifications previously proposed by numerous workers including Ulrich and Bassler (1926), Hass (1941), and Lindström (1970).

1.7 PALAEOECOLOGY OF CONODONTS

The palaeoecologic controls on the distribution of the conodont animal are poorly understood in part because most studies are either biostratigraphic or morphologic and very few attempts have been made to study their palaeoecology as an end in itself. Most general observations arise from studies of their distribution and these indicate that, whilst many conodont species were extremely widespread, others either were restricted geographically by isolation or were confined to very specialized environments. The majority of species were present in most marine environments but the abundance of many species varies and consistency has not yet been proved.

Two principal models have been proposed to explain the observed distribution of conodont species and its implications for the mode of life of the conodont animal. Seddon and Sweet (1971) sought to impose a strictly pelagic, depth-controlled, mode of life on the conodont animal whereas Druce (1973) presupposed that distance from shore was the major controlling factor. The latter concept was taken further by Barnes and Fähraeus (1975) and Le Fevre *et al.* (1976), who suggested that the majority of late Ordovician and early Silurian conodonts could be divided into laterally segregated communities of nekto-benthonic habit and related to depth of water, and a small number of pelagic forms which could be found at any depth. (See also Klapper and Barrick, 1977).

Salinity has been suggested by a number of authors as a factor controlling the distribution of conodonts. No faunas have yet been recorded from nonmarine strata although their presence in the brackish water phase of many Silesian marine transgressive horizons suggests that at least some species were tolerant of low salinity environments. Barnes and Fähraeus (1975) and von Bitter (1976) have suggested that some species were adapted to withstand euryhaline and hypersaline conditions respectively. The majority of species occur in what appear to be normal marine, stenohaline conditions as suggested by Clark (1981).

Temperature controls may well be a major factor in their distribution although their importance has not yet been investigated. The absence of conodont faunas in cold water regions during the Devonian, Carboniferous and Permian Periods and the separation into provinces during the Ordovician Period may well have been due to temperature control.

Control of conodont dispersal, possibly at a larval stage, by ocean currents has been suggested by Klapper and Johnson (1980) and Higgins (1981b) for the Devonian and Carboniferous faunas respectively. Both in the Devonian and the Carboniferous Periods conodont faunas are known only from the tropical latitudes when the disposition of landmasses allowed circum-equatorial currents to prevail which may have controlled the distribution of faunas.

The presence of two main conodont faunal provinces in Ordovician time has been known since the 1950s and were defined as such by Sweet and Bergström (1974). The North American Midcontinent Province includes interior North America, parts of the eastern Great Basin, western belts of the Appalachian Mountains, much of the Canadian Arctic Islands and part of the Siberian Platform. The North Atlantic Province includes NW Europe, parts of the South America and part of the eastern Appalachians. According to Bergström (p. 49) the North Atlantic Province occupied high latitudes and was characterized by cold water environments and the Midcontinent Province by low latitude, warm temperature environments. The majority of British and Irish faunas, south of the Highland Border Fault, are of the North Atlantic type whereas those further north belong to the Midcontinent Province. This apparent anomaly equates well with plate reconstructions for early Ordovician time which place northern Scotland adjacent to the North American Plate at tropical latitudes. Some biofacies control at a local level is evident (see Bergström, p. 51) but too little is known of the sedimentology of the conodont-bearing horizons to reach firm conclusions.

In rocks of Silurian age Aldridge (1976 and this volume) has related conodont distribution to water depth, pointing to the virtual restriction of species of the genus *Icriodella* to shallow, high energy environments during the Llandovery Epoch. Aldridge (1976) associated conodont communities with the macrofossil communities of Ziegler *et al.* (1968) in an attempt to relate faunal diversity, abundance and species to depth of environment. He concluded that coniform elements show a pattern of increased abundance with increasing depth whereas other elements are controlled more obviously by environmental energy.

Devonian conodont distribution is probably better known than that of any other period. Klapper and Johnson (1980) have recently summarized Devonian conodont distribution in a worldwide survey, concluding that Devonian conodonts were restricted to tropical latitudes but, within this climatic realm shallow water faunas of Lower and Middle Devonian age include many endemic elements which might form the basis of conodont provinces. In general species of the genera *Icriodus* and *Pelekysgnathus* tend to be restricted to shallow water environments and therefore likely to be endemic. Several authors (Chatterton, 1976; Sandberg, 1976; Weddige and Ziegler, 1976) have attempted to relate conodont distribution in Devonian rocks to environment, and biofacies have been recognized based on diversity, abundance and faunal association. Whilst energy of the environment was emphasized by Weddige and Ziegler, Chatterton related changes to temperature and salinity to faunal associations. Sandberg established five biofacies for the late Devonian Period of the Western USA based on relative abundance of genera such as *Palmatolepis* and *Polygnathus* suggesting that genera such as *Palmatolepis* fit the depth stratification model of

Seddon and Sweet (1971) whereas others, such as *Polygnathus*, did not. This anomaly was attributed to the diversity of environments occupied by different species of *Polygnathus*.

In Devon and Cornwall, the presence of an Icriodus biofacies can be recognized throughout the Devonian rocks and indicates shallow water environments. On the other hand the palmatolepid-bispathodid biofacies of Sandberg (1976) can be recognized in late Devonian rocks indicating deep water conditions. Clearly conodont biofacies will be of considerable value in the reconstruction of Devonian palaeogeography in SW England.

Carboniferous rocks in Great Britain and Ireland are characterized by a wide variety of environments; the Dinantian Subperiod exhibits a multitude of shallow water carbonate environments whereas the Silesian Subperiod was characterized by basinal shales commonly alternating with nonmarine, coastal plain sediments. In the Dinantian rocks the complexity of zonal schemes reflects the environments and Austin (1976) has attempted to analyse the role played by environment in controlling the faunas. He related distribution to depth of water, recognizing genera such as *Clydagnathus, Cavusgnathus* and *Mestognathus* as being typical of shallow water shelf environments whereas genera such as *Scaliognathus, Siphonodella* and *Elictognathus* were deep water, basin inhabitants. He further suggested that the controlling factor was energy of the environment. During Viséan and Namurian times some element of provincialism was proposed by Higgins (1981b), suggesting that shallow water elements became endemic in midcontinent USA and Europe including species of *Mestognathus* and *Paragnathodus*. Higgins suggested that provincialism accounted for the absence of, or low abundance and diversity of species of the genera *Adetognathus* and *Rhachistognathus* in Europe. (See also Merrill and von Bitter, 1976).

Permian faunas are as yet poorly known but low faunal diversity, including monospecific occurrences of *Merillina divergens*, suggest that the extremely shallow, hypersaline environments of the British Permian rocks strongly affected the conodont faunas.

1.8 APPLICATIONS OF CONODONTS

The widespread distribution, abundance and chemical composition have led to extensive use of conodonts in the solution of stratigraphic and geochemical problems. Although not, as once thought, ubiquitous in all marine environments they are more widely distributed than most fossil groups and, combined with their rapid evolution, this has made them one of the most effective biostratigraphic groups in the Palaeozoic Era. The chemical stability of the mineral apatite protects the conodont elements from the effects of heat and chemical attack to a degree unknown in fossils composed of calcium carbonate. This allows them to survive extremes of metamorphism and dolomitization and remain identifiable and yet, at the same time, the chemical effects can be utilized because the effect of heat is to cause colour change, turning them into effective geologic thermometers and therefore maturity indicators for hydrocarbon exploration. In addition as apatite is a chemically closed system at low temperatures, investigation of the trace-element composition of the conodonts is leading to their use as indicators of original sea water isotope composition.

(a) Biostratigraphy

More than 100 conodont biostratigraphic zones are defined in the Palaeozoic Era and Triassic System, with the exception of the Cambrian System, zonations exist for the major part of each system (Sweet and Bergström, 1981). However, in Britain there remain many gaps in the conodont record which are in part due to lack of study but also to either a lack of suitable host-rocks or extreme metamorphism. Unsuitable host-rocks include non-calcareous sandstones and highly indurated shales for which convenient techniques for bulk extraction do not exist. Nevertheless there are many shale sequences (e.g. in the Carboniferous System), which are suitable for investigation but whose conodont faunas are unknown.

The stratigraphy and correlation of British Palaeozoic rocks is covered in the Special Report Series of the Geological Society of London. These recent publications cover the Cambrian System (Cowie *et al.*, 1972), Ordovician System (Williams *et al.*, 1972), Silurian System (Cocks *et al.*, 1971), Devonian System (House *et al.*, 1977), Dinantian Subsystem (George *et al.*, 1976), Silesian Subsystem (Ramsbottom *et al.*, 1978) and Permian System (Smith *et al.*, 1974). Conodont faunas did not figure very prominently in these summaries, in contrast to their prominence in other countries, which largely reflects the lack of study of these faunas in Great Britain and Ireland.

Cambrian conodonts are particularly poorly known. In the world as a whole Lower and Middle Cambrian conodonts consist of simple coniform proto- and para-conodonts which are insufficiently known to provide a zonation. Representatives of these have been recorded in Great Britain from the *Hyolithus* Limestone, Comley Limestone and possibly from the Hartshill Formation of Lower Cambrian age from the Welsh Borderland (see pp. 33–34). Middle Cambrian conodonts are unknown. Euconodonts first appeared in the Upper Cambrian and have been used, together with the paraconodonts, to zone rocks straddling the Cambrian–Ordovician boundary (Müller, 1973; Miller, 1975) in Iran and North America respectively. Faunas of Upper Cambrian age in Great Britain are only slightly better known and are represented by three species, *Prooneotodus tenuis*, *Cordylodus proavus* and *Westergaardodina* cf. *biscuspidata* (see pp. 33–34).

Ordovician conodonts in Great Britain and Ireland are much better known than those of Cambrian age. More than 130 faunas have been recorded and are collated (pp. 34–46) in this volume. The provincialism of Ordovician conodont faunas (see p.22; Barnes *et al.*, 1973) had an impact on the British area. Only one suite of faunas, those of the Durness Limestone, have clear North American Midcontinent affinities, the remainder having mixed but mainly North Atlantic affinities. Lower Ordovician faunas are poorly known but appear to indicate a considerable potential for biostratigraphic purposes. Faunas occur in the black shale facies of the Southern Uplands in association with graptolites and in the upper part of the carbonate Durness Limestone Group of NW Scotland. Though the faunas in these two areas belong to different provinces there are species common to the Arenig components, such as *Oistodus lanceolatus* which offer a means of correlation. Faunas of probable Llanvirn age are also recorded from Scotland (pp. 41–44). Faunas of Llandeilian age are recorded from the type area of that series and are of considerable value for intercontinental correlation (see Bergström, pp. 47–48). Caradoc and Ashgill faunas have received by far the greatest attention and they form the major number of the localities listed. The stages of the Caradoc Series cannot be recognized on the basis of the conodont faunas although faunas from the lower part are different from those of the upper. Similarly the stages of the Ashgill Series cannot be differentiated by their conodont faunas although two zones, the *Amorphognathus superbus* and *A. ordovicicus* Zones, appear to be represented (see Bergström, p. 48). The proposed Ordovician–Silurian boundary stratotype at Dobb's Linn is in a clastic succession which is unlikely to yield many conodont faunas although this boundary elsewhere is marked by considerable changes in the conodont faunas.

In rocks of Silurian age, conodont faunas are generally better known than those of the Ordovician System although most data comes from the Llandovery Series (Aldridge 1972, 1975). Aldridge and his students have conducted an extensive search for conodont faunas from the Llandovery of Wales, the Welsh Borderland and Scotland. These studies have shown that few faunas occur in the type section of the Llandovery Series but that diverse collections from the Welsh Borderland allow the recognition of four conodont zones. Early Wenlock was a time of rapid decline of conodont faunas and faunas younger than those of the Llandovery–Wenlock boundary beds are poorly known in Britain. Those from the boundary beds have been studied in the Wenlock type area and traced throughout the Welsh Borderland (see summary by Aldridge, p. 69). Wenlock faunas are principally known from the Welsh Borderland and the West Midlands where species of the genus *Ozarkodina* will probably offer the best biostratigraphic possibilities. Faunas of Lower Ludlow age are known mainly from Ireland from a very few localities but those of Upper Ludlow age are better known and occur extensively in the Welsh Borderland but no zonation has yet been formulated.

In the Devonian System, conodont study has been confined to Devon and Cornwall and with the exception of off-shore areas will not extend much to the north because of the largely nonmarine nature of the rocks. Even within Devon and Cornwall, despite its historic importance, conodonts from the Lower Devonian and, to a lesser extent, from the Middle Devonian are poorly known and it is only from the Upper Devonian that a moderately complete faunal succession has been determined. Extensive revision of known faunas is needed before detailed comparison with what is now the international Upper Devonian standard conodont sequence is possible.

Carboniferous faunas are better known than those of any other system in Britain. Study of the Dinantian Subsystem faunas has been extensive in both Europe and North America and zonations having widespread use have been proposed (Sandberg *et al.*, 1978, Lane *et al.*, 1980) for the lower positions of the Mississippian Subsystem (the Tournaisian Series and the early part of the Viséan Series) but these are based on cosmopolitan genera such as *Siphonodella* and *Gnathodus* which are common in the deeper-water environments. The distribution of these genera is more erratic in the British area in part because of breaks in the sequence and in part because of the multiplicity of environments in the dominantly shallow-water sequences representing the Dinantian Subsystem in Great Britain and Ireland. This latter phenomenon has led to a large number of zonal schemes for different areas which have been difficult to correlate both with each other and with the so-called standard schemes derived from other parts of the world. Varker and Sevastopoulo have attempted to produce a conflated scheme derived from the preceding ones but still differing from those outside this region and not precisely correlatable with other schemes. On the assumption that a biozone should not be extended beyond the geographical limits of its key forms, the zonal situation in the shallow-water shelf sequences of Great Britain and

Ireland will probably remain different in name but, as the ranges of individual elements become better known, correlation will be improved.

Work on the Dinantian conodonts of Great Britain has produced an important advance in the study of conodonts in general. The early work (Rhodes *et al.*, 1969) pointed to the fact that the conodont animal was environmentally controlled and this work was published at a time when such ideas were unfashionable.

In the Silesian Subsystem, conodont studies are made difficult both by the restriction of marine horizons to thin bands and by the dearth of limestones. The latter problem can be overcome by extracting faunas from the shales which usually contain rich, although often broken, faunas. Namurian faunas have been extensively described from the Craven Basin but there is still considerable scope for improvement of the zonal scheme and particularly for its extension to Northern England, Scotland and Ireland. There is also considerable potential in applying the scheme to the complexly folded Silesian rocks of Devon and Cornwall where the resistance of conodonts to metamorphism would render them particularly useful. Westphalian faunas are barely known although records of their presence suggest they are very common. N. Riley of the British Geological Survey is currently studying faunas of this age. Comparison of Silesian faunas with those of North America may be made difficult by the provinciality which Higgins (1975) feels occurs at this level but it is a subtle provinciality with few endemic forms occurring in either area; the differences are those of emphasis and stratigraphic range which may become less obvious with further study.

Permian conodont faunas in Great Britain were unknown until the persistence of A. Swift and R. J. Aldridge led to their discovery. Marine Permian rocks in Great Britain are largely restricted to the Upper Permian, consist mainly of primary dolomites, with a restricted marine invertebrate fauna, and are never likely to yield neither rich or varied conodont faunas. However, the faunas which are present enable correlation with better-known sequences elsewhere (Sweet, 1970) to be achieved.

(b) Organic metamorphism of conodonts

Conodont elements extracted from sediments which have undergone little depth of burial are generally pale yellow in colour (often transparent) and exhibit well preserved internal and surface structure. Metamorphic effects produced by increasing depth of burial lead to colour changes ranging from shades of brown, through black and grey and eventually to crystal-clear elements.

Although colour variations were apparent to earlier workers, Ellison (1944) was the first to note that elements heated in a test-tube give off water and turn dark grey. This process was attributed to carbonization by Lindström (1964) and the presence of small amounts of organic matter (Clark and Müller, 1968; Pietzner *et al.*, 1968) implied that this interpretation was correct. Major systematic studies by Epstein *et al.* (1974, 1975, 1977) made available a scheme for the use of colour change in geothermometry and, in so doing, added a further dimension to the study of conodonts, (see also Bergström, 1980). Their work followed three main lines of study.

Firstly, colour variations of conodont elements were mapped on a regional scale in well-known basins (Epstein *et al.*, 1977), indicating that elements become darker with increasing depth of burial.

Secondly, elements were heated in controlled experiments, producing the same sequence of colour changes noted in the field. From this data, the following colour alteration index (CAI) was constructed (Epstein *et al.*, 1977).

CAI	C°
1	>50–80
1½	50–90
2	60–140
3	110–200
4	190–300
5	<300

Conodont elements having an index of CAI 5 are black in colour. At higher temperatures, black

elements become grey, then white and finally
clear but the temperatures at which these changes
occur have not been published. Elements from
garnet-grade metamorphic rocks were figured by
Epstein *et al.* (1977) who stated that crystal-clear
elements can be produced by heating in open air
at 950 °C for 4 h. Because the colour changes are
both time and temperature dependent, a method
is needed for the determination of maximum and
minimum temperatures of particular examples.
Epstein *et al.* (1977) made extensive use of the
Arrhenius plot for this purpose.

    Thirdly, Epstein *et al.* (1977) correlated CAI
with other thermal indices including the most
commonly used indices in hydrocarbon exploration, vitrinite reflectance and palynomorph
thermal alteration index (TAI).

    Determining the CAI can be done by collect-
ing a representative set of standard colour elements
which can be related to the Epstein *et al.* scale by
reference to the colour chart in their 1977 publication and the use of Munsell colour chips. Colour
can vary both within an element and between
elements of different morphologies from the
same sample. It is therefore important to compare
similar elements from different samples and to
use the colour of thinner parts of the elements
(e.g. on ramiform elements) as the main guide to
CAI of a sample.

    The practical applications of conodonts as
geologic thermometers are twofold. Firstly, CAI
values are used as an indicator of maturity in
hydrocarbon exploration. Epstein *et al.* (1977)
stated that CAI 1.5–2.0 is at the upper margin
of the oil window and that CAI 4.5 is near the
upper margin for dry gas production. It should be
noted that there are exceptions to these rules.
Experimental data shows that, whilst confined
pressure alone does not appear to affect colour of
elements, in combination with water considerable
retardation of the carbonization process occurs.
In addition, Wardlaw and Harris (1984) noted that
warm saline solutions can produce anomalously
high CAI readings. Secondly, CAI values can be
used to indicate anomalously high temperature
zones which may be indicative of mineralized
zones or high heat flow at plate margins.

(c) Isotope chemistry of conodonts

Trace-element chemistry of conodonts shows great
promise as a further use of conodonts but its study
is still at a very early stage. Preliminary work
suggests that there is a strong relationship between
thermal alteration and isotope content of conodonts which implies that unaltered specimens are
needed for constructions of original sea water
composition. However, there are situations where
knowledge of the isotope composition of altered
specimens is important and can add considerably
to the study of basin history.

    Radiogenic dating of conodonts is possible
which leads to the intriguing possibility of linking
radiogenic and biostratigraphic dating in the
Palaeozoic. Two approaches have been followed.
Sachs *et al.* (1980) irradiated early Carboniferous
conodonts and from the resulting fission tracks
determined a siphonodellid as being 380± 140
million years in age. The high degree of error may
be reduced by using larger samples but, even at
this stage, the radiogenic date is very close to the
accepted age of 360 million years for the base of
the Carboniferous System. As suggested by Sachs
et al., fission track dating of thermally altered
conodonts should yield dates of the uplift phase of
basins, which, coupled with CAI data, will add
considerably to the burial and/or uplift history of
basins. The second approach was that of Kovach
and Zartman (1981) who used the U–Th–Pb
method of age determination. The U–Th–Pb
content is low, but ages ranging from 260 to
360 million years for the Ames Limestone Member
of the Glenshaw Formation (Virgilian, Upper
Carboniferous) of eastern Ohio and ages of 315–
341 million years for the older Brush Creek
Limestone Member of the Glenshaw Formation
(early Missourian) of northwest West Virginia
indicate that this method also has potential.
Neutron radiation of the specimens indicates that
the uranium is differently distributed in the two
samples.

    Strontium isotopes in conodonts have been
studied by Kovach (1981) who showed that strontium concentrations range from 1560 to 20 900
ppm and show a tendency to decrease from early
Ordovician to early Triassic, which may be a

reflection of changing composition of sea water or an evolutionary trend in the conodont structure. Kovach and Futa (1983) investigated the neodymium composition of conodonts from the Ordovician and Carboniferous Systems. The sample from the Ordovician System yielded significantly lower ratios of ^{143}Nd to ^{144}Nd than did the four samples from the Carboniferous System. At present the neodymium isotopic composition varies from one ocean basin to another thus raising the possibility of reconstructing Palaeozoic ocean basins on the basis of isotopic composition, in relation to plate movements.

Rare earth elements in conodonts determined by neutron activation analysis have been studied by Wright Clark (1983). This work shows that rare earth elements, including ratios of cerium to lanthanum, vary among depositional environments but are consistent among contemporaneous faunas from the same environment. This raises the possibility of using rare earths to determine Eh/pH and provenance in Palaeozoic rocks.

1.9 REFERENCES

Aldridge, R. J. 1972. Llandovery conodonts from the Welsh Borderland. *Bull. Brit Mus. (Nat. Hist.), Geol.*, **22**, 125–231, 9 plates.

Aldridge, R. J. 1975. The stratigraphic distribution of conodonts in the British Silurian. *J. Geol. Soc., London*, **131**, 607–618, 3 plates.

Aldridge, R. J. 1976. Comparison of macrofossil communities and conodont distribution in the British Silurian. In: C. R. Barnes (Ed.), *Conodont Paleoecology, Spec. Paper Geol. Assoc. Can.*, **15**, 92–104.

Aldridge, R. J. 1982. A fused cluster of coniform conodont elements from the late Ordovician of Washington Land, Western North Greenland. *Palaeontology*, **25**, (2) 425–430, 1 plate.

Armstrong, W. G. and Tarlo, L. B. H. 1966. Amino-acid components in fossil calcified tissues. *Nature (London)*, **210**, (5035), 481–482.

Austin, R. L. 1976. Evidence from Great Britain and Ireland concerning West European Dinantian conodont paleoecology. In: C. R. Barnes (Ed.), *Conodont Paleoecology, Spec. Paper Geol. Assoc. Can.*, **15**, 201–224.

Austin, R. L. and Rhodes, F. H. T. 1969. A conodont assemblage from the Carboniferous of the Avon Gorge, Bristol. *Palaeontology*, **12** (3), 400–405.

Baesemann, J. F. 1973. Missourian (Upper Pennsylvanian) conodonts of Northeastern Kansas. *J. Paleontol.*, **47**, 689–710, 3 plates.

Barnes, C. R. 1967. A questionable natural conodont assemblage from Middle Ordovician limestone, Ottawa, Canada. *J. Paleontol.*, **41**, 1557–1560.

Barnes C. R. (Ed.) 1976. *Conodont Paleoecology, Spec. Paper Geol. Assoc. Can.*, **15**, 1–324.

Barnes, C. R. and Fahraeus, L. E. 1975. Provinces, communities, and the proposed nektobenthic habit of Ordovician conodontophorids. *Lethaia*, **8**, 133–149.

Barnes, C. R., Rexroad, C. D. and Miller, J. F. 1973. Lower Paleozoic conodont provincialism. In: F. H. T. Rhodes (Ed.), Conodont Paleozoology, *Spec. Paper Geol. Soc. Am.*, **141**, 157–190.

Barnes, C. R, Sass, D. B. and Monroe, E. A. 1970. Preliminary studies of the ultrastructure of selected Ordovician conodonts. *Life Sci. Contrib., R. Ont. Mus.*, **76**, 1–24, 10 plates.

Barnes, C. R. and Slack, D. J. 1975. Conodont ultrastructure: the subfamily Acanthodontinae. *Life Sci. Contrib., R. Ont. Mus.*, **106**, 1–21.

Behnken, F. H. 1975. Leonardian and Guadalupian (Permian) conodont biostratigraphy in Western and Southwestern United States. *J. Paleontol.*, **49**, 284–315, 2 plates.

Bengtson, S. 1976. The structure of some Middle Cambrian conodonts, and the early evolution of conodont structure and function. *Lethaia*, **9**, 185–206.

Bergström, S. M. 1980. Conodonts as paleotemperature tools in Ordovician rocks of the Caledonides and adjacent areas in Scandinavia and the British Isles. *Geol Fören. Stockholm Förh.*, **102**, 377–392.

Briggs, D. E. G., Clarkson, E. N. K. and Aldridge, R. J. 1983. The conodont animal. *Lethaia*, **16**, 1–14.

Chatterton, B. D. E. 1976. Distribution and paleoecology of Eifelian and early Givetian conodonts from Western and Northwestern Canada. In: C. R. Barnes (Ed.), *Conodont Paleoecology, Spec. Paper Geol. Assoc. Can.*, **15**, 143–157.

Clark, D. L. 1981. Paleoecology. In: R. A. Robison (Ed.), *Treatise on Invertebrate Paleontology, Part W, Supplement 2, Conodonta*, Geological Society of America and University of Kansas Press, Lawrence, Kansas.

Clark, D. L. Sweet,, W. C., Bergström, S. M., Klapper, G., G. Austin, R. L., Rhodes, F. H. T., Müller, K. J., Ziegler, W., Lindström, M., Miller, J. F. and Harris, A. G. 1981. In: R. A. Robison (Ed.), *Treatise on Invertebrate Paleontology, Part W, Supplement 2. Conodonta*, Geological Society of America and University of Kansas Press, Lawrence, Kansas, W1–W202.

Clark, D. L. (Ed.) 1984. Conodont biofacies and provincialism. *Spec. Paper Geol. Soc. Am.*, **196**, 1–340.

Clark, D. L. and Müller, K. J. 1968. The basal opening of conodonts. *J. Paleontol.*, **42**, 561–570.

Cocks, L. R. M., Holland, C. H., Rickards, R. B. and Strachan, I. 1971. A correlation of Silurian rocks in the British Isles. *Geol. Soc. London Spec. Rep.*, **1**, in *J. Geol. Soc. London*, **127**, 103–136.

Collinson, C. W. 1963. Techniques for the collecting and processing of conodonts. *Circ. State Geol. Surv., Ill.* **343**, 1–16.

Conway Morris, S. 1976. A new Cambrian lophophorate

from the Burgess Shale of British Columbia. *Palaeontology,* **19,** 199−222, 4 plates.

Conway Morris, S. 1980. Conodont function: fallacies of the tooth model. *Lethaia,* **13** (1), 107−108.

Cowie, J. W., Rushton, A. W. A. and Stubblefield, C. J. 1972. A correlation of Cambrian rocks in the British Isles. *Geol. Soc. London Spec. Rep.,* **2,** 1−74.

Demanet, F. 1939. Filtering appendices on the branchial arches of Coelacanthus lepturus Agassiz. *Geol. Mag.,* **76,** 215−219.

Denham, R. L. 1944. Conodonts. *J. Paleontol,* **18,** 216−218.

Dow, V. E. 1960. Magnetic separation of conodonts. *J. Paleontol.,* **34,** 738−743.

Dow, V. E. 1965. Magnetic separation of conodonts. In: B. Kummel and D. M. Raup, (Eds.), *Handbook of Paleontologic Techniques,* W. H. Freeman, San Francisco, California, 263−267.

Druce, E. C. 1973. Upper Paleozoic and Triassic conodont distribution and the recognition of biofacies. In F. H. T. Rhodes (Ed.), Conodont Paleozoology, *Spec. Paper Geol. Soc. Am.,* **141,** 191−237.

Dubois, E. P. 1943. Evidence on the nature of conodonts. *J. Paleontol.,* **17,** 155−159, 1 plate.

Ellison, S. P. Jnr. 1944. The composition of conodonts. *J. Paleontol.,* **18,** 133−140.

Epstein, A. G., Epstein, J. B. and Harris, L. D. 1974. Incipient metamorphism, structural anomalies, and oil and gas potential in the Appalachian basin determined from conodont color. *Abstracts Geol. Soc. Am.,* **6** (7), 723−724.

Epstein, A. G., Epstein, J. B. and Harris, L. D. 1975. Conodont color alteration − an index to diagenesis of organic matter, *Abstracts Annu. Meet. Am. Assoc. Pet. Geol. Soc. Econ. Paleontol. Mineral,* **2,** 21−22.

Epstein, A. G., Epstein, J. B. and Harris, L. D. 1977. Conodont color alteration − an index to organic metamorphism. *U.S. Geol. Surv., Prof. Paper,* **995,** 1−27.

George, T. N., Johnson, G. A. L., Mitchell, M., Prentice, J. E., Ramsbottom, W. H. C., Sevastopulo, G. D. and Wilson, R. B. 1976. A correlation of Dinantian rocks in the British Isles. *Geol. Soc. London Spec. Rep.,* **7,** 1−87.

Gross, W. 1954. Zur Conodonten-Frage. *Senckenbergiana Lethaea,* **35,** 73−85, 5 plates.

Halstead, L. B. 1968. The pattern of vertebrate evolution. W. H. Freeman, San Francisco, California, 1−209.

Harley, J. 1861. On the Ludlow bone-bed and its crustacean remains. *Q. J. Geol. Soc. London,* **17,** 542−552, 1 plate.

Hass, W. H. 1941. Morphology of conodonts. *J. Paleontol.,* **15,** 71−81, 5 plates.

Hauf, P. L. and Airey, J. 1980. The handling, hazards, and maintenance of heavy liquids in the geologic laboratory. *U.S. Geol. Surv. Circ.,* **827,** 1−24.

Higgins, A. C. 1975. Conodont zonation of the late Viséan−early Westphalian strata of the south and central Pennines of Northern England. *Bull. Geol. Surv. Gt. Brn.,* **53,** 1−90, 18 plates.

Higgins, A. C. 1981a. Coprolitic conodont assemblages from the Lower Westphalian of North Staffordshire.

Palaeontology, **24** (2), 437−441.

Higgins, A. C. 1981b. The distribution of conodonts in relation to the palaeogeography of late Viséan− Namurian time. In: J. W. Neale and M. D. Brasier (Eds.), *Microfossils from Recent and Fossil Shelf Seas,* Ellis Horwood, Chichester, Sussex, 37−51.

Higgins, A. C. and Spinner, E. G. 1969. Techniques for the extraction of selected microfossils. *Geology,* 12−28.

Hinde, G. J. 1879. On conodonts from the Chazy and Cincinnati Group of the Cambro−Silurian and from the Hamilton and Genesee Shale divisions of the Devonian in Canada and the United States. *Q. J. Geol. Soc. London,* **35,** 351−369.

Hitchings, V. H. and Ramsay, A. T. S. 1978. Conodont assemblages: a new functional model. *Palaeogeogr., Palaeoclimatol., Palaeoecol.,* **24,** 137−149.

House, M. R., Richardson, J. B., Chaloner, W. C., Allen, J. R. L., Holland, C. H. and Westoll, T. S. 1977. A correlation of Devonian rocks of the British Isles. *Geol. Soc. London Spec. Rep.,* **8,** 1−110.

Jeppsson, L. 1969. Notes on some Upper Silurian multi-element conodonts. *Geol. Fören. Stockholm Förh.,* **91,** 12−24.

Jeppsson, L. 1971. Element arrangement in conodont apparatuses of *Hindeodella* type and in similar forms. *Lethaia,* **4,** 101−123.

Jeppsson, L. 1972. Some Silurian conodont apparatuses and possible conodont dimorphism. *Geol. Palaeontol.,* **6,** 51−69, 2 plates.

Klapper, G. and Barrick, J. E. 1977. Conodont ecology: pelagic versus benthic. *Lethaia,* **11,** 15−23.

Klapper, G. and Johnson, J. G. 1980. Endemism and dispersal of Devonian conodonts. *J. Paleontol.,* **54** (2), 400−455, 4 plates.

Klapper, G. and Philip, G. M. 1971. Devonian conodont apparatuses and their vicarious conodont apparatuses. *Lethaia,* **4,** 429−452.

Kovach, J. 1981. The strontium contents of conodonts and possible use of the strontium concentrations and strontium isotopic composition of conodonts for correlation purposes. *Abstracts Geol. Soc. Am.,* **13,** 285.

Kovach, J. and Futa, K. 1983. Conodonts as possible indicators of variations in the neodymium isotopic composition of Paleozoic seawater. *Abstracts Geol. Soc. Am.,* **15,** 247.

Kovach, J. and Zartman, R. W. 1981. U−Th−Pb dating of conodonts. *Abstracts Geol. Soc. Am.,* **13,** 285.

Landing, E. 1977. *'Prooneotodus' tenuis* (Müller, 1959) apparatuses from the Taconic allochthon, Eastern New York: construction, taphonomy and the protoconodont 'supertooth' model. *J. Paleontol.,* **51,** 1072−1084, 2 plates.

Lane, H. R. 1969. Symmetry in conodont element pairs. *J. Paleontol.,* **42,** 1258−1263.

Lane, H. R., Sandberg, C. A. and Ziegler, W. 1980. Taxonomy and phylogeny of some Lower Carboniferous conodonts and preliminary standard post-*Siphonodella* zonation. *Geol. Palaeontol.,* **14,** 117−164, 10 plates.

Lange, F. G. 1968. Conodonten-Gruppenfunde aus Kalken des tieferen Oberdevon. *Geol. Palaeontol.*, **2**, 37–57, 6 plates.

Le Fevre, J., Barnes, C. R. and Tixier, M. 1976. Paleoecology of late Ordovician and early Silurian conodontophorids, Hudson Bay Basin. In: C. R. Barnes (Ed.) Conodont Paleoecology, *Spec. Paper Geol. Assoc. Can.,* **15,** 69–89.

Lindström, M. 1964. *Conodonts,* Elsevier, Amsterdam, 1–196.

Lindström, M. 1970. A suprageneric taxonomy of the conodonts. *Lethaia,* **3,** 427–445.

Lindström, M. 1973. On the affinities of conodonts. In: F. H. T. Rhodes (Ed.) *Conodont Paleozoology. Spec. Paper Geol. Soc. Am.,* **141,** 85–102.

Lindström, M. 1974. The conodont apparatus as a food-gathering mechanism. *Palaeontology,* **17,** 729–744.

Lindström, M., McTavish, R. A. and Ziegler, W. 1972. Feinstrukturelle Untersuchungen an Conodonten, 2, Einige Prioniodontidae aus dem Ordovicium Australiens. *Geol. Paleontol.,* **6,** 33–43, 3 plates.

Lindström, M. and Ziegler, W. 1971. Feinstrukturelle Untersuchungen an Conodonten. 1. Die Uberfamilie Panderodontacea. *Geol. Palaeontol.,* **5,** 9–33, 8 plates.

Lindström, M. and Ziegler, W. 1981a. Surface microornamentation and observations on internal composition. In: R. A. Robison (Ed.) *Treatise on Invertebrate Paleontology, Part W, Supplement 2, Conodonta,* Geological Society of America and University of Kansas Press, Lawrence, Kansas, W41–W52.

Lindström, M. and Ziegler, W. (Eds.) 1972. *Symp. on Conodont Taxonomy,* in *Geol. Palaeontol.,* SB. 1.

Loomis, F. B. 1936. Are conodonts gastropods? *J. Paleontol.,* **10,** 663–664.

Martinsson, A. and Bengtson, S. (Eds.) 1983. Taxonomy, ecology and identity of conodonts. *Proc. ECOS III, Lund, 1982,* in *Foss. Strata,* **15,** 1–192.

Mashkova, T. V. 1972. *Ozarkodina steinhornensis* (Ziegler) apparatus, its conodonts and biozone. *Geol. Paleontol., Sunderb.,* **1,** 81–90, 2 plates.

Melton, W. G. and Scott, H. W. 1973. Conodont-bearing animals from the Bear Gulch Limestone, Montana. In: F. H. T. Rhodes (Ed.), *Conodont Paleozoology, Spec. Paper Geol. Soc. Am.,* **141,** 31–65.

Merrill, G. K. and von Bitter, P. H. 1976. Revision of Conodont Biofacies Nomenclature and Interpretations of Environmental Controls in Pennsylvanian rocks of Eastern and Central North America. *Life Sci. Contrib., R. Ont. Mus.,* **108,** 1–46.

Miller, J. F. 1975. Conodont faunas from the Cambrian and Lowest Ordovician of Western North America. *Abstracts Geol. Soc. Am.,* **7,** 1200–1201.

Miller, J. F. and Rushton, A. W. A. 1973. Natural conodont assemblages from the Upper Cambrian of Warwickshire, Great Britain. *Abstracts Geol. Soc. Am.,* **5,** 338–339.

Moore, R. C. (Ed.) 1962. Conodont classification and nomenclature. *Treatise on Invertebrate Paleontology, Part W, Micellanea,* Geological Society of America and University of Kansas Press, Lawrence, Kansas.

Müller, K. J. 1973. Late Cambrian and early Ordovician conodonts from Northern Iran. *Geol. Surv. Iran Rep.,* **30,** 1–77, 11 plates.

Müller, K. J. 1981. Zoological affinities of conodonts. In R. A. Robison (Ed.), *Treatise on Invertebrate Paleontology, Part W, Supplement 2, Conodonta,* Geological Society of America and University of Kansas Press, Lawrence, Kansas, W78–W82.

Pander, C. H. 1856. *Monographie der fossilen Fische des Silurischen Systems der Russisch-Baltischen Gouvernements,* Akademie der Wissenschaften, St. Petersburg, 1–91, 7 plates.

Pietzner, H., Vahl, J., Werner, H. and Ziegler, W. 1968. Zur chemischen Zusammensetzung und Mikromorphologie der Conodonten. *Palaeontographica,* **128,** 115–152, 10 plates.

Pollock, C. A. 1969. Fused Silurian conodont clusters from Indiana. *J. Paleontol.,* **43,** 929–935, 3 plates.

Ramsbottom, W. H. C., Calver, M. A., Eager, R. M. C., Hodson, F., Holliday, D. W., Stubblefield, C. J. and Wilson, R. B. 1978. A correlation of Silesian rocks of the British Isles. *Geol. Soc. London Spec. Rep.,* **10,** 1–81.

Rexroad, C. B. and Nicoll, R. S. 1964. A Silurian conodont with tetanus? *J. Paleontol.,* **38,** 771–773.

Rhodes, F. H. T. 1952. A classification of Pennsylvanian conodont assemblages. *J. Paleontol.,* **26,** 886–901, 4 plates.

Rhodes, F. H. T. 1953a. Some British Lower Palaeozoic conodont faunas. *Philos. Trans. R. Soc. London, Ser. B,* **237,** 261–334, 4 plates.

Rhodes, F. H. T. 1953b. Nomenclature of conodont assemblages. *J. Paleontol.,* **27,** 610–612.

Rhodes, F. H. T. 1954. The zoological affinities of conodonts. *Biol. Rev. Cambridge Philos. Soc.,* **29,** 419–452.

Rhodes, F. H. T. 1962. Recognition, interpretation and taxonomic position of conodont assemblages. In: R. C. Moore (Ed.), *Treatise on Invertebrate Paleontology, Part W, Miscellanea,* Geological Society of America and University of Kansas Press, Lawrence, Kansas, W70–W83.

Rhodes, F. H. T. (Ed.) 1973. *Conodont Paleozoology, Spec. Paper Geol. Soc. Am.,* **141,** 1–296.

Rhodes, F. H. T. and Austin, R. L. 1981. Natural assemblages of elements: Interpretation and Taxonomy. In: R. A. Robison (Ed.), *Treatise on Invertebrate Paleontology, Part W, Supplement 2, Conodonta,* Geological Society of America and University of Kansas Press, Lawrence, Kansas, W68–W78.

Rhodes, F. H. T and Austin, R. L. In press. Conodont assemblages from the Carboniferous of Britain. *C. R. 9ème Congr. Int. de Stratigraphie et de Geologique du Carbonifère, Washington and Champaign-Urbana, 1979,* **5** 000–000.

Rhodes, F. H. T., Austin, R. L. and Druce, E. C. 1969. British Avonian (Carboniferous) conodont faunas and their value in local and intercontinental correlation. *Bull. Br. Mus. (Nat. Hist.), Geol. Suppl.,* **5,** 1–313, 31 plates.

Sachs, H. M., Denkinger, M., Bennett, C. L. and Harris, A. G. 1980. Radiometric dating of sediments using fission tracks in conodonts. *Nature (London),* **288,** 359–361.

Sandberg, C. A. 1976. Conodont biofacies of late Devonian *Polygnathus styriacus* Zone in Western United States. In C. R. Barnes (Ed.), *Conodont Paleoecology, Spec. Paper Geol. Assoc. Can., 15*, 171–186.

Sandberg, C. A., Ziegler, W., Leuteritz, K. and Brill, S. M. 1978. Phylogeny, speciation and zonation of *Siphonodella* (Conodonta, Upper Devonian and Lower Carboniferous). *Newsl. Stratigr., 7* (2), 102–120.

Schmidt, H. 1934. Condonten-Funde in ursprunglichen Zusammenhang. *Paläeontol., Z., 16*, 76–85, 1 plate.

Schmidt, H. 1950. Nachträge zur Deutung der Conodonten. *Decheniana, 104*, 11–19.

Schmidt, H. and Müller, K. J. 1964. Weitere Funde von Conodonten-Gruppen aus dem oberen Karbon des Sauerlandes. *Paläeontol. Z., 38*, 105–135.

Scott, H. W. 1934. The zoological relationships of the conodonts. *J. Paleontol., 8*, 448–455, 2 plates.

Scott, H. W. 1942. Conodont assemblages from the Heath Formation, Montana. *J. Paleontol., 16*, 293–300, 4 plates.

Scott, H. W. 1973. New conodontochordata from the Bear Gulch Limestone (Namurian, Montana). *Mich. State Univ. Paleontol. Ser., 1*, 81–100, 3 plates.

Seddon, G. and Sweet, W. C. 1971. An ecologic model for conodonts. *J. Paleontol., 45*, 869–880.

Smith, D. B., Brunston, R. G. W., Manning, P. I., Simpson, S. and Shotton, F. W. *1974. A correlation of Permian rocks in the British Isles. Geol. Soc. London Spec. Rep., 5*, 1–45.

Sweet, W. C. 1970. Uppermost Permian and Lower Triassic conodonts of the Salt Range and Trans-Indus Ranges, West Pakistan. In: B. Kummel and C. Teichert (Eds.) *Stratigraphic boundary problems, Permian and Triassic of West Pakistan, Univ. Kansas, Dep. Geol., Spec. Publ., 4*, 207–275, 5 plates.

Sweet, W. C. 1981. Morphology and composition of elements, macromorphology of elements and apparatuses. In: R. A. Robison (Ed.) *Treatise on Invertebrate Paleontology, Part W, Supplement 2, Conodonta*, Geological Society of America and University of Kansas Press, Lawrence, Kansas, W5–W20.

Sweet, W. C. and Bergström, S. M. (Eds) 1971. *Symp. Conodont Biostratigraphy,* in *Mem. Geol. Soc. Am., 127*, 1–499.

Sweet, W. C. and Bergström, S. M. 1972. Multielement taxonomy and Ordovician conodonts. *Geol. Palaeontol., Sonderb., 1*, 29–42.

Sweet, W. C. and Bergström, S. M. 1974. Provincialism exhibited by Ordovician conodont faunas. In: C. A. Ross (Ed.) *Paleogeographic Provinces and Provinciality, Soc. Econ. Paleontol. Min. Spec. Publ., 21*, 189–202.

Sweet, W. C. and Bergström, S. M. 1981. Biostratigraphy and evolution. In: Robinson, R. A. (Ed.), *Treatise on Invertebrate Paleontology, Part W, Supplement 2, Conodonta*, Geological Society of America and University of Kansas Press, Lawrence, Kansas, W92–W101.

Ulrich, E. O. and Bassler, R. S. 1926. A classification of the toothlike fossils, conodonts, with descriptions of American Devonian and Mississippian species. *U.S. Natl. Mus. Proc., 58*, 12, 1–63, 11 plates.

von Bitter, P. H. 1976. Paleoecology and distribution of Windsor Group (Viséan–?Early Namurian) conodonts, Port Hood Island, Nova Scotia, Canada. In: C. R. Barnes (Ed.), *Conodont Palaeoecology, Spec. Paper Geol. Assoc. Can., 15*, 225–241.

Wardlaw, B. and Harris, A. G. 1984. Conodont-based thermal maturation and Paleozoic rocks in Arizona. *Am. Assoc. Pet. Geol. Bull., 68* (9), 1101–1106.

Weddige, K. and Ziegler, W. 1976. The significance of *Icriodus: Polygnathus* ratios in limestones from the type Eifelian, Germany. In: C. R. Barnes (Ed.), *Conodont Palaeoecology, Spec. Paper Geol. Assoc. Can., 15*, 187–199.

Williams, A., Strachan, I., Bassett, D. A., Dean, W. T., Ingham, J. K., Wright, A. D. and Whittington, H. B. 1972. Correlation of Ordovician rocks in the British Isles. *Geol Soc. London, Spec. Rep., 3*, 1–74.

Wright-Clark, J. 1983. Rare earth elements in conodont apatite: Variations with geological age and with depositional environments. *Abstracts Geol. Soc. Am., 15*, 247.

Ziegler, W. 1970 On microstructure and surface ornamentation of conodonts. *Abstracts Geol. Soc. Am., 2*, 410.

Ziegler, W. (Ed.) 1973. *Catalogue of Conodonts, I,* Schweizerbart'sche Stuttgart, 1–504, 27 plates.

Ziegler, W. (Ed.) 1975. *Catalogue of Conodonts, II,* Schweizerbart'sche, Stuttgart, 1–404, 25 plates.

Ziegler, W. (Ed.) 1977. *Catalogue of Conodonts, III,* Schweizerbart'sche, Stuttgart, 1–574, 39 plates.

Ziegler, W. (Ed.) 1981. *Catalogue of Conodonts, IV,* Schweizerbart'sche, Stuttgart, 1–445, 40 plates.

Ziegler, A. M., Cocks, L. R. M. and Bambach, R. K., 1968. The composition and structure of Lower Silurian marine communities. *Lethaia, 1*, 1–27.

Zittel, K. A. and Rohon, J. V. 1886. Über Conodonten. *Bayer Akad. Wiss. München Math-Phys. K. l. Sitzungsber., 16*, 108–136, 2 plates.

2

Conodonts of the Cambrian and Ordovician Systems from the British Isles

S. M. Bergström and **M. J. Orchard**
with contributions by
G. D. Sevastopulo, A. C. Higgins, N. M. Savage, R. J. Aldridge, M. D. Brasier and **A. W. A. Rushton**

2.1 HISTORY OF CONODONT STUDIES
(by M. J. Orchard)

Cambrian conodonts from Britain have only been known for little over a decade. Taylor and Rushton (1971) published the first record, and Miller and Rushton (1973) were the first to deal with them taxonomically. Their specimens of *Prooneotodus* were preserved on Upper Cambrian mudstone bedding surfaces; interestingly, an element had been recorded half a century earlier (as a trilobite spine) by G. Barrow (Taylor and Rushton, 1971, p. 33).

Subsequent accounts of conodonts from the Tremadoc and older rocks in Britain are few. Matthews and Missarzhevsky (1975, p. 294, Plate 3, Fig. 7) listed and figured an early Cambrian (Atdabanian) *Hertzina* from the *Strenuella* Limestone at Comley, Shropshire, and a questionable representative of the same genus was recorded from the Hartshill Formation in the Nuneaton

area of Warwickshire. Hinz (1983) and Brasier (1984) have recently added more data from these Lower Cambrian limestones, two species of *Hertzina* having now been identified from both the *Hyolithes* Limestone at Nuneaton and the Comley Limestone in Shropshire.

No Middle Cambrian conodonts are at present known from Britain, but additional Upper Cambrian and Tremadoc occurrences have been described by Rushton (1982) and by Bulman and Rushton (1973) respectively.

The history of study on Ordovician conodonts from the British Isles dates from a little over 80 years ago when John Smith, whilst taking a 'look round amongst the hills' at the head of the Snar Valley in the Southern Uplands of Scotland, discovered abundant conodonts preserved on the surface of shale interbedded with radiolarian chert. Smith (1907) found ten similar conodont localities in Southern Scotland and he was immediately impressed with the potential of conodonts for marking 'zonal bands' (Smith, 1907, p. 241). Almost half a century later, in a landmark work, Rhodes (1953) described conodonts from the Llandeilo Limestone in South Wales and from two Caradoc limestones in North Wales, the Gelli-grin and Pen-y-garnedd, now collectively referred to as the Cymerig Limestone. This paper marked the beginning of systematic Ordovician conodont study in Britain. During the 1950s, further conodont studies by Rhodes (1955) on the Keisley Limestone of Westmorland, by Lindström (1957) and Lamont and Lindström (1957) on strata in Southern Scotland, and by Lindström (1959) on the Crug Limestone of South Wales provided additional data and substantiated the value of conodonts as stratigraphic tools in Britain.

A taxonomic updating of Rhodes' (1953) study was carried out by Berström (1964), who also recorded additional new faunas from the Castell and Birdshill Limestones in South Wales. Further conodont data from Scotland was provided by Lindström (1964, pp. 8, 84, 85 and 141), Walton (1965, pp. 181 and 182) and Higgins (1967), the latter describing an early Ordovician conodont fauna from the Durness Limestone of northernmost Scotland that was remarkable in that it clearly had North American Midcontinent affinities.

In a state-of-the-art paper, Bergström (1971) summarized the distribution of Ordovician conodonts from the British Isles and began a modern phase of study, that of multielement conodont taxonomy. Conodont faunas from each of the previously known localities in Wales, and several new ones both there and in Southern Scotland and Ireland, were summarized in terms of their important multielement species, many of which were newly defined in the same paper. Bergström (1971) also introduced a conodont zonation for the Middle and Upper Ordovician of the Baltoscandic area and discussed its application in Britain. Recently, Orchard (1980) presented new data from the Upper Ordovician rocks of the North of England and from Wales. In particular, the conodont faunas of the type area of the Ashgill Series were described for the first time.

Some of the localities and faunas identified by Bergström (1971) have recently been discussed in more detail (Bergström 1981, 1983; Bergström et al., 1984). Also, 34 conodont localities from the British Isles were discussed by Bergström (1980) in terms of their colour alteration index (CAI) and the implied geothermometry of the host rocks. In a recent study (Savage and Bassett, in press), conodonts from Caradoc and Ashgill strata in Wales and the Welsh Borderland are described and some new localities recorded.

2.2 CONODONT LOCALITIES
(by M. J. Orchard)

(a) Tremadoc Series and older

Conodonts of this age are known from the Harlech Dome of North-west Wales, from the Welsh Borderland, from the English Midlands and from a single borehole in Buckinghamshire. In Wales the Cambrian System is represented by several thousand metres of basinal mudstone and sandstone which accumulated in the 'Welsh Trough', whereas in England there are much thinner contemporaneous successions of sandstone, mudstone and limestone shelf–sea deposits. Known conodont localities are indicated in Fig. 2.1 and details are given below.

C1.   Ogof-ddû, E of Criccieth. *Prooneotodus* sp. is recorded from beds transitional between the Merioneth Series and Tremadoc Series (Rushton, 1982, p. 43, Fig. 2).

C2.   Bryn-illin-fawr forestry road. *Prooneotodus tenuis* (including a fused cluster) and *Cordylodus proavus* occur in the Dol-cyn-afon Member of the Cwmhesgen Formation (Mawddach Group). These occurrences are referred to the *Acerocare* Zone of the Late Cambrian Merioneth Series (Rushton, 1982, p. 44, Fig. 3).

C3.   Comley, Shropshire. *Hertzina elongata* and *Hertzina*? cf. *bisulcata* are recorded from the early Cambrian Comley ('*Strenuella*') Limestone (Matthews and Missarzhevsky, 1975, p. 294, Plate 3, Fig. 7; Hinz, 1983; Brasier, 1984, pp. 235 and 236).

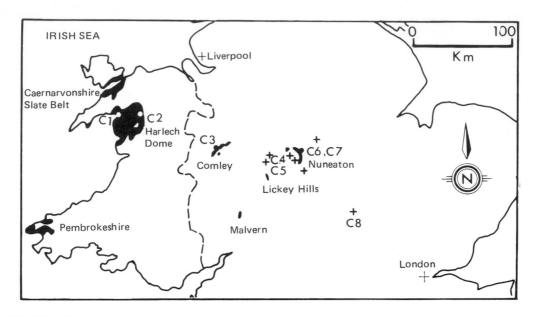

Fig. 2.1 — Map shows outcrop of Cambrian rocks in England and Wales and the location of Cambrian conodont localities C1—C6.

C4, C5 Warwickshire coalfield. *Prooneotodus tenuis* is recorded from the late Cambrian Monks Park Shales in several boreholes. Taylor and Rushton (1971, pp. 25 and 37, Plates 1 and 2) record it (as 'Problematicum B') in Merevale Nos. 1 and 2 Boreholes, and also in core taken at a depth of 2853 ft in the Hollyfast Borehole, and in the Dosthill area. The stratigraphic position indicates the Upper *Peltura scarabaeoides* or *Acerocare* Zone (Miller and Rushton, 1973, p. 338). In Merevale No. 3 Borehole *Westergaardodina?* occurs in the Outwoods Shales at the top of the *Olenus* Zone, and *Furnishina* cf. *asymmetrica* in the Monks Park Shales at the base of the *Parabolina spinulosa* Zone (Taylor and Rushton, 1971, p. 13). *Prooneotodus* is present also in cores (up to the (*Clonograptus tenellus* Zone) from several boreholes in Warwickshire (A. W. A. Rushton, unpublished).

C6, C7 Woodlands Quarry, Hartshill, near Nuneaton, Warwickshire. *Hertzina elongata* and *H.?* cf. *bisulcata* are known from beds 1 and 10 respectively of the *Hyolithes* Limestone within the Home Farm Member of the Hartshill Formation (Matthews and Missarzhevsky, 1975, p. 294; Brasier, 1984, pp. 235 and 236).

C8.   Tatternhoe Borehole, 8 miles NE of Buckingham. *Westergaardodina* cf. *bicuspidata* is recorded from mudstone interbedded with grey and red-stained siltstone, sandstone and shale of Tremadoc age. The conodonts are associated with the graptolite *Dictyonema flabelliforme* below Liassic rocks (Bulman and Rushton, 1973, pp. 14, 30 and 31).

(b) Arenig Series and younger
Far more conodont data are available from rocks of this age, faunules being known from most regions of Ordovician outcrop in the British Isles (Fig. 2.2). Below, data from the following regions are listed separately: Wales and the Welsh Borderland, the North of England, Southern Scotland, Northern Scotland and Ireland.

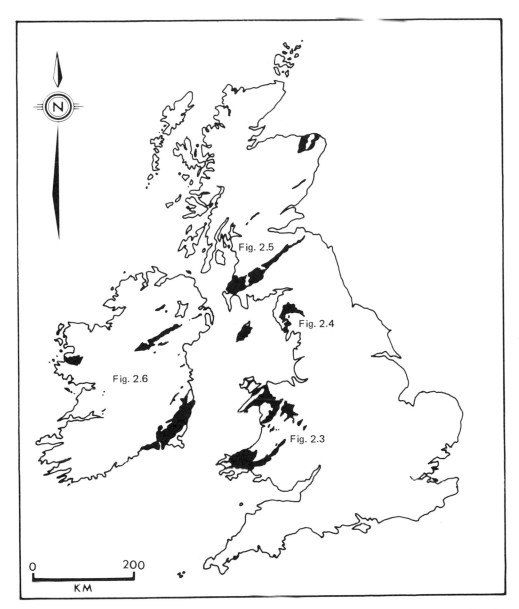

Fig. 2.2 – Map shows outcrop of Ordovician rocks in the British Isles, and the location of Figs. 2.3–2.6.

(i) Wales and the Welsh Borderland

Ordovician rocks in Wales are extremely variable. They include andesitic volcanics, muddy sandstones, graptolitic shales and local limestone accumulations, often developed on an unstable sea floor surrounding volcanic islands. Local unconformities occur both here and in the Welsh Borderland, where the sequences are generally thinner and dominated by calcareous mudstones and shelly sandstones deposited in the shallower-water shelf environment with a shoreline not far to the east.

There are 21 published locations of conodonts in the Ordovician rocks of this area (Fig. 2.3); more have been recorded by Savage and Bassett (in press). Many of those recorded by Bergström (1971, 1980) remain undescribed in detail, but a summary of published accounts, with some updating, and some new data follow.

1.   Abereiddy Bay, north side near entrance to disused quarry. *Amorphognathus tvaer-*

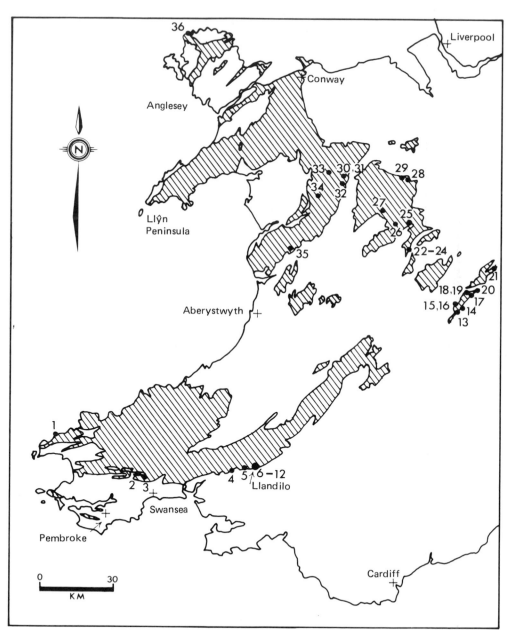

Fig. 2.3 – Map shows outcrop of Ordovician rocks in Wales and the Welsh Borderland and the Ordovician conodont localities 1–36.

ensis, Phragmodus n. sp. cf. *inflexus* (=?*P. polovicus* Dzik) and *Plectodina flexa* were recorded by Bergström (1964, 1971, Fig. 7, 1980 and herein) from the Castell Limestone of the Llandeilo Series.

2.   Robeston Wathen, disused quarry. Undetermined species of *Amorphognathus, Aphelognathus* or *Plectodina* and several coniform elements occur in the Robeston Wathen Limestone of the Ashgill Series (Orchard, 1980, pp. 12 and 13). Savage and Bassett (in press) record *Amorphognathus ordovicicus* from this unit.

3.   Bryn-banc quarries, 3 km E of Narberth. *Amorphognathus tvaerensis, Eoplacognathus elongatus* and *Icriodella* cf. *I. praecox* are recorded from the Narberth Group, which extends from the Llandeilo to Caradoc Series (Bergström, 1980, 1983; Bergström *et al.,* 1984).

4,5.   Llandilo. Savage and Bassett (in press) record additional faunules from the Birdshill Limestone (see loc. 6) W of Llandilo.

6.   Llandilo, quarry WNW of Birdshill Farm, W of town. *Amorphognathus superbus* (an advanced form), *Icriodella superba, Rhodesognathus elegans* and *Ozarkodina? pseudofissilis* are reported to be the dominant multielement species in the Birdshill Limestone (Ashgill Series). In addition, *Prioniodus* sp., *Plectodina* sp. and coniform elements occur (Bergström, 1964, 1971, 1980; Orchard, 1980). Savage and Bassett (in press) also discuss the Birdshill Limestone fauna but determine the *Amorphognathus* sp. as *A. ordovicicus* based on Pb elements. These authors do not record holodontiform M elements, but those recovered by Orchard (1980) clearly do not belong to *A. ordovicicus.*

7.   Penybanc, NW of Llandilo. Savage and Bassett (in press) record species of *Amorphognathus* and *Plectodina* from an outcrop which they refer tentatively to the Mydrim Shales.

8.   Llandilo, quarry at Crug Farm, 0.5 mile N of town. Conodonts from the Crug Limestone (Ashgill Series) were first described by Lindström (1959), and later by Bergström (1964, 1971, 1980) and Orchard (1980). The fauna resembles that of the Birdshill Limestone but in addition includes *Aphelognathus rhodesi* (*A. furcatus* in Orchard, 1980) and more common *Ozarkodina? pseudofissilis.* Also, the *Icriodella* morphs, which are less common than in the Birdshill Limestone, have more discrete nodes than topotype *I. superba.* Further, some *Amorphognathus* holodontiform M elements appear more advanced than those of *A. superbus* (Orchard, 1980; Savage and Bassett, in press).

9.   Llandilo, 500 m WSW of Dynevor Castle. *Amorphognathus* cf. *tvaerensis, Icriodella superba* and *Plectodina flexa* are recorded from the uppermost beds of the Llandeilo Flags at this locality (Bergström, 1971, 1980, 1983).

10.   Llandilo, 300 ft ESE of Keepers Lodge at the Golden Grove Quarry, Llanfihangel Aberythych. This is locality 1 of Rhodes (1953), developed in the Lower Llandeilo Flags. Bergström (1964, 1971, 1980) has updated the faunal list which includes *Amorphognathus inaequalis, Prioniodus prevariablis, Plectodina flexa* and '*Erismodus*' sp. (see locs. 18 and 19).

11, 12.   Llandilo, Ffairfach railway cutting. Bergström (1971, 1980, 1983) and Bergström *et al.* (1984) have listed conodonts from this section. The conglomeratic unit in the uppermost part of the Ffairfach Grit contain *Eoplacognathus lindstroemi, Amorphognathus inaequalis, Baltoniodus prevariabilis* and *Plectodina* sp. Above these beds at the same locality, the Lower Llandeilo Flags yield a similar fauna which lacks *Eoplacognathus.*

13–15.   Southern Shropshire, southern Caradoc Series succession. Savage and Bassett (in press) record species of *Plectodina* and *Prioniodus* from the Costonian Stage Coston Formation; *Icriodella superba, Plectodina* n. sp. 2 and *Rhodesognathus elegans* from the Marshbrookian Stage Cheney Longville Formation.

16. Rock House, Onny Valley. Conodonts from the Costonian Stage Hoar Edge Grit are mentioned but not listed by Bergström (1980).

17. Hatton Bridge, Church Stretton. From the Caradoc Series Acton Scott Formation, Bergström (1971, 1980) records *Icriodella superba, Rhodesognathus elegans* and *Plectodina* sp. Savage and Bassett (in press) record further elements.

18, 19. Wyresytch quarry, SW end of Ragleth Hill, Church Stretton. Bergström (1971, 1980) reported *Icriodella superba* and '*Erismodus*' sp. from strata assigned to the Caradocian Series Harnage Group. Savage and Bassett (in press) identify the same(?) fauna as *I. superba* and *Plectodina* n. sp. 2, specifically from the Harnagian Stage Smeathen Wood Formation.

20. Southern Shropshire, southern Caradocian Series succession. Savage and Bassett (in press) record *Icriodella superba* and *Plectodina* n. sp. 1 from the Woolstonian Stage Alternata Limestone.

21. Evenwood Quarry, 13 km SE of Shrewsbury *Amorphognathus* cf. *tvaerensis, Icriodella* cf. *I praecox, Rhodesognathus elegans* (or a closely allied species – see Section 2.4), *Plectodina* n. sp. and '*Erismodus*' (see locs. 18 and 19) sp. are recorded from the Costonian Stage Hoar Edge Grit by Bergström (1971, 1980). Bergström (1983, Figs. 6C and 6D) illustrated an *Icriodella* apparatus from this locality. Savage and Bassett (in press) record additional elements, including the type material of *Plectodina* n. sp. 1 from nearby.

22–24. Gwern y Brain, near Welshpool. A small fauna from the Onnian Stage Pen-y-garnedd Phosphorite, Nod Glas Formation, includes *Amorphognathus* cf. *A.*

complicatus (Orchard, herein). Savage and Bassett (in press) record two *Amorphognathus-* and *Rhodesognathus*-bearing faunules from low and high in the Nod Glas Formation. The lower one also includes *Icriodella superba* and *Plectodina* n. sp. 1, whereas the higher one includes *Phragmodus* and *Protopanderodus*.

25. Gelli Farm. E. of Llanfyllin. Savage and Bassett (in press) record a small fauna from the Dolhir Formation, including *Ozarkodina pseudofissilis* and species of *Icriodella* and ?*Amorphognathus*.

26. Greenhall Park quarry, E of Llanfyllin. Savage and Bassett (in press) record *Icriodella superba* and *Plectodina* n. sp. 1 from the Pen-y-garnedd Formation at this locality.

27. Pen-y-garnedd, quarry 900 ft E of Powis Arms. This is locality 3 of Rhodes (1953). The conodonts from this outcrop of the Caradoc Series Cymerig Limestone were later discussed by Bergström (1964, 1971) who listed *Amorphognathus superbus, A. complicatus, Icriodella superba, Rhodesognathus elegans* and *Plectodina* species.

28. Ty-draw Hill quarry ESE of Ddolhir. Savage and Bassett (in press) record *Amorphognathus ordovicicus, Phragmodus undatus, Protopanderodus liripipus* and *Icriodella* from the Ashgill Series Glyn Formation.

29. Quarry ESE of Ddolhir. A small conodont faunule with a CAI value of 5 was noted by Bergström (1980, p. 390) from the Ashgill Series Ddolhir Limestone. It consists of simple coniform elements.

30. Bala, quarry 1750 ft N of Plas Rhiwaldog, 600 ft E of Y Garnedd. This is locality 2 of Rhodes (1953), the Gelligrin Limestone. In most respects the conodont fauna is the same as the limestone at Pen-y-garnedd (loc. 27), but Bergström (1964, 1971) did not record *A. complicatus*. Orchard (1980) discussed and figured this faunule too, including several elements not originally found by Rhodes

(1953). Some of the elements called 'Bryantodina? aff. polita' by Orchard (1980) are the same as others referred to Plectodina n. sp. 1 of Savage and Bassett (in press).

31. Bala, quarries on Brun Pig, S of the town. This represents a further exposure of the Cymerig Limestone. Details were given by Bergström (1964).

32. Hillside exposure SE of Llangower. Orchard (1980, pp. 12–14) recorded Amorphognathus ordovicicus, Hamarodus europaeus and Birksfeldia circumplicata from the Ashgill Series Rhiwlas Limestone at this locality. In addition, rare elements of Icriodella and Ozarkodina? occur with abundant coniform elements.

33, 34. W and SW of Bala. Additional exposures of Rhiwlas Limestone have yielded Amorphognathus ordovicicus and/or Panderodus (Savage and Bassett, in press).

35. Pistyll Gwyn Waterfalls, Afon Pumryd, Llanymawddwy. Orchard (1980, pp. 12–14) recorded a faunule closely similar to that from the Rhiwlas Limestone (loc. 32) within the Ashgill Series Abercwmeiddaw Mudstones Group (collected by P. Magor).

36. Anglesey, shore exposure 1 km ESE of Carmel Head. Bergström (1980, 1981) reported Prioniodus variabilis, Pygodus sp. = P. anserinus, Eoplacognathus elongatus, Periodon aculeatus, Plectodina sp. and Amorphognathus sp. cf. A. kielcensis from a limestone olistostrome within the Garn Formation, which also contains Complexodus pugionifer (Bergström, herein).

(ii) The North of England

Ordovician rocks outcrop over a large area in the Lake District and in the Cross Fell, Cautley-Dent and Craven Inliers to the east. In the Lake District, several thousand metres of argillites, sandstones and volcanics make up the bulk of the sequence at the top of which lies the Coniston Limestone (McNamara, 1979; Moseley, 1984). Correlatives of the latter occur in inliers to the east where the Upper Ordovician succession is dominated by calcareous mudstones with minor volcanics and local limestones (Ingham, 1966) which developed on the eastern and northern fringes of an emergent Lake District area.

Conodont collections from this region (Fig. 2.4) are all late Ordovician in age, and largely from the Ashgill Series. The work of Orchard (1980) aimed to intercalibrate conodonts from these rocks with the shelly zonal scheme established by Ingham (1966) in the Howgill Fells, the type area for the Ashgill Series (Ingham and Wright, 1970). Orchard (1980) provides details of the individual collections, a summary of which follows, together with some data from Bergström (1980) and Aldridge (herein).

37. Lake District, High Pike Haw. Birksfeldia sp., Amorphognathus sp., Belodina sp. and Staufferella sp. occur at the base of the Cautleyan Stage Kentmere Limestone Member of the Applethwaite Formation (Orchard, 1980).

38. Lake District, Old Pits Beck. Amorphognathus ordovicicus, Strachanognathus parvus and Birksfeldia sp. occur in the Rawtheyan Stage White Limestone (Orchard, 1980).

39. Lake District, Hol (=Skelgill) Beck, Troutbeck. Amorphognathus sp. indet. and coniform elements with a CAI = 5 from the Rawtheyan Stage White Limestone (Bergström, 1980, p. 390, and herein).

40, 41. Lake District, Brow Gill. Coniform elements are known from the base and top of the Cautleyan Stage Kentmere Limestone Member of the Applethwaite Formation. Nearby a rich faunule occurs in the overlying Rawtheyan Stage mucronata Beds. The latter includes Birksfeldia circumplicata, Amorphognathus ordovicicus, Hamarodus europaeus, Strachanognathus parvus, and Coelocerodontus trigonius (Orchard, 1980).

42–55. Taythes Inlier, Cautley: Taythes Gill,

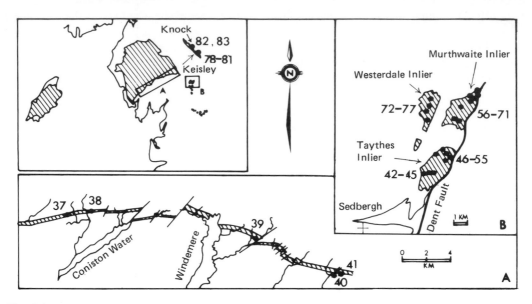

Fig. 2.4 – Map shows outcrop of Ordovician rocks in the north of England and the Ordovician conodont localities 37–83. 4A shows the Coniston Limestone localities of the Southern Lake District; Fig. 4B shows the localities in the Howgill Fells inliers.

Birksfield Beck, Ecker Secker Beck. 14 faunules from Cautleyan, Rawtheyan and Hirnantian strata (Orchard, 1980). The significant faunules here came from the latest Rawtheyan Stage Cystoid Limestone and include the original locality for *Birksfeldia circumplicata*. In association are *Amorphognathus ordovicicus, Hamarodus europaeus, Strachanognathus parvus, Pseudooneotodus mitratus* and other coniform taxa.

56–71. Murthwaite Inlier, Cautley: Sally Beck, Sally Brow, High Sprintgill, Low Sprintgill, River Rawthey. 16 faunules from Pusgillian, Cautleyan and Rawtheyan strata of the Cautley Mudstones (Orchard, 1980). The Pusgillian faunules include diminutive specimens of *Amorphognathus, Plectodina* or *Aphelognathus, Ozarkodina* and *Rhodesognathus,* probably referable to the *superbus* Zone. Cautleyan faunules lack most of these taxa but include *Amorphognathus ordovicicus* and *Birksfeldia* sp. Rawtheyan faunules contain mostly coniform elements.

72–77. Westerdale Inlier, Cautley: Backside Beck. Six faunules of Rawtheyan age from the Cautley Mudstones (Orchard, 1980). Notable are *Amorphognathus ordovicicus* and *Birksfeldia* sp.

78, 79. Cross Fell, Keisley Quarry. Rhodes (1955) described a fauna from the Keisley Limestone exposed in this quarry which was subsequently referred by Bergström (1971) to the *A. ordovicicus* Zone. Orchard (1980) sampled the outcrop and studied both Rhodes's collection and another provided by R. J. Aldridge. Only the latter included holodontiform elements, which Orchard (1980) referred to *Amorphognathus lindstroemi*; here, these elements are regarded as part of *A. duftonus* Rhodes. In addition, the collections, which originate from the upper part of the limestone, include *Hamarodus europaeus, Birksfeldia* sp. and *Strachanognathus parvus.* In contrast, the lower more argillaceous part of the limestone yielded species of *Icriodella* and *Aphelognathus* (Orchard, 1980).

80, 81   Cross Fell, beds exposed at the sharp
          bend in the lane to Keisley Quarry. These
          beds overlie the Keisley Limestone and
          were thought by Temple (1968) to belong
          to the Llandovery Series but Ingham and
          Wright (in Williams *et al.*, 1972, p.
          47) recorded a *Hirnantia* fauna and concluded
          that they were of late Ashgill age. A few
          conodonts from these beds were also of
          Ordovician aspect (Aldridge, 1975, p.
          609). From two adjacent calcareous
          horizons, Aldridge (herein) reports species
          of *Amorphognathus, Icriodella, Eocarnio-
          dus, Walliserodus?, Dapsilodus* and *Pan-
          derodus*.

82, 83   Cross Fell, Swindale Beck, Knock. The
          Rawtheyan Stage Swindale Limestone in-
          cludes *Amorphognathus* sp. and coniform
          elements. Calcareous horizons within the
          overlying Hirnantian Stage Ashgill Shales
          have yielded *A. ordovicicus* and *Hamaro-
          dus europaeus* (Orchard, 1980).

(iii) *Southern Scotland*

The Ordovician sequence in the Southern Uplands
of Scotland generally consists of mudstones and/or
coarse clastics with local volcanics and minor carbonates. In some areas the sequence is very thick
and includes conglomerates, whereas elsewhere
there are relatively thin successions of fine grained
mudstones and cherts.

    Ordovician conodonts are known from several
widely separated areas in this region (Fig. 2.5),
generally within relatively deep water sediments,
and often in association with graptolites and/or
radiolarians. Conodonts have been known from
this area since the turn of the century, but few
have been systematically described. The following
is an update of known localities:

84, 85   Morroch Bay, 1.5 miles SE of Portpatrick.
          Two accounts of conodonts from this
          locality are published. Lamont and
          Lindström (1957) found (what would
          now be called) *Spinodus spinatus* and a
          questionable *Periodon aculeatus* in indian-

red shale. Lindström (1957) illustrated
28 specimens of conodonts associated
with 19 species of graptolites, including
the zonal index *Climacograptus wilsoni*,
within black shale. These conodonts
appear to represent *Periodon* and various
coniform taxa.

86–91.   Girvan, Aldons Quarry (loc. 86), quarry
          0.5 km WSW of Minuntion Farm (loc.
          87), Benan Burn (locs. 88–90) and
          Brockloch Quarries (loc. 91). Berg-
          ström (1980) mentions conodonts from
          the Stinchar Limestone (Barr Group)
          from each of these localities. In Benan
          Burn the limestone contains *Pygodus
          serra* in its lower part and *P. anserinus* in
          its upper part. Elsewhere in the Stinchar
          Limestone, *Cahabagnathus sweeti, Proto-
          panderodus varicostatus, Belodina moni-
          torensis* and *Belodella* n. sp B occur. The
          underlying Confinis Flags contain un-
          diagnostic conodonts (Bergström, 1971).

92.   Girvan, Laggan Burn. Bergström (1971
          and herein) records from the Balclatchie
          Group a 'beautiful' fauna, which includes
          *Amorphognathus tvaerensis, Periodon acu-
          leatus, 'Aphelognathus'* sp., *Spinodus
          spinatus, Cahabagnathus* cf. *carnesi, Belo-
          dina* sp. and *Protopanderodus liripipus*.

93, 94.   Girvan, Whitehouse Bay. The Whitehouse
          Beds and overlying Shalloch Formation at
          this locality contain *Amorphognathus*
          sp(p)., *Phragmodus undatus, Belodina* sp.
          and *Plectodina* sp. (Bergström, 1980;
          Sweet and Bergström, 1976, pp. 135 and
          136). The younger unit is referable to the
          A. ordovicicus Zone, and has yielded
          Birksfeldia? sp. *Protopanderodus liripipus,
          Scabbardella altipes* and *Panderodus*
          (Bergström, herein).

95.   Girvan, Penwhapple Burn, S of Knock-
          gerran. A faunule recorded from the
          Cascade Grits (Bergström, 1980) includes
          Amorphognathus sp., *Aphelognathus* sp.,
          Dapsilodus mutatus, Phragmodus sp. and
          Protopanderodus liripipus (Bergström,
          herein).

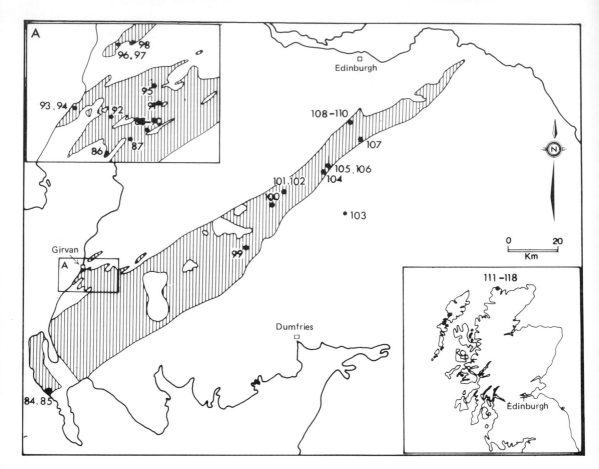

Fig. 2.5 – Map shows outcrop of Ordovician rocks in Scotland and the Ordovician localities 84–118. Insets show details of the Girvan area, and the position of the Durness locality.

96, 97   Girvan, Craighead Hill. Two localities are noted by Lamont and Lindström (1957, p. 65) in red chert associated with pillow lavas included within the Ballantrae Group. The conodonts include *Periodon aculeatus* and '*Acontiodus*' sp.

98.   Girvan, Craighead Quarries. Bergström (1980) mentions a conodont faunule from the Craighead Limestone which includes *Amorphognathus* sp., *Plectodina* sp., *Periodon grandis* and *Belodina compressa* (Bergström, herein).

99.   Fardingmulloch, 5.5 km W of Enterkinfoot, Dumfrieshire. Lamont and Lindström (1957) record *Periodon aculeatus* from dark-red chert at this locality and

note that *Pygodus anserinus* occurs in John Smith's original collection from hereabouts.

100.   Crawford, Lanarkshire, Ravengill Burn. A well-preserved Arenig faunule was found in ochreous shale by Lamont and Lindström (1957, pp. 61 and 62), who present a composite list of 22 form species. Of these, *Oepikodus evae* is the diagnostic species (Lindström, 1971). Löfgren (1978, p. 38) provided a nomenclaturally updated list as follows: *O. evae, Protopanderodus rectus, Paroistodus parallelus, P. proteus, Drepanoistodus forceps, Drepanodus arcuatus, Oistodus lanceolatus* and *Paracordylodus gracilis*.

101,   Crawford, Normangill Burn. Two faunas
102.   were reported by Lamont and Lindström
        (1957). One was associated with grapto-
        lites in black shale and included *Pygodus
        anserinus* and *Periodon aculeatus*. The
        second occurred as moulds in pale-greenish
        or yellowish chert with thin lamellae of
        shale: a composite fauna from these beds
        included the above taxa plus coniform
        elements.

103.   Dob's Linn, N of Moffat. From cherty
        shale (Glenkiln Shale?) at the basal part
        of the Main Cliff at this locality, Lamont
        and Lindström (1957) record an unspeci-
        fied conodont fauna. H. Williams (per-
        sonal communication) has made addi-
        tional collections.

104—   Tweed Valley area, quarry SE of Glen-
106.   cotho, Wrae Hill, and Drumelzier Quarry
        respectively. Limestones from each of
        these localities were reported by Berg-
        ström (1971, 1980, 1981) to contain
        diverse conodont faunas, including *Pygo-
        dus serra, P. aculeatus, Protopanderodus
        varicostatus, Spinodus spinatus, Eoplaco-
        gnathus* sp., *Strachanognathus parvus* and
        Prioniodus prevariabilis, an association of
        late Llanvirn Series or slightly younger
        age. Earlier Bergström *et al.* (1974, p.
        1652) listed additional coniform ele-
        ments from the Wrae Limestone, including
        Dapsilodus(?), *Cornuodus, Drepanoisto-
        dus* and *Panderodus. Polonodus* is also
        known from the Wrae Limestone (Or-
        chard, herein).

107.   Eddleston Valley. Lindström (1964, pp.
        80, 84, 85 and 141) and Walton (1965,
        pp. 181 and 182) recorded ten form
        species from the Winkston Limestone.
        The most recent update is provided by
        Bergström (1981) who noted the fauna
        is the same as that of the Tweed Valley
        Limestones (locs. 104—106).

108—   Lamancha, Peebleshire. Lamont and
110.   Lindström (1957) recorded three cono-
        dont localities in dark-red chert in this
        area. One occurs 0.4 km ENE of Noble-
house, W of Lamancha, the second (in
association with graptolites) occurs 0.4
km S of Ruddenleys farmhouse, S of
Lamancha, and the third (associated with
pillow lavas) occurs about 0.25 km NNW
of the same farmhouse. All three yielded
*Pygodus serra, P. anserinus, Periodon
aculeatus* and *Spinodus spinatus.*

(iv) Northern Scotland
In the North-west Highlands, the Cambrian and
Ordovician Systems are represented by the limestones and dolomites of the Durness Limestone,
the topmost member of which, the Durine Member,
has yielded the only conodonts hitherto known
from the region (Fig. 2.5). Additional elements
are now known from the underlying Croisaphuill
Formation (Higgins, herein), although there is
uncertainty regarding the separation of the two
units (Whittington, in Williams *et al.*, 1972, p. 50).

111—   Durness Village. Higgins (1967) reported
115.   five productive samples of Durine Lime-
        stone from outcrops in and to the W of
        the village. These samples were collected
        at the base (D18 and D19), at 400 ft
        (D10) and at 700 ft (D15 and D16)
        above the base of the formation and
        yielded a composite fauna of 16 form
        species of conodonts which were assessed
        as late Arenig or early Llanvirn Series by
        Higgins. Lindström (1971, p. 38) partly
        reassessed this fauna and concluded that
        their age could be precisely determined
        as the *hirundo* Zone of the late Arenig
        Series. Further revision by Löfgren
        (1978) appraised '*Scandodus' brevibasis*
        as implying a date from within the inter-
        val *Paroistodus originalis — Microzar-
        kodina flabellum parva* zones, i.e. late
        Volkhovian Stage, or middle to late
        Arenig Series. However, this species
        does range into the Llanvirn Series.
        Löfgren (1978) also proposed a correla-
        tion with the North American Midconti-
        nent faunas 2 or lowermost 3 of Sweet
        et al. (1971) based on *Oistodus multi-*

corrugatus. Most recently, Ethington and Clark (1981, pp. 55, 68 and 88) have synonymized additional Durness specimens as *Pteracontiodus cryptodens* and ?*'Microzarkodina' marathonensis*. In addition, Higgins (herein) records *Ulrichodina*? cf. *simplex, Protopanderodus gradatus,* and *Histiodella* sp. Bergström (herein) records further diagnostic Midcontinent elements (see Section 2.6).

116–
118
Durness. Higgins (herein) records three collections of conodonts from the (base, +3 m and +20 m) Croisaphuill Formation, 100 m E of Loch Croispol, and about 100 m lower in the section than the Durine faunules. A composite list comprises *Protopanderodus gradatus, Scolopodus* cf. *emarginatus, Paltodus* aff. *sexplicatus* and *'Oistodus'* sp. 6 of Ethington and Clark (1981). This fauna is assigned to the *Acodus deltatus–Macerodus dianae* interval of Ethington and Clark (1981), i.e. Middle or Upper Canadian in age (Higgins, herein).

(v) *Ireland* (by G. D. Sevastopulo)

The Irish Caledonides comprise several northeasterly-striking belts (Fig. 2.6) distinguished by their stratigraphy and tectonic history, which may be correlated, at least approximately, with similar belts in Britain. All of them, except the furthest northwesterly Dalradian Belt contain Ordovician rocks.

The Murrisk Belt, best known in the area in the west from which it takes its name, is the continuation along strike of the Midland Valley of Scotland. It contains several inliers of volcanics of island arc type, and varied (mostly basinal) sedimentary rocks.

The Longford Down Belt is analogous to the Southern Uplands of Scotland. It can be divided into a northern division of volcanics, greywackes, black shales and cherts, and a southern division in which the Ordovician rocks occur as small inliers within Silurian greywackes.

The Leinster Belt (the northern boundary of which has been interpreted as the line of closure

of the Iapetus Ocean – see Fig. 2.7) can be subdivided into several northeasterly-striking divisions of distinctive Ordovician geology. These include a division of island arc volcanics, some of which are capped by limestones such as those of the Lambay, Portrane and the Chair of Kildare Inliers. Elsewhere, varied sedimentary rocks of both shallow- and deeper-water origin occur.

Study of Irish Ordovician conodonts is at a reconnaissance stage. Relatively few faunas are known, partly because of the generally unpromising nature of most Irish Ordovician rocks. Published information is limited to faunal lists or records of unspecified conodont faunas. For completeness, all these localities are included in the list below. They may be located by reference to the Irish National Grid.

119,
120.
Tourmakeady, County Mayo. Bergström (1980) reported conodonts with a CAI of approximately 3.5 from the Tourmakeady Limestone, 200 m W of Gortbunacullin Farm (M 109 718). Judging by its outcrop pattern, the limestone in the Tourmakeady area consists of a series of lenses (many of them of carbonate breccia). Conodonts have been recovered from at least one other locality (M 053 653) which has yielded *Juanognathus* sp., *Oistodus lanceolatus* and *Periodon flabellum* (Marigold White, personal communication). Brachiopods from the limestones are of mid-Arenig age (Williams and Curry, 1984).

121–
124.
County Galway, north. Within the coarse turbidites of the Rosroe Formation there are several lenses of allochthonous carbonate. They occur at Killary Bay Little (L 775 643), Dernasliggaun (L 821 619), Currarevagh (L 965 591) and S of Lough Nafooey at L 979 589. All have yielded conodonts but the only substantial fauna collected so far is from Currarevagh. It includes *Coleodus*? sp., *Periodon aculeatus* and *Protopanderodus* sp. Graptolites from the Rosroe Formation indicate an early to middle Llanvirn age.

125.
Acton, County Armagh. The discovery of

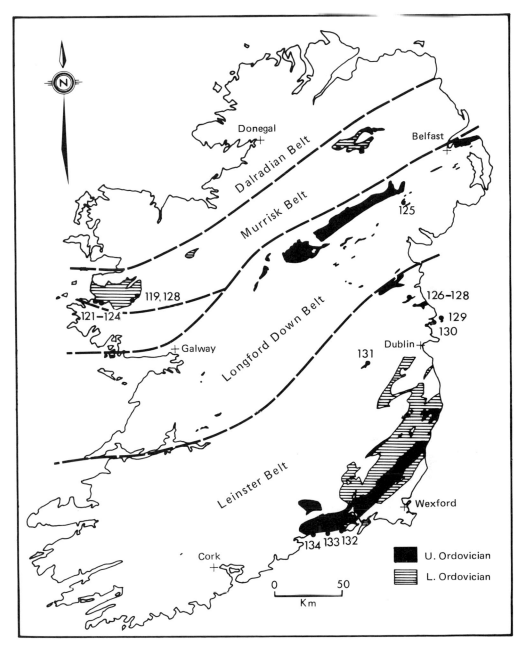

Fig. 2.6 — Map shows the outcrop of Ordovician rocks in Ireland, the principal tectonic belts and the Ordovician conodont localities 119–134.

conodonts of late Llanvirn age in a faulted inlier of red and green mudstones and black cherts near Acton has recorded in the Annual Report for 1974 of the Institute of Geological Sciences. Bergström (1980) referred to the same fauna, reporting a CAI value of 6–7 and recording the locality as a stream section in 'Crother's Valley Field' (J 0425 4124). He noted that the fauna was similar in age and preservation to those described from the Southern Uplands of Scotland by Lamont and Lindström (1957).

126–   Bellewstown, County Meath. The Bellews-
128.   town Beds were at one time exposed at two localities (O 083 671 and O 077669) in the northern part of the Balbriggan inlier. Shelly faunas from the silty limestones and calcareous siltstones were regarded by Harper and Rast (1964) as being of late Llanvirn age. Brenchley *et al.* (1977) reported two conodont faunas from the limestones, one assigned to the Llandeilo Series (by Bergström) and the other to the early Caradoc Series (by Higgins). New collections of limestone boulders from the float around both localities have yielded conodonts. The faunas include a single *Pygodus* sp. juv. cf. *P. serra* and common *Eoplacognathus robustus* (Brenda Thornbury, personal communication).

129,   Lambay Island and Portrane, County
130.   Dublin. Limestones similar in age to those at the Chair of Kildare are known to yield conodonts.

131.   Chair of Kildare, County Kildare. Bergström (1971) referred to conodonts, including *Amorphognathus ordovicicus*, from the limestones of Ashgill age at the Chair of Kildare.

132–   Tramore area, County Waterford. Berg-
134.   ström (1971) recorded the occurrence of the *Eoplacognathus lindstroemi* Subzone in the Tramore Limestone and noted that older and younger horizons were likely to be present in the formation. Bergström (1980) recorded CAI values of 5 for two collections of conodonts from Newton Head (loc. 131) and Dunabrattin Head (loc. 132) near Tramore. A small fauna from 14 m above the base of the Tramore Limestone at Tramore (loc.

130; S 580 008) contains *Eoplacognathus* sp. transitional between *E. robustus* and *E. lindstroemi*.

2.3   DEPOSITORY OF COLLECTIONS OF IMPORTANCE

Collections are housed as follows.

(a) The British Museum (Natural History)
The collections here include the figured material of Higgins (1967).

(b) The National Museum of Wales, Cardiff
This Museum houses the Savage and Bassett (in press) collection.

(c) The British Geological Survey
Collections here include the specimens of Rushton (1982) and Miller and Rushton (1973) and the John Smith collection.

(d) Universities
The Rhodes (1953) collection is at the Department of Geology, University of Birmingham. The Keisley fauna (Rhodes, 1955) is in the collections of the Department of Geology, University of Durham. The collection of the late S. C. Matthews is at the Department of Geology, University of Bristol. All material illustrated by Orchard is housed at the Sedgwick Museum, University of Cambridge. Specimens referred to in this volume from the Aldridge, Brasier and Sevastopulo collections are housed at the Geology Departments of the Universities of Nottingham, Hull, and Trinity College, Dublin, respectively. The extensive Bergström collection is located at the Department of Geology and Mineralogy, The Ohio State University, and material illustrated by Lindström (1959) is at the Geological Institute, University of Lund.

(e) Additional material
Additional material is contained in the Higgins collection at the Geological Survey of Canada, Calgary. The Lamont and Lindström (1957) specimens form part of the Lamont collection, the location of which is uncertain.

2.4 AN OUTLINE OF THE LIMITS AND INTERNAL DIVISIONS OF THE ORDOVICIAN SYSTEM AND THEIR CONODONT CORRELATION

(by S. M. Bergström)

An extensive and authoritative summary of the stratigraphical classification of the Ordovician System of the British Isles was published a little more than a decade ago (Williams *et al.*, 1972). Following general practice in Britain, the base of the Ordovician System was taken to be the base of the Arenig Series, and the top to be the top of the Hirnantian Stage of the Ashgill Series. Neither of these levels was defined precisely on the basis of graptolites or any other widespread index fossil group, and historical priority, especially the original scope of the system proposed by Lapworth (1879), undoubtedly was given primary importance when selecting these horizons as systemic boundaries. In a recent summary, Whittington *et al.* (1984) critically reviewed the scope of the series of the British Ordovician System and their biostratigraphic basis. Significantly, they note that no precise biostratigraphic definitions of the bases of each series and no boundary stratotypes have ever been formally proposed, and the exact biostratigraphic scope of most, if not all, series is open to question. An additional problem is the fact that these series, apart from the Llanvirn Series, have their typical development in shelly facies with largely endemic megafossils but have been widely interpreted, in most cases on very tenuous evidence, in terms of standard graptolite zones. This has unfortunately led to the propagation of some incorrect correlations, even internationally, e.g. the equation of the Llandeilo Series with the *Glyptograptus teretiusculus* Zone, and the Arenig Series with the *Paratetragraptus approximatus, Didymograptus extensus* and *D. hirundo* Zones (cf. Zalasiewicz, 1984). It is to be expected that such mistakes will be corrected during the ongoing reassessment of the series in their type areas, and it is also to be expected that this work will result in the proper definition of series units and selection of appropriate stratotypes. During the last decade, extensive world-wide work has been carried out by the Cambrian–Ordovician Boundary and the Ordo-vician–Silurian Boundary Working Groups of the International Commission of Stratigraphy with the ultimate goal of identifying stratigraphic levels and stratotypes for the systematic boundaries that will receive international approval. Although the work of the former group is not yet completed, recent deliberations show clearly that a large majority of its members is against placing the lower boundary of the system at the base of the Arenig Series. However, ratification is likely in the near future of a Working Group recommendation to define the base of the Silurian System as the base of the *Akidograptus acuminatus* Zone as it is developed at Dob's Linn in Southern Scotland. Pending inter-national decisions regarding the boundaries, the practice advocated by Williams *et al.* (1972) is followed herein, i.e. the Arenig Series is regarded as the oldest series of the Ordovician System, which also includes the Llanvirn, Llandeilo, Caradoc and Ashgill Series. No formal stages are currently used in the Arenig, Llanvirn and Llandeilo Series but the Caradoc and the Ashgill Series are subdivided into eight and four stages respectively.

Apart from the Llanvirn Series, the British series and stages have traditionally been defined on shelly fossils, and microfossils including conodonts have until recently been of little, if any, importance for the biostratigraphic classification. However, recent conodont work has direct bearing on the biostratigraphic scope and the definition of some series units, and it is appropriate to review some of those data here. For a correlation between the British series and conodont zone units, see Table 1.

Few conodont occurrences are known from certain Arenig strata (locs. 100, 119 and 120), and none from well-dated beds near the base of the Arenig and the Llanvirn Series; hence conodonts provide no assistance in defining these series boundaries. The basal part of the Llandeilo Series in its type area as well as the topmost portion of subjacent strata (the Ffairfach Group) have pro-duced moderately abundant but taxonomically not very varied conodont faunas (locs. 10–12), which indicate that the base of the type Llandeilo Series represents a level close to the base of the *Amorphognathus inaequalis* Subzone of the *Pygodus anserinus* Zone (Bergström, 1983; Bergström *et al.,* 1984). Based on conodont–graptolite zone relation (Bergström, in press), this level is no older than the uppermost *Glyptograptus teretiusculus* Zone in Baltoscandia. This is in agreement with the fact that graptolites of the *G. teretiusculus* Zone, as well as the index of the next younger zone, the *Nemagraptus gracilis* Zone, have been found in early Llandeilan rocks west of Llandilo (Addison, in Williams *et al.,* 1972). This means that, if the standard practice of defining the top of the Llanvirn Series as the top of the *Didymograptus murchisoni* Zone is followed, there is a post-Llanvirn pre-Llandeilo interval corresponding to a major part of the *G. teretiusculus* Zone that logically is not referable to either series (Bergström *et al.,* 1974, 1984; Jaanusson, 1979; Bergström, 1983). Obviously, a change in the classical scope of these series is needed to embrace this interval.

The upper Llandeilo Series in the type area (loc. 9) and the Llandeilo–Caradoc transition strata at Narberth west of Llandilo (loc. 3) contain conodonts which indicate that the top of the Llandeilo Series is likely to correspond to a level in the lowermost *A. tvaerensis* Zone (Bergström, 1983; Bergström *et al.,* 1984). Basal Caradoc (Costonian Stage) strata in the Caradoc type area in Shropshire (loc. 21) have yielded similar faunules also containing sparse specimens identified as *Rhodesognathus elegans* by Bergström (1971); these may well be conspecific with *R. elegans polonicus* (Dzik, 1976) and the form referred to as *'Prioniodus' (Rhodesognathus)* n. sp. aff. *Prioniodus variabilis* (Bergström, 1962) and *Prioniodus gerdae* (Bergström, 1971) by Lindström *et al.* (1974). The Polish specimens of this form, which is distinctive enough to merit recognition as a separate species, originate from the lowermost *Baltoniodus gerdae* Subzone and may be very slightly younger than the Costonian occurrences, which appear to represent the *B. variabilis* Subzone.

Although there are no notable differences between conodont faunas from the lower and upper Caradoc Series (Bergström, 1971; Savage and Bassett, in press), the various Caradocian stages defined on shelly fossils cannot be differ-

entiated at the present time using conodonts. Despite considerable efforts by several workers, the precise stratigraphic position of the *Amorphognathus tvaerensis–A. superbus* zonal boundary remains undetermined although it is clearly located in strata older than the Woolstonian Stage (?) Cymerig Limestone from which *A. superbus* was originally described. Savage and Bassett (in press) record *A.* aff. *tvaerensis* from the Nod Glas Formation (Onnian Stage) but, as noted by these workers, the specimens are atypical of *A. tvaerensis* and are not useful in locating the *A. tvaerensis–A. superbus* zonal boundary.

The Caradoc–Ashgill boundary is recognized on shelly fossils although recent work in Norway suggests that it may be approximately coeval with the *Dicranograptus clingani–Pleurograptus linearis* zonal boundary in the graptolite succession (Williams and Bruton, 1983). At present, this boundary cannot be defined by means of conodonts in Britain or elsewhere. Faunas from the Pusgillian Stage (lowermost Ashgill Series) include phylogenetically advanced specimens of the zonal index *A. superbus*, suggesting that the *A. superbus–A. ordovicicus* zonal boundary is either in the Upper Pusgillian Stage or Lower Cautleyan Stage (Bergström, 1971, 1983, Orchard, 1980). The *A. ordovicicus* Zone faunas show some changes through the Middle and Upper Ashgill Series (Orchard, 1980) but no formal subzones have been recognized and the data at hand do not permit discrimination of each of the Ashgill stages recognized on shelly fossils. There is a marked change in the conodont faunas in the Ordovician–Silurian boundary interval but none of the British sections studied thus far provides a continuous record of this faunal turnover and its relations to the system boundary. The proposed boundary stratotype at Dob's Linn is developed entirely in clastic rocks and there is little prospect of finding diagnostic conodonts, or other microfossils, through the boundary interval, although some conodonts are known from the locality (loc. 103).

2.5 CONODONT ZONATION
(by S. M. Bergström)

Since the 1950s, two main conodont faunal

provinces have been recognized in the Ordovician Systems, the North Atlantic and the North American Midcontinent Provinces. The former province is characterized by cold- or deep-water and in most cases mid- to high-latitude faunas whereas the Midcontinent Province includes primarily warm-water low-latitude faunas. The profound differences between these faunas has necessitated the use of a separate zonal scheme for each province. For details of the North Atlantic Province zonal units, see Lindström (1971), Bergström (1971, 1983) and Löfgren (1978). Ethington and Clark (1971, 1981), Sweet *et al.* (1971), McCracken and Barnes (1981), Repetski (1982) and Sweet (1984), among others, have discussed the conodont biostratigraphy of the Midcontinent Province.

Apart from that of the Durness Limestone, which is clearly a Midcontinent type, conodont faunas from the British Isles are dominated by taxa best known from the North Atlantic Province, and these faunas can readily be classified in terms of the North Atlantic Province zonal scheme. That scheme with the known ranges of selected taxa is given in Table 1, which includes many taxa that are as yet unrecorded from the British Isles. Some of the species listed are not restricted to the North Atlantic Province but are known also from the Midcontinent Province.

Although it is outside the scope of the present summary to discuss the North Atlantic Province zonal scheme in detail, it should be pointed out that the various zonal units are not all of the same type. That is, most of, if not all, the Arenig units are assemblage zones or range zones based on the vertical ranges of, in most cases, phylogenetically not directly related taxa. By contrast, the Llanvirn to Ashgill units are based on taxa in rapidly evolving lineages and represent phylozones or lineage zones in the sense of Hedberg (1972). For a discussion of the Middle and Upper Ordovician zonal units, see Bergström (1983).

There are vast gaps in the biostratigraphic coverage of published British conodont localities. Whereas the upper Llanvirn to Ashgill faunas are relatively well known, stratigraphically older faunas remain virtually unknown. The principal reason for this is undoubtedly the unfavourable lithology for conodont extraction in the Arenig and Llanvirn rocks, where clastics and volcanics dominate and acid-soluble carbonates are rare. However, as shown by the presence in shales of the Scottish *Oepikodus evae* faunule (loc. 100), the Lower Ordovician clastic successions in Britain do contain conodonts and work in those strata certainly has the potential to yield interesting results.

2.6 FACIES AND ITS CONTROL UPON THE CONODONT FAUNAS
(by S. M. Bergström)

During the Ordovician Period, both the geographic location and the internal geography of the regions which now comprise the British Isles were greatly different from today. Scotland and Northern Ireland, and probably northernmost England, were separated, perhaps by thousands of kilometres, from the rest of the present British Isles by the Iapetus Ocean. Most recent palaeogeographic reconstructions place the northern parts of the British Isles near, or adjacent to the North American Plate at a low latitude, whereas Southern Britain is interpreted to have been located at middle to high latitudes (Fig. 2.7). This latitudinal separation is reflected in the composition of some British conodont faunas and may be considered a kind of 'provincial facies control'. There is also a facies control caused by specific conditions in the different depositional environments within each of these regions, e.g. those related to differences in water depth. Some examples of both these kinds of facies control are discussed below.

The most striking case of provincial facies control currently known in Britain is the fauna of the Durine Member of the Durness Limestone in northwesternmost Scotland. Previous studies have noted the marked similarity of its megafossils (Poulsen, 1951) and lithology (Swett and Smit, 1972) to those of coeval strata in Eastern North America and, in recent years, northwesternmost Scotland has commonly been interpreted to represent a detached fragment of the North American Plate. Not only is the Durine faunule unique in Britain but also it differs markedly from

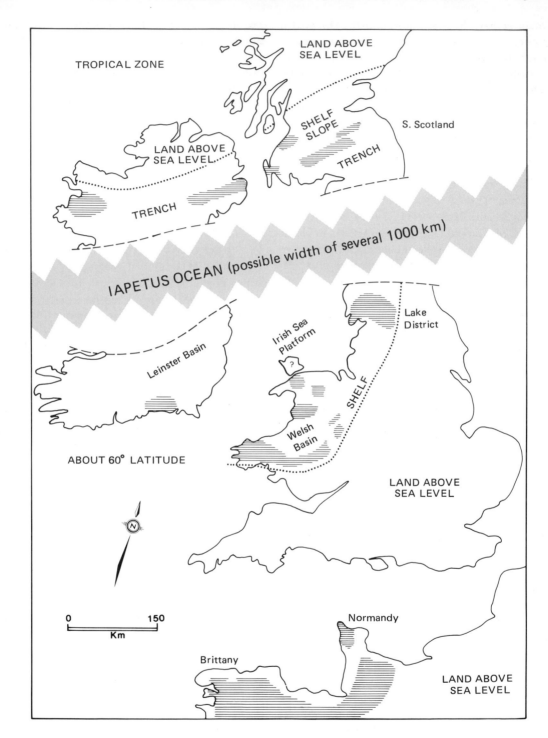

Fig. 2.7 — A palaeogeographical—palaeoenvironmental reconstruction of Britain during Ordovician time.

coeval faunas described from other parts of Europe. Higgins (1967) recognized its strong affinity to North American Midcontinent faunas, particularly that of the Joins Formation of Oklahoma, and collections made recently by S. M. Bergström and J. Repetski have confirmed this affinity by adding to the Durine faunal list such highly characteristic Midcontinent Province taxa as *Chosonodina rigbyi, Dischidognathus* n. sp. and *Histiodella altifrons*. The Durine fauna appears to compare most closely with the Midcontinent *Pteracontiodus cryptodens–Histiodella altifrons-Multioistodus auritus* interval, and possibly the *Histiodella sinuosa* interval, of Ethington and Clark (1981). In terms of North American classification, it is clearly early Whiterockian in age, but it has virtually nothing diagnostic in common with Baltoscandian faunas and its North Atlantic equivalents are much less clear (see locs. 111–115).

An early Arenig (*Oepikodus evae* Zone) faunule reported from Ravengill (loc. 100) in the Southern Uplands of Scotland (Lamont and Lindtröm, 1957) has virtually nothing in common with the Durine fauna but is closely similar to coeval faunas in Baltoscandia. The Ravengill fauna occurs in graptolitic green and ochreous shales associated with radiolarian cherts in a succession generally interpreted to have been laid down in very deep water. The striking difference between the Durine and Ravengill faunules could conceivably be depth-related, the Durine faunule being deposited in very shallow water. In Eastern North America, Lower and Middle Ordovician Midcontinent Province faunas are known from shallow-water shelf strata in relatively close proximity to relatively deep-water deposits bearing North Atlantic Province taxa (Bergström *et al.*, 1972; Landing, 1976; Fåhraeus and Nowlan, 1978). In contrast, faunules similar to the Ravengill one are known from Baltoscandian strata that are likely to have been deposited in relatively shallow water. If Scotland occupied a low-latitude position in lower and early Middle Ordovician times as suggested by Fig. 2.7, the occurrence of cold-water North Atlantic taxa such as those at Ravengill in the tropical zone could be interpreted as a case of 'species submergence', i.e. a shift of the normal living environment of high latitude taxa into deeper and colder water in the low-latitude zone, in analogy with a case from the Middle Ordovician rocks of Eastern North America described by Bergström and Carnes (1976).

The next younger British conodont faunules are also from Scotland. The Stinchar Limestone and Confinis Flags of the Girvan area (locs. 86–91) have produced low-abundance faunules of the *Pygodus serra* and *P. anserinus* Zones (Bergström, 1971) which exhibit very close similarity to those of coeval strata in Eastern North America. The same close North American affinity is shown by the brachiopods in the same strata (Williams, 1962). As noted below, the Stinchar faunule differs rather conspicuously from slightly younger faunules from Wales and this might be interpreted as another case of provincial facies control. The common occurrence of *Girvanella* together with other evidence suggests that the Stinchar Limestone was deposited in relatively shallow water, perhaps at a depth of no more than a few tens of metres. Conodont faunules of similar age and composition, although lacking representatives of *Cahabagnathus, Belodina* and *Belodella*, occur in limestone clasts in the late Middle Ordovician olistostromes in the Tweed region (locs. 104–106) north-east of Girvan. The source deposit of these limestone clasts remains an enigma because no lithically similar carbonate unit is known in Southern Scotland. The fauna recorded from these units (Bergström *et al.*, 1974) is considerably more varied taxonomically than that of Llandeilo Series deep-water cherts and chert-shales in the same region (locs. 99, 101, 102, and 108–110) which includes *Pygodus, Spinodus, Peridon* and coniform elements (Lamont and Lindström, 1957), all quite widespread taxa which may have had a pelagic mode of life. The difference between this faunule and those of the Tweed region olistostromes and the Stinchar Limestone is likely to have been caused by local environmental conditions among which difference in water depth might have been important.

There are few published data on the sedimentology and depositional environments of most of the conodont-bearing carbonate units in the Middle and Upper Ordovician rocks of Wales and the Welsh Borderland, and few generalizations can be made regarding possible facies control of conodont occurrences. There is little doubt that the conodont faunules from the transgressive basal Caradoc Series (Costonian Stage) in the Onny Valley and at Evenwood in South Shropshire (Bergström, 1971; Savage and Bassett, in press) represent shallow-water environments. The type Llandeilo Series at Llandilo, which grades upwards into graptolitic dark shale, is likely to have been laid down in deeper water, as was the case with the conodont-bearing limestone beds known as the Castell Limestone at Abereiddy Bay (loc. 1) (Bergström, 1964).

By and large, the taxonomic compositions of the late Llandeilo and Costonian faunas in Wales and the Welsh Borderland are quite similar, both having representatives of *Plectodina, Amorphognathus, Icriodella, Panderodus, Drepanoistodus* and hyaline forms. *Baltoniodus*, well represented in the Llandeilo Series, is sparse in the Costonian Stage of South Shropshire, and the same applies to *Amorphognathus*; in contrast, the Welsh Borderland Costonian Series Stage yields *Rhodesognathus*, a genus not yet known from the Llandeilo Series. In this case the difference in depositional environments is not strongly expressed in the composition of the conodont faunules but, as noted, there are differences in the frequency of individual taxa. A much more conspicuous difference is evident at a comparison between the faunules of the Lower Llandeilo and subjacent Ffairfach Group at Llandilo (locs. 10–12) and those of the broadly equivalent Stinchar Limestone (locs. 86–91) and the clasts in the Tweed region olistostromes (locs. 104–106) in South Scotland. The latter deposits lack the common representation of *Plectodina, Amorphognathus, Baltoniodus* and *Eoplacognathus* so typical of the Welsh strata but contain *Pygodus, Belodina, Belodella, Cahabagnathus, Spinodus, Periodon, Strachanognathus* and other taxa not known at Llandilo. All the latter genera are known, however, from coeval deposits in Baltoscandia. As noted above, the difference between the Scottish and Welsh faunas may be attributed to provincial facies control.

A Middle Ordovician (*B. variabilis* Subzone) faunule of a type so far unique in Wales but with decidedly Baltoscandian affinity has recently been recorded (Bergström, 1981) from pale-coloured limestone clasts in a debris flow of the Garn Formation on Anglesey (loc. 36). This faunule includes specimens of *Amorphognathus, Baltoniodus, Pygodus, Complexodus, Spinodus, Strachanognathus, Periodon, Walliserodus, Eoplacognathus* and *Plectodina*, and, among these, only the latter genus is not represented in coeval strata in Baltoscandia. Although it may be significant that the Garn conodonts occur in a region having brachiopods interpreted to be of Baltoscandian type (Williams, 1969, Fig. 27), the specific environmental conditions responsible for these unusual faunal occurrences are not obvious. There is no known source for the limestone clasts which appear to represent a relatively shallow-water depositional environment, but the considerable size of some clasts (1 m or more across) suggests a source not very distant from their present occurrence. The remarkable difference between this faunule and those of the Costonian Stage of the Welsh Borderland may reflect the contrast between a more or less oceanic setting on one hand, and a continental platform setting on the other, but further studies are needed to clarify the nature of the apparent environmental control of the compositions of the two faunules, which are of about the same age and not very widely separated geographically.

As a whole, the Ashgill faunules in Britain do not exhibit striking regional differences attributable to provincial facies control. The occurrence of the Midcontinent Province *Phragmodus undatus* in the Shalloch Formation at Whitehouse Bay in the Girvan area (locs. 93 and 94), and in the Glyn Formation in North Wales (loc. 28), indicates faunal exchange with that Province. However, the associated species at Girvan are *Amorphognathus ordovicicus, Belodina* sp., *Birksfeldia* sp., *Panderodus* sp., *Plectodina* sp., *Protopanderodus liripipus* and *Scabbardella altipes*, which are provincially rather undiagnostic; all these species occur elsewhere in the British Ashgill Series (Orchard, 1980). Examples of local facies control on the distribution of individual species in the Ashgill Series have

been given by Orchard (1980), and some biofacies
differentiation has been noted by Sweet and Bergström (1984), but the general aspect of the British
Ashgill faunas is one of relative uniformity. Interestingly, these Ashgill faunules compare far more
closely with the coeval ones in Baltoscandia than

is the case with most older Ordovician faunules.
This may perhaps be attributed to the fact that
sea-floor spreading processes by Ashgill time had
resulted not only in a substantial narrowing of the
Iapetus Ocean but also in moving Britain to a
similar latitudinal belt as Baltoscandia.

Plates 1–5
Photographs and descriptions compiled by M. J. Orchard from material provided by the persons indicated as the collector in the following descriptions; these persons are responsible for the determinations.

Plate 2.1

'Prooneotodus' tenuis Müller 1959
Plate 2.1, Figs. 1and 7. Diagnosis: elongate slender, slightly curved sheath-like protoconodonts with an elliptical to subcircular cross-section.
Part and counterpart of two half-apparatuses preserved on a bedding plane. B.G.S. RX136A,B, × 6. S. Jusypiw collection. Upper Cambrian (*Acerocare* Zone) Cwmhesgen Formation, North Wales (loc. C2).

Hertzina elongata Müller 1959
Plate 2.1, Figs. 2–5. Diagnosis: slightly curved, weakly laterally compressed protoconodont with a flat to gently concave posterior face, a convex anterior surface, flat lateral faces and a postero-lateral carina on each side.
Lateral and basal views: Figs. 2 and 3, HUP 79/1/155, × 100; Figs. 4 and 5, HUP 79/1/156, × 120. M. D. Brasier collection. Bed 1 ii–iii, Lower Cambrian *Hyolithes* Limestone, Nuneaton (loc. C6).

Hertzina? cf. *bisulcata* Müller 1959
Plate 2.1, Figs. 6 and 8. Diagnosis: A straight protoconodont with no significant degree of taper, a concave posterior face, a convex anterior face and strongly concave lateral faces.
Lateral and terminal views, HUP 79/1/165, × 120, × 100, M. D. Brasier collection. Bed 10iii, Lower Cambrian *Hyolithes* Limestone, Nuneaton (loc. C7).

Pteracontiodus cryptodens (Mound 1965)
Plate 2.1, Figs. 9, 10 and 15. Diagnosis: acodiform element has a straight or sharply recurved tricostate cusp and a base produced anteriorly, laterally and posteriorly.
Lateral views, × 70. A. C. Higgins collection. Sample D16, Durine Formation, Durness (loc. 115).

Paltodus aff. *P. sexplicatus* (Jones 1971) sensu Abaimova 1975.
Plate 2.1, Fig. 11. Diagnosis: coniform element with up to six strong, asymmetrically arranged costae that begin just above the base and extend to the tip of the cusp.
Lateral view, × 70. A. C. Higgins collection. Base of Croisaphuill Formation, Durness (loc. 116).

Scolopodus cf. *emarginatus* Barnes and Tuke 1970
Plate 2.1, Fig. 12. Diagnosis: proclined to suberect coniform element with smooth or faintly striate faces, a rounded anterior margin, and a deep posterior groove with adjacent sharp margins. Basal cavity deep and conical with a deep notch in the wider posterior end.
Lateral view, × 70. A. C. Higgins collection. Base of Croisaphuill Formation, Durness (loc. 116).

'Oistodus' sp. 6, Ethington and Clark 1981
Plate 2.1, Fig. 13. Diagnosis: geniculate element with a sharp-edged broad cusp; outer surface convex, inner surface has a carina extending along its length. Posterior expansion of base short, anterior drawn out. Base strongly flared.
Lateral view, × 70. A. C. Higgins collection. 3 m above base, Croisaphuill Formation, Durness (loc. 117).

Scandodus brevibasis (Sergeeva 1963)
Plate 2.1, Fig. 14. Table 1. Diagnosis: acondontiform element is bilaterally symmetrical with a rounded anterior face and two anteriorly located lateral costae.
Lateral view, × 7. A. C. Higgins collection. Sample D16, Durine Formation, Durness (loc. 115).

Protopanderodus gradatus Serpagli 1974
Plate 2.1, Figs. 16 and 18. Diagnosis: Scandodiform element (Fig. 16) is asymmetric, has a short base and a recurved cusp with rounded anterior and sharp posterior margins. Scolopodiform element (Fig. 18) is symmetrical and has a groove on either side of the cusp near its posterior margin.
Lateral views, × 70. A. C. Higgins collection. Fig. 16, sample D16, Durine Formation, Durness (loc. 115). Fig. 18, 20 m above base, Croisaphuill Formation, Durness (loc. 118).

Oistodus multicorrugatus Harris 1962
Plate 2.1, Fig. 17. Diagnosis: alate coniform element consists of a sharply recurved cusp with antero-laterally directed keels forming the edges of a triangular anterior face.
Lateral view, × 70. A. C. Higgins collection. Sample D15, Durine Formation, Durness (loc. 114).

Plate 2.1

Ulrichodina? cf. *simplex* Ethington and Clark 1981
Plate 2.1, Fig. 19. Diagnosis: proclined coniform element is knife-shaped blade with sharp anterior and posterior cusp edges; lateral costa present. Base widely flared, shallowly excavated, and has a prominent antero-basal sinus on each side.
Lateral view, ×70. A. C. Higgins collection. Sample D10, Durine Formation, Durness (loc. 113).

Drepanoistodus sp.
Plate 2.1, Fig. 20. Diagnosis: drepanodiform element is recurved and more or less symmetrical with sharp anterior and posterior edges. The base is expanded on the inner side.
Lateral view, ×70. A. C. Higgins collection. Sample D16, Durine Formation, Durness (loc. 115).

PLATE 2.2

Spinodus spinatus (Hadding 1913)
Plate 2.2, Figs. 1 and 4. Table 1. Diagnosis: an apparatus of ramiform elements with posteriorly directed processes that bear long discrete denticles.
Lateral views: Fig. 1, dolabrate element SM A110000, ×68; Fig. 4, tertiopedate element A110001, ×75. M. J. Orchard collection. Wrae Limestone, Southern Uplands (loc. 105). *E. variabilis–E. suecicus* Zones.

Belodella nevadensis (Ethington and Schumacher 1969)
Plate 2.2, Fig. 2. Diagnosis: *Belodella* with a costate multidenticulate biconvex non-geniculate element and a typical geniculate element.
Lateral view, non-geniculate element OSU 38536, ×80. S. M. Bergström collection. Stinchar Limestone, basal metre of unit 7 of Williams (1962), Brochloch Quarry, Girvan area (loc. 91). *Pygodus anserinus* Zone.

Protopanderodus cf. *varicostatus* (Sweet and Bergström 1962)
Plate 2.2, Fig. 3. Table 1. Diagnosis: *Protopanderodus* with a relatively short base, several prominent, variably arranged lateral costae, and a rounded anterio-basal margin.
Lateral view, SM A110002, ×50. M. J. Orchard collection. Wrae Limestone, Southern Uplands (loc. 105). *E. variabilis–E. suecicus* Zones.

Pygodus serra (Hadding 1913)
Plate 2.2, Fig. 5. Diagnosis: *Pygodus* with three denticle rows on triangular anterior platform of stelliscaphate element.
Upper view, dextral stelliscaphate element OSU 38537, ×65. S. M. Bergström collection. 8 m above base, Stinchar Limestone, Minuntion Quarry, Girvan area (loc. 87). *Pygodus serra* Zone.

Periodon aculeatus Hadding 1913
Plate 2.2, Figs. 6 and 7. Table 1. Diagnosis: a *Periodon* with persistent denticulation in the geniculate elements. Ramiform elements with well-developed denticulation on the anterior processes, a restricted basal cavity, and between four and six denticles between cusp and biggest posterior denticle.
Inner lateral views: Fig. 6, dextral digyrate P element SM A110003; Fig. 7, sinistral geniculate M element SM A110004, ×75. M. J. Orchard collection. Wrae Limestone, Southern Uplands (loc. 105). *E. variabilis–E. suecicus* Zones.

Eoplacognathus robustus Bergström 1971
Plate 2.2, Figs. 8 and 12. Table 1. Diagnosis: an *Eoplacognathus* in which the stelliplanate Pa element has a short, distally blunt postero-lateral process, longer than that in *E. foliaceus* and *E. reclinatus* but shorter than that in *E. lindstroemi*. The pastiniplanate Pb element has a long, relatively straight anterior process and short posterior and lateral processes, the whole unit appearing less y-shaped than *E. lindstroemi*.
Upper views. Fig. 8, sinistral Pb element TCD 25638, ×72; Fig. 12, sinistral Pa element (anterior is to the right) TCD 25637, ×60. G. D. Sevastopulo collection. Bellewstown Limestone: Fig. 8, boulder E6 (O 083671); Fig. 12, boulder 12W (O 077669), west of Bellewstown, Ireland (locs. 126–128). *Pygodus serra* Zone.

Polonodus sp.
Plate 2.2, Fig. 9. Table 1. Diagnosis: an arched pectiniform element with a prominent cusp and a rugose ornament of coalescing nodes.
Upper view of posteriorly broken sinistral scaphate element SM A110005, ×75. M. J. Orchard collection. Wrae Limestone, Southern Uplands (loc. 105). *E. variabilis–E. suecicus* Zones.

Cahabagnathus sweeti (Bergström 1971)
Plate 2.2, Fig. 10. Table 1. Diagnosis: *Cahabagnathus* with a straight main denticle row in the pastiniplanate and an unbranched antero-lateral process in the stelliplanate element.
Upper view, dextral pastiniplanate element OSU 38539, ×53. S. M. Bergström collection. Stinchar Limestone, basal metre of unit 7 of Williams (1962), Brochloch Quarry, Girvan area (loc. 91). *Pygodus anserinus* Zone.

Plate 2.2

Eoplacognathus lindstroemi Hamar 1964
Plate 2.2, Figs. 11 and 13. Table 1. Diagnosis: the sinistral stelliplanate Pa element has a straight antero-posterior axis, and a postero-lateral process almost as long as the posterior process. The sinistral pastiniplanate Pb element has a slightly sinuous, very long anterior process, and posterior and lateral processes of approximately equal length, diverging from one another at an angle that makes the unit y-shaped.
Upper views; Fig. 11, sinistral Pb element SM A110006; Fig. 13, dextral Pa element (posterior branch of bifid antero-lateral process is broken) A110007, ×65. M. J. Orchard collection. Sample F3, Ffairfach Grit, Llandilo (loc. 11). *Pygodus anserinus* Zone.

Amorphognathus inaequalis Rhodes 1953
Plate 2.2, Fig. 14. Table 1. Diagnosis: the pastiniscaphate Pa element has strongly developed anterior and posterior processes and two lateral processes that tend to be simple or only incipiently bifid. The tertiopedate M element has three denticulate processes, and several subequal apical denticles; the position of the cusp is relatively clearly defined.
Upper view, sinistral Pa element SM A110008, ×69. M. J. Orchard collection. Sample F2, Ffairfach Grit, Llandilo (loc. 11). *Pygodus anserinus* Zone.

Plate 2.3

Strachanognathus parvus Rhodes 1955
Plate 2.3, Fig. 1. Table 1. Diagnosis: coniform lamellar conodont with a single prominent proclined denticle anterior to the suberect cusp. Base short with apex of shallow basal cavity located beneath base of denticle.
Lateral view, sinistral element OSU 38526, ×125. S. M. Bergström collection. Garn Formation, Anglesey (loc. 36). *Baltoniodus variabilis* Subzone.

Baltoniodus variabilis (Bergström 1962)
Plate 2.3, Fig. 2. Table 1. Diagnosis: *Baltoniodus* with inner ledged margin of the pastinate Pa element developed into a prominent triangular platform. Upper view, dextral Pa element OSU 38541, ×75. S. M. Bergström collection. Garn Formation, Anglesey (loc. 36). *Baltoniodus variabilis* Subzone.

Pygodus anserinus Lamont and Lindström 1957
Plate 2.3, Fig. 3. Table 1. Diagnosis: *Pygodus* with four denticle rows on the triangular platform of the stelliscaphate element.
Upper view, dextral stelliscaphate element OSU 38529, ×75. S. M. Bergström collection. Garn Formation, Anglesey (loc. 36). *Baltoniodus variabilis* Subzone.

Protopanderodus liripipus Kennedy, Barnes and Uyeno 1979
Plate 2.3, Fig. 4. Table 1. Diagnosis: *Protopanderodus* with a posteriorly extended adenticulate base and flange-like antero-basal margin.
Lateral view, OSU 38531, ×52. S. M. Bergström collection. Balclatchie Group, Laggan Burn, Girvan area (loc. 92). *Amorphognathus tvaerensis* Zone.

Protopanderodus varicostatus (Sweet and Bergström 1962)
Plate 2.3, Fig. 5. Table 1. Diagnosis: *Protopanderodus* with a relatively short base, a few prominent costae on the cusp, and an extended antero-basal margin.
Lateral view, OSU 38530, ×75. S. M. Bergström collection. Garn Formation, Anglesey (loc. 36). *Baltoniodus variabilis* Subzone.

Complexodus pugionifer (Drygant 1974)
Plate 2.3, Fig. 6. Table 1. Diagnosis: pastiniscaphate Pa element with prominent postero-lateral process having transversely widened, in many cases double, rows of often irregularly spaced denticles.
Lateral view, Pa element OSU 38527, ×125. S. M. Bergström collection. Garn Formation, Anglesey (loc.36). *Baltoniodus variabilis* Subzone.

Icriodella cf. *praecox* Lindström, Racheboeuf and Henry 1974
Plate 2.3, Figs. 7, 10 and 12–14. Diagnosis: the pastiniscaphate Pa element has simple denticle rows on both the anterior and the posterior processes; lateral process adentate. The tertiopedate S elements bear relatively large and discrete denticles like those ot *I. superba* rather than *I. praecox* sensu stricto.
Figs. 7 and 12, posterior and lateral views, S elements OSU 37185, 37182, ×84. Fig. 10, lateral view, bipennate M element OSU 37183, ×84; Figs. 13 and 14, lateral and upper views, Pa elements OSU 38181, ×22, and OSU 37180, ×84. S. M. Bergström collection. Fig. 13, from sample W66–13, Costonian of Evenwood Quarry, near Shrewsbury (loc. 21); others from sample 79B40-1, Bryn-banc, E of Narberth (loc. 3). *Amorphognathus tvaerensis* Zone.

Plate 2.3

Amorphognathus tvaerensis Bergström 1962
Plate 2.3, Figs. 8, 9, 11 and 16. Table 1. Diagnosis: *Amorphognathus* with two postero-lateral processes, one bifid and one simple, in the dextral pastiniscaphate Pa element. Tertiopedate M element with rather long but weakly denticulate anterior process and several apical denticles, the posterior of which may be directed backwards; cusp indistinct.
Fig. 11, upper view, dextral Pa element OSU 38532, ×65; Figs. 8 and 9, outer lateral views, sinistral and dextral pastinate Pb elements OSU 38534, 35, ×65; Fig. 16, posterior view, sinistral M element OSU 38533, ×80. S. M. Bergström collection. Balclatchie Group, Laggan Burn, Girvan area (loc. 92). *Amorphognathus tvaerensis* Zone.

Eoplacognathus elongatus (Bergström 1962)
Plate 2.3, Fig. 15. Table 1. Diagnosis: *Eoplacognathus* with conspicuous V-shaped bend in main denticle row in pastiniplanate Pa element. The pastiniplanate Pb element has a relatively straight anterior process and a relatively long posterior process compared with *E. lindstroemi*.
Upper view, sinistral Pa element (anterior is lower right) OSU 38528, ×50. S. M. Bergström collection. Garn Formation, Anglesey (loc. 36). *Baltoniodus variabilis* Subzone.

Plate 2.4

Amorphognathus superbus Rhodes 1953
Plate 2.4, Figs. 1–4 and 8. Table 1. Diagnosis: the pastiniscaphate Pa element has two bifid lobes, the posterior one of which has a particularly prominent anterior branch. The sinistral pastinate Pb element has a characteristic sinuous lower inner margin. The tertiopedate M elements have about three relatively large apical denticles and three distinct processes, all of which may be denticulated.
Figs. 1, 3, outer lateral views, dextral and sinistral Pb elements NMW 81.5G.28, 29, ×48. Fig. 2, inner lateral view, sinistral M element. NMW 81,5G,30, ×48; Fig. 4, upper view, sinistral Pa element (longest lobe broken) SM A110008, ×65; Fig. 8, postero-lateral view, dextral M element (apical denticules and posterior and inner lateral processes broken), SM A110009, ×90. Figs. 1–3, N. N. Savage collection; Figs. 4 and 8, M. J. Orchard collection. Figs. 1–3, Cymerig Limestone, Bala (loc. 30) (topotype material); Fig. 4, Birdshill Limestone, near Llandilo (loc. 6); Fig. 8, Crug Limestone, near Llandilo (loc. 8). *Amorphognathus superbus* Zone.

Rhodesognathus elegans (Rhodes 1953)
Plate 2.4, Figs. 5 and 10. Table 1. Diagnosis: pastinate Pa elements with an angle of about 120° between the anterior and posterior processes; posterior process with an inner lateral flare. Pastinate Pb elements with an angle of about 90° between the rather short posterior process and the slightly recurved anterior process. Short outer lateral process joins anterior process at denticle in front of cusp in both elements.
Outer lateral views: Fig. 5, Pa element SM A110010, ×75; Fig. 10, Pb element SM A110011, ×75; Fig. 5, Crug Limestone (loc. 8); Fig. 10, Birdshill Limestone (loc. 6), near Llandilo. M. J. Orchard collection. *Amorphognathus superbus* Zone.

Amorphognathus cf. *complicatus* Rhodes 1953
Plate 2.4, Fig. 6. Table 1. Diagnosis: pastiniscaphate Pa element characterized by an unbranched, anteriorly directed inner bar.
Upper view, sinistral Pa element (outer lateral process and other process extremities are broken) SM A110012, ×65. M. J. Orchard collection. Nod Glas Formation, near Welshpool (loc. 22). *Amorphognathus superbus* Zone.

Icriodella superba Rhodes 1953
Plate 2.4, Figs. 7 and 9. Table 1. Diagnosis: the pastiniscaphate Pa element has the nodes of the anterior platform aligned and largely fused by transverse ridges. The tertiopedate Pb element is pyramidal and has long adenticulate processes. The ramiform S elements are similar but have denticulate processes.
Fig. 7, lateral view, Pb element SM A 10013, ×65; Fig. 9. upper view, dextral Pa element SM A108124 (topotype), ×50. M. J. Orchard collection. Fig. 7, Birdshill Limestone, near Llandilo (loc. 6), Fig. 9, Cymerig Limestone, near Bala (loc. 30). *Amorphognathus superbus* Zone.

Aphelognathus rhodesi Lindström 1959
Plate 2.4, Figs. 11–13, 15 and 16. Diagnosis: the angulate Pa element has anterior and posterior processes subequal in length, with no or very small denticles just in front of the cusp, and large denticles farther anteriorly. The denticles posterior of the cusp tend to be fused to it.
Lateral and posterior (12 only) views, ×75: Fig. 11, sinistral digyrate Sb element SM A108188; Fig. 12, alate Sa element SM A108187; Fig. 13, sinistral dolobrate M element SM A108191; Fig. 15, dextral bipennate Pb element SM A108189; Fig. 16, dextral angulate Pa element SM A110015. M. J. Orchard collection. Crug Limestone, near Llandilo (loc. 8) (topotype material). *Amorphognathus superbus* Zone.

Plate 2.4

Milaculum n. sp. A
Plate 2.4, Fig. 14. Diagnosis: a subquadrate concavo-convex *Milaculum* with the upper surface covered by regularly arranged, low and subequal nodes aligned in two perpendicular directions.
Upper view, SM A110016, ×90. M. J. Orchard collection. Robeston Wathen Limestone, South Wales (loc. 2).
Remarks: this element, although not a conodont, is found also in the acid residues of the Ashgillian Cautley Mudstones and the lower Keisley Limestone. *Amorphognathus ordovicicus* Zone.

Ozarkodina? pseudofissilis (Lindström 1959)
Plate 2.4, Figs. 17 and 10. Table 1. Diagnosis: only Pa and Pb elements are definitely known. The Pa element is a carminate element with uniform denticulation and an inwardly twisted posterior process that is both shorter and lower than the anterior process. The Pb element is a relatively deep agulate element with processes of subequal length.
Fig. 17, outer lateral view, sinistral Pb element SM A108231, ×115; Fig. 20, inner lateral view, sinistral Pa element SM A110017, ×65. M. J. Orchard collection. Crug Limestone, near Llandilo (loc. 8) *Amorphognathus superbus* Zone.

Plectodina n. sp. 2 of Savage and Bassett
Plate 2.4, Fig. 18. Diagnosis: all the elements are large and have broad bases containing conspicuous white matter. The denticles are typically discrete and widely spaced.
Inner lateral view, dextral Pb element (anteriorly broken) NMW 81.6G.32, ×36, N. M. Savage collection. Smeathen Wood Formation, Ragleth (loc. 19). *Amorphognathus tvaerensis* Zone.

Plectodina n. sp. 1 of Savage and Bassett
Plate 2.4, Fig. 19. Diagnosis: a species in which the angulate Pa element is characteristically broad and bears discrete stout denticles, and a basal cavity which is widely expanded along the posterior two thirds of the element.
Outer lateral view, sinistral Pa element, NMW 81.6G.22, ×49. N. M. Savage collection. Hoar Edge Grit, Bullhill Gutter (see loc. 21). *Amorphognathus tvaerensis* Zone.

Plate 2.5

PLATE 2.5
All from the *Amorphognathus ordovicicus* Zone.

Amorphognathus duftonus Rhodes 1955
Plate 2.5, Figs. 1 and 6. Table 1. Diagnosis: the tertiopedate M element has a single apical denticle that bears a small, often downward-directed, triangular or barb-like denticle on its inner lateral edge. The outer lateral process is reduced to an adenticulate anticusp.
Fig. 1, upper view, dextral pastiniscaphate Pa element, OSU 38538, ×65; Fig. 6, inner antero-lateral view, dextral M element, SM A108133, ×100. Fig. 1, S. M. Bergström collection; Fig. 6, R. J. Aldridge collection. Upper part of Keisley Limestone, Keisley Quarry (loc. 79).
Remarks: in Britain known also from the Rawtheyan Cystoid Limestone of the Howgill Fells.

Amorphognathus ordovicicus Branson and Mehl 1933
Plate 2.5, Figs. 2, 3, 5, 8 and 9. Table 1. Diagnosis: the pastiniscaphate Pa element has two lateral lobes, the inner one of which is strongly bifid; the outer lateral lobe is less prominent and may also be bifid. Tertiopedate M elements have a single prominent cusp-like apical denticle and two denticulate processes; the outer lateral process is reduced to an adenticulate anticusp.
Fig. 2, inner lateral view, sinistral tertiopedate Sb element SM A104071, ×100; Fig. 3, posterior view, sinistral pastinate Pb element SM A104056, ×75; Fig. 5, inner antero-lateral view, dextral M element SM A108195, ×120; Fig. 8, Inner lateral view, dextral pastinate Pb element SM A104059, ×120; Fig. 9, outer lateral view, sinistral M element SM A110018, ×80. M. J. Orchard collection. Figs. 2 and 9, sample BFB4, Cystoid Limestone, Birksfield Beck, Howgill Fells (locs. 42–55); Figs. 3, 5 and 8, sample CL3, *mucronata* Limestone, Brow Gill, Lake District (loc. 41).

Hamarodus europaeus (Serpagli 1967)
Plate 2.5, Figs. 4, 7 and 12. Table 1. Diagnosis: the Pa element is a laterally compressed, deeply excavated thin-walled non-geniculate coniform element with a proclined to suberect cusp and with very narrow denticulated anterior and posterior processes. The M element is geniculate coniform, and the S elements from a symmetry transition of bipennate through alate elements. Inner lateral views: Fig. 4, sinistral bipennate Sc element SM A108209, ×95; Fig. 7, sinistral Pa element SM A110014, ×100; Fig. 12, sinistral M element SM A108208, ×95. Figs. 4 and 12, M. J. Orchard collection; Fig. 7, S. M. Bergström collection. Figs 4 and 12, sample BFB4, Cystoid Limestone, Birksfield Beck, Howgill Fells (locs. 42–55); Fig. 7, sample E62–3, top of Keisley Limestone (loc. 79).

Plate 2.5

'Pseudooneotodus' mitratus (Moskalenko 1973)
Plate 2.5, Fig. 10. Diagnosis: a very broad, squat, wholly excavated coniform element with a triangular to subquadrate basal outline and very low nodes on the edges of the poorly differentiated processes.
Upper view, dextral element SM A110019, ×90. M. J. Orchard collection. Sample BFB4 Cystoid Limestone, Birksfield Beck, Howgill Fells (locs. 42–55).

Birksfeldia circumplicata Orchard 1980
Plate 2.5, Figs. 11, 14–16, 18, 19 and 22. Table 1. Diagnosis: seximembrate apparatus includes pastinate P elements in which the anterior process is turned strongly inwards. The Pa element is weakly arched and has a prominent cusp and a strongly denticulated anterior (-lateral) process. The Pb element has three subequal processes. The M element is doloborate; the Sc element is similar but differs in having a small denticulate anterior process and a reclined rather than erect cusp. The Sb and Sa elements are tertiopedate, with between one and three irregularly denticulated processes.
Fig. 11, inner lateral view, sinistral Pa element (early growth stage) SM A110019; Fig. 14, inner lateral view, sinistral Sc element SM A110020; Fig. 15, Postero-lateral view, dextral Sa element SM A110021; Fig. 16, inner antero-lateral view, dextral Pa element SM A110022. Fig. 18, inner lateral view, sinistral Pb element SM A110023; Fig. 19, outer lateral view, dextral Sb element AM A110024; Fig. 22, inner lateral view, sinistral M element SM A110025. All ×57. M. J. Orchard collection. Sample BFB4, Cystoid Limestone, Birksfield Beck, Howgill Fells (locs. 42–55) (topotype material).

Scabbardella altipes (Henningsmoen 1948)
Plate 2.5, Fig. 13. Diagnosis: recurved, laterally compressed non-geniculate coniform elements showing variation in cross-section from drepanodiform through acodiform to distacodiform.
Inner lateral view, acodiform element SM A108213, ×60. M. J. Orchard collection. Sample ESB3, Cystoid Limestone, Ecker Secker Beck, Howgill Fells (locs. 42–55).

Dapsilodus mutatus (Branson and Mehl 1933)
Plate 2.5, Fig. 17. Diagnosis: acodiform and distacodiform non-geniculate elements with a long posterior extension of the base and a relatively short recurved cusp.
Inner lateral view, acodiform element SM A1081139, ×100. R. J. Aldridge collection. Upper part of Keisley Limestone (loc. 79).

Eocarniodus gracilis (Rhodes 1955)
Plate 2.5, Figs. 20 and 21. Diagnosis: variably arched and flexed, relatively small elements with subcentral cusps and short denticulate processes. Platform flanges may be developed in some elements. Fig. 20, SM A108201, ×120; Fig. 21, SM A108202, ×140. M. J. Orchard collection. Fig. 20, sample BFB4, Cystoid Limestone, Birksfield Beck, Howgill Fells (locs. 42–55); Fig. 21, sample CL3, *mucronata* Limestone, Brow Gill, Lake District (loc. 41).

2.7 REFERENCES

Abaimova, G. P. 1975. Ranneordovikskie konodontiy srednego techeniya r. leny. *Tr. Sib. Nauchno-Issled. Inst. Geol. Geofiz. Miner. Syrya*, **207**, 1–129, [Early Ordovician conodonts from the River Lena.]

Aldridge, R. J. 1975. The stratigraphic distribution of conodonts in the British Silurian. *J. Geol. Soc. London*, **131**, 607–618, 3 plates.

Barnes, C. R. and Tuke, M. F. 1970. Conodonts from the St. George Formation (Ordovician), Northern Newfoundland. *Geol. Surv. Canada, Bull.*, **187**, 79–97, plates 18–20, Ottawa.

Bergström, S. M. 1962. Conodonts from the Ludibundus Limestone (Middle Ordovician) of the Tvären area (SE Sweden). *Ark. Mineral. Geol.*, **3**, 1, 1–61, 5 plates.

Bergström, S. M. 1964. Remarks on some Ordovician conodont faunas from Wales. *Acta Univ. Lundensis, II*, **3**, 1–66.

Bergström, S. M. 1971. Conodont biostratigraphy of the Middle and Upper Ordovician of Europe and Eastern North America. In: W. C. Sweet and S. M. Bergström (Eds.) *Symp. on Conodont Biostratigraphy* in *Mem. Geol. Soc. Am.*, **127**, 83–161, 2 plates.

Bergström, S. M. 1980. Conodonts as paleotemperature tools in Ordovician rocks of the Caledonides and adjacent areas in Scandinavia and the British Isles. *Geol. För. Stockholm Förh.* **102** (4), 377–392.

Bergström, S. M. 1981. Biostratigraphical and biogeographical significance of conodonts in two British Middle Ordovician olistostromes, *Abstracts Geol. Soc. Am.*, **13**, 271.

Bergström, S. M. 1983. Biogeography, evolutionary relationships and biostratigraphic significance of Ordovician platform conodonts. *Foss. Strata*, **15**, 35–58.

Bergström, S. M. In press. Biostratigraphic integration of Ordovician graptolite and conodont zones – a regional review. *Blackwell Scientific Publications*.

Bergström, S. M. and Carnes, J. B. 1976. Conodont biostratigraphy and paleoecology of the Holston Formation (Middle Ordovician) and associated strata in Eastern Tennessee. *Spec. Paper Geol. Assoc. Can.*, **15**, 27–57.

Bergström, S. M., Epstein, A. G. and Epstein, J. B. 1972. Early Ordovician North Atlantic Province conodonts in Eastern Pennsylvania. *U.S. Geol. Surv. Prof. Paper*, **800-D**, D37–D44.

Bergström, S. M., Rhodes, F. H. T. and Lindström, M. 1984. Conodont biostratigraphy of the type of Llandeilo and associated strata in Ordovician Wales. *Abstracts Geol. Soc. Am.*, **16** (3), 125.

Bergström, S. M., Riva, J. and Kay, M. 1974. Significance of Conodonts, Graptolites, and Shelly Faunas from the Ordovician of Western and North–Central Newfoundland, *Can. J. Earth Sci.*, **11**, 1625–1660.

Branson, E. B. and Mehl, M. G. (1933). Conodonts from the Maquoketa Thebes (Upper Ordovician) of Missouri. *Univ. Missouri Stud.*, **8**, 121–132.

Brasier, M. D. 1984. Microfossils and small shelly fossils from the Lower Cambrian *Hyolithes* Limestone at Nuneaton, English Midlands. *Geol. Mag.*, **121**, 229–253.

Brenchley, P. J., Harper, J. C., Mitchell, W. I. and Romano, M. 1977. A reappraisal of some Ordovician successions in Eastern Ireland. *Proc. R. Irish Acad. Sect. B*, **77**, 65–85.

Bulman, O. M. B. and Rushton, A. W. A. 1973. Tremadoc faunas from boreholes in Central England. *Bull. Geol. Surv. Gt. Br.*, **43**, 1–40.

Drygant, D. M. 1974. Prostye Konodonty Silura i nizov Devona Volyno-Podolya: *Paleontol. Sb. Lvov. Univ.*, **10**, 64–70, 2 plates. [Simple conodonts of the Silurian and lowermost Devonian of the Volyn-Podolian area.]

Dzik, J. 1976. Remarks on the evolution of the Ordovician conodonts. *Acta Palaeont. Pol.*, **21**, 395–455.

Ethington, R. L. and Clark, D. L. 1971. Lower Ordovician conodonts of North America. *Mem. Geol. Soc. Am.*, **127**, 63–82.

Ethington, R. L. and Clark, D. L. 1981. Lower and Middle Ordovician Conodonts from the Ibex Area, Western Millard County, Utah. *Geol. Stud., Brigham Young Univ.*, **288** (2), 1–155.

Ethington, R. L. and Schumacher, D. 1969. Conodonts of the Copenhagen Formation (Middle Ordovician) in central Nevada. *J. Paleontol.*, **43**, 440–484.

Fåhraeus L. E and Nowlan G S. 1978. Franconian (late Cambrian) to early Champlanian (Middle Ordovician) conodonts from the Cow Head Group Western Newfoundland *J. Paleontol.* **52**, 444–471.

Hadding, A. 1913. Undre dicellograptusskiffern i Skåne jämte några därmed ekvivalenta bildningar: *Lunds Univ. Arsskr Avd. 2*, **9**, 15, 1–90, 8 plates.

Hamar, G. 1964. The Middle Ordovician of the Oslo region, Norway. 17. Conodonts from the Lower Middle Ordovician of Ringerike. *Norsk Geol. Tidsskr.*, **44**, 243–292, 6 plates.

Harper, J. C. and Rast, N. 1964. The faunal succession and volcanic rocks of the Ordovician near Bellewstown, Co. Meath. *Proc. R. Irish Acad. Sect. B.*, **64** 1–23.

Harris, R. W. 1962. New conodonts from Joins (Ordovician) Formation of Oklahoma. *Oklahoma Geol. Notes*, **22**, 199–211, 1 plate.

Hedberg, H. (Ed.) 1972. International Subcommission on Stratigraphic Classification, Report 7b. Summary of an international guide to stratigraphic classification, terminology, and usage. *Lethaia*, **5**, 297–323.

Henningsmoen, G. 1948. The *Tretaspis* Series of the Kullatorp Core. *Bull. Geol. Inst. Univ. Uppsala*, **32**, 374–432.

Higgins, A. C. 1967. The age of the Durine Member of the Durness Limestone Formation at Durness. *Scott. J. Geol.*, **3**(3), 382–388.

Hinz, I. 1983. Zur unterkambrischen Mikrofauna von Comley und Umgebung in Shropshire. *Unpublished thesis*, Bonn University.

Ingham, J. K. 1966. The Ordovician rocks in the Cautley and Dent Districts of Westmorland and Yorkshire. *Proc. Yorks. Geol. Soc.*, **35**, 455–505.

Ingham, J. K. and Wright, A. D. 1970. A revised classification of the Ashgill Series. *Lethaia*, **3**, 233–242.

Jaanusson, V. 1979. Ordovician in: R. A. Robinson and C. Teichert (Eds.) *Treatise on Invertebrate Paleontology, Part A, Introduction, Fossilization (Taphonomy), Biogeography, and Biostratigraphy*. Geological Society of America and University of Kansas Press, Lawrence, Kansas, A136–A166.

Jones, P. J. 1971. Lower Ordovician conodonts from the Bonaparte Gulf Basin and the Daly River Basin, Northwestern Australia. *Austral. Bur. Min. Resources, Geol. Geophys. Bull.*, **117**, 1–80, 9 plates, Canberra.

Kennedy, D. J., Barnes, C. R. and Uyeno, T. T. 1979. A Middle Ordovician conodont faunule from the Tetagouche Group, Camel Back Mountain, New Brunswick. *Canad. J. Earth Sci.*, **16**, 540–551, 1 plate.

Lamont, A. and Lindström, M. 1957. Arenigian and Llandeilian cherts identified in the Southern Uplands of Scotland by means of conodonts, etc. *Trans. Edinburgh Geol. Soc.*, **17** (1), 60–70, 1 plate.

Landing, E. 1976. Early Ordovician (Arenigian) conodont and graptolite biostratigraphy of the Taconic allochthon, Eastern New York. *J. Paleontol.*, **50**, 614–646.

Lapworth, C. 1879. On the tripartite classification of the Lower Palaeozoic rocks. *Geol. Mag.*, **6**, 1–15.

Lindström, M. 1957. Two Ordovician Conodont Faunas found with zonal Graptolites. *Geol. Fören. Stockholm Förh.*, **79**, 161–178.

Lindström, M. 1959. Conodonts from the Crug Limestone (Ordovician, Wales). *Micropaleontology*, **5**, 427–452, 4 plates.

Lindström, M. 1964. *Conodonts*, Elsevier, Amsterdam, 1–196.

Lindström, M. 1971. Lower Ordovician Conodonts of Europe. In: W. C. Sweet and S. M. Bergström (Eds.) *Symp. on Conodont Biostratigraphy*, in *Mem. Geol. Surv. Am.*, **127**, 21–61.

Lindström, M., Racheboeuf, P. R. and Henry, J.-L. 1974. Ordovician conodonts from the Postolonnec Formation (Crozon Peninsula, Massif Armoricain) and their stratigraphic significance. *Geol. Palaeontol.*, **8**, 15–28.

Löfgren, A. 1978. Arenigian and Llanvirnian Conodonts from Jämtland, Northern Sweden. *Foss. Strata*, **13**, 1–129, 16 plates.

Matthews, S. C. and Missarzhevsky, V. V. 1975. Small shelly fossils of late Pre-Cambrian and early Cambrian age: a review of recent work. *J. Geol. Soc. London*, **131**, 289–304.

McCracken, A. D. and Barnes, C. R. 1981. Conodont biostratigraphy and paleoecology of the Ellis Bay Formation, Anticosti Island, Quebec with special reference to late Ordovician–early Silurian chronostratigraphy and the systemic boundary. *Bull. Geol. Soc. Can.*, **329**, 51–134.

McNamara, K. 1979. The age, stratigraphy and genesis of the Coniston Limestone Group in the Southern Lake District. *Geol. J.*, **14**, 41–67.

Miller, J. F. and Rushton, A. W. A. 1973. Natural conodont assemblages from the Upper Cambrian of Warwickshire, Great Britain. *Abstracts Geol. Soc. Am.*, **5**, 338–339.

Moskalenko, T. A. 1973. Conodonts of the Middle and Upper Ordovician on the Siberian Platform. *Acad. Sci. U.S.S.R., Siberian Branch, Trans. Inst. Geol. Geophys.*, **137**, 1–143, 18 plates.

Moseley, F. 1984. Lower Palaeozoic lithostratigraphical classification in the English Lake District. *Geol. J.*, **19**, 239–247.

Mound, M. C. 1965. Two new conodont genera from the Joins Formation (Lower Middle Ordovician) of Oklahoma. *Proc. Biol. Soc. Washington*, **78**, 193–200.

Müller, K. J. 1959. Kambrische Conodonten. *Z. dt. geol. Ges.*, **111**, 434–485, 5 plates.

Orchard, M. J. 1980. Upper Ordovician conodonts from England and Wales. *Geol. Palaeontol.*, **14**, 9–44.

Poulsen, C. 1951. The position of the East Greenland Cambro-Ordovician in the palaeogeography of the North Atlantic region. *Medd. Dan. Geol. Foren.*, **12**, 161–162.

Repetski, J. E. 1982. Conodonts from the El Paso Group (Lower Ordovician) of westernmost Texas and Southern New Mexico. *New Mexico Bur. Mines Miner. Res. Mem.*, **40**, 1–121.

Rhodes, F. H. T. 1953. Some British Lower Palaeozoic conodont faunas. *Philos. Trans. R. Soc. London, Ser. B*, **237**, 647, 261–334, 4 plates.

Rhodes, F. H. T. 1955. The conodont fauna of the Keisley Limestone. *Q. J. Geol. Soc. London*, **111** (2), 117–142, 4 plates.

Rushton, A. W. A. 1982. The biostratigraphy and correlation of the Merioneth–Tremadoc Series boundary in North Wales. In: M. G. Basset and W. T. Dean (Eds.), *The Cambrian–Ordovician Boundary: Sections, Fossil Distributions and Correlations,Geol. Ser.*, **3**, National Museum of Wales, Cardiff, 41–59.

Savage, N. M. and Bassett, M. G. In press. Caradoc–Ashgill conodont faunas from Wales and the Welsh Borderland. *Palaeontology*.

Sergeeva, S. P. 1963. Konodont' i iz nixhnego ordovika leningradskogo oblasti. *Paleont. Zhurn.*, **1962**, 94–108, 2 plates.

Serpagli, E. 1967. I condonti dell' Ordoviciano superiore (Ashgilliano) delle Alpi Carniche. *Boll. Soc. Paleont. Ital.*, **6**, 30–111, 26 plates.

Serpagli, E. 1974. Lower Ordovician conodonts from precordilleran Argentina (Province of San Juan). *Boll. Soc. Paleont. Ital.*, **13**, 17–98, 25 plates.

Smith, J. 1907. On the occurrence of conodonts in the Arenig–Llandeilo formations of the Southern Uplands of Scotland *Trans. Nat. Hist. Soc. Glasgow*, **7**, 235–252, 5 plates.

Sweet, W. C. 1984. Graphic correlation of upper Middle and Upper Ordovician rocks, North American Midcontinent Province, U.S.A. In D. L. Bruton (Ed.) *Aspects of Ordovician System, Palaeontol. Contrib. Univ. Oslo*, **295**, 23–25.

Sweet, W. C. and Bergström, S. M. 1976. Conodont biostratigraphy of the Middle and Upper Ordovician of the United States Midcontinent. In M. G. Bassett (Ed.) *The Ordovician System, Proc. of a Palaeontological Association Symp., Birmingham, September 1974*, 121–151

Sweet, W. C. and Bergström, S. M. 1984. Conodont

provinces and biofacies of the late Ordovician. In: D. L. Clark (Ed.) *Spec. Paper Geol. Soc. Am.,* **196,** 69–87.

Sweet, W. C., Ethington, R. L. and Barnes, C. R. 1971. North American Middle and Upper Ordovician conodont faunas. In: W. C. Sweet and S. M. Bergström (Eds.) *Symp. in Conodont Biostratigraphy,* in *Mem. Geol. Soc. Am.,* **127,** 163–193.

Swett, K. and Smit, D. E. 1972. Paleogeography and depositional environments of the Cambro-Ordovician shallow-marine facies of the North Atlantic. *Bull. Geol. Soc. Am.,* **83,** 3223–3248.

Taylor, K. and Rushton, A. W. A. 1971. The pre-Westphalian geology of the Warwickshire Coalfield. *Bull. Geol. Surv. Gt. Br.,* **35.**

Temple, J. T. 1968. The Lower Llandovery (Silurian) brachiopods from Keisley, Westmorland. *Palaeontogr. Soc. (Monogr.),* 1–58, 10 plates.

Walton, E. K. 1965. Lower Palaeozoic rocks – stratigraphy. In: G. Y. Craig (Ed.) *The Geology of Scotland,* Oliver and Boyd, Edinburgh, 161–200.

Whittington, H. B., Dean, W. T., Fortey, R. A., Rickards, R. B., Rushton, A. W. A. and Wright, A. D. 1984. Definition of the Tremadoc Series and the series of the Ordovician System in Britain. *Geol. Mag.,* **121,** 17–33.

Williams, A. 1962. The Barr and Lower Ardmillan Series (Caradoc) of the Girvan district, South-west Ayrshire, with descriptions of the Brachiopoda. *Mem. Geol. Soc. London,* **3,** 1–267.

Williams, A. 1969. Ordovician faunal provinces with reference to brachiopod distribution. In; A. Wood (Ed.), *The Pre-Cambrian and Lower Palaeozoic Rocks of Wales,* University of Wales Press, Cardiff, 117–154.

Williams, A. and Curry, G. B. 1984. Lower Ordovician Brachiopoda from the Tourmakeady Limestone, Co. Mayo, Ireland. *Bull. Br. Mus. (Nat. Hist.) Geol.,* **38,** 185–272.

Williams, A., Strachan, I., Bassett, D. A., Dean, W. T., Ingham, J. K., Wright, A. D. and Whittington, H. B. 1972. A correlation of Ordovician rocks in the British Isles. *Geol. Soc. London Spec. Rep.,* **3,** 1–74.

Williams, S. H. and Bruton, D. L. 1983. The Caradoc–Ashgill boundary in the Central Oslo region and associated graptolite faunas. *Nor. Geol. Tidsskr.,* **63,** 147–191.

Zalasiewicz, J. A. 1984. A re-examination of the Arenig Series. *Geol. J.,* **19,** 105–124.

3

Conodonts of the Silurian System from the British Isles

R. J. Aldridge

3.1 HISTORY OF CONODONT STUDIES

Shortly after Pander (1856) first described conodont elements, Harley (1861) recognized them in
washed residues from the Ludlow Bone Bed of
Shropshire. By careful examination with a hand-
lens, he distinguished elements of two types,
which he illustrated and named as *Astacoderma
serratum* and *A. spinosum*; these specimens would
currently be placed in the multielement species
Ozarkodina confluens and *Distomodus? dubius*
respectively. Further searches for Silurian conodonts in the nineteenth century were undertaken
by John Smith, who in 1879 exhibited specimens
to the Natural History Society of Glasgow (Young,
1881, p. 78). Smith's material came from weathered
shales and rotten limestones of Shropshire and
Dudley, but none of his specimens has ever been
described or illustrated. Smith and Jones (1881),
however, did provide a list of the localities that
yielded the collections.

Apart from a note by Whittard (1928, p. 743)
mentioning the occurrence of conodont elements
in the Pentamerus Beds of Shropshire, no further
records of British Silurian conodonts appeared
until Rhodes (1953) published full descriptions of
middle Ludlow faunas from Shropshire and the
West Midlands. Rhodes' Silurian work formed
part of a sampling programme covering several
Lower Palaeozoic localities in England and Wales
and his results served to stimulate considerable
interest in Ordovician and Silurian conodonts.
Since 1953, numerous papers and theses have
dealt wholly or partially with British Silurian
conodont faunas.

Conodont faunas from the British Llandovery
Series have been more fully documented than
those of the higher Silurian series. The first descriptions were provided by Brooks and Druce
(1965), who recovered forty elements from a
limestone conglomerate at the base of the Wych

Formation of Gullet Quarry in the Malvern Hills. Additional material from the same locality was reported by Jones *et al.* (1969), who also examined collections from another upper Llandovery limestone exposure at the nearby Hollybush Quarry. These finds were followed by a wider pilot study of faunas throughout Wales and Welsh Borderland (Aldridge, 1972), later supplemented by additional collections from the same region and from Scotland (Aldridge, 1975b; Mohamed, 1983). Samples from the type area at Llandovery have yielded very few conodont specimens (Aldridge, 1972; Cocks *et al.,* 1984), but the diverse collections from the Welsh Borderland allowed the provisional recognition of four local assemblage biozones spanning the Aeronian and Telychian Stages (Fig. 3.3).

Strata close to the Llandovery–Wenlock boundary commonly yield rich and diverse conodont faunas, and the detailed distribution of species across the base of the Wenlock Series in the type area has been determined from bed-by-bed sampling (Mabillard and Aldridge, 1985). The *amorphognathoides* Zone of Walliser (1964) spans the base of the Wenlock Series, and at the boundary stratotype the interval with *Pterospathodus amorphognathoides* is only 95 cm thick. Elsewhere, however, this index species ranges through considerably thicker sequences of strata. Faunas spanning the Llandovery–Wenlock boundary away from the type area have been recorded in detail by Mabillard (1981), who has employed conodonts and other microfossils in the correlation of the base of the Wenlock Series throughout the Welsh Borderland and South Wales. A note on Llandovery–Wenlock conodonts of the Woolhope Inlier has also been published by Davis (1974) and a description of faunas from the Coralliferous Group of South-west Dyfed by Mabillard and Aldridge (1983).

The earliest Wenlock Epoch was a time of rapid decline in the diversity of conodont faunas in both Britain and, as far as is known, the rest of the world (Aldridge, 1976; Aldridge and Mabillard, 1981; Aldridge and Jeppsson, 1984). Published records of post-crisis Wenlock conodonts in Britain are few. The first fauna to be illustrated was from Usk, South Wales (Austin and Bassett, 1967), and other contributions have noted conodonts from the Barr Limestone of the West Midlands (Aldridge, in Bassett, 1974) and from various localities in the Welsh Borderland (Aldridge, 1975a, 1975b; Aldridge *et al.,* 1981). These papers have emphasized the importance of species of *Ozarkodina* in the Wenlock Series, particularly the presence of *O. sagitta rhenana* in the lower part, the appearance of *O. confluens* in the Coalbrookdale Formation and the abundance of *O. bohemica bohemica* in the Much Wenlock Limestone Formation.

Conodonts are sparse in strata spanning the Wenlock–Ludlow boundary and in the lower Ludlow Series (Aldridge, 1975b). Faunas of this age, however, have been reported from the Annascaul Formation of the Dingle Peninsula. Ireland (Aldridge, 1980), where separate limestone exposures from Caherconree Mountain are characterized by *Ozarkodina sagitta* and *Kockelella variabilis* respectively. In the Welsh Borderland, faunas from younger Ludlow strata are relatively well known. Rhodes' (1953) descriptions are of faunas from the middle Ludlow Series of Shropshire and the West Midlands, and additional material of similar age collected by Newall included specimens of *K. variabilis* (Rhodes and Newall, 1963). In unpublished theses, Eccleston (1958) described small collections from Ludlow and the Woolhope Inlier and Druce (1967) reported uppermost Ludlow conodonts from Diddlebury, Shropshire. Collinson and Druce (1966) published an abstract recording the latter fauna, and Walliser (1966) also listed a few species from the Whitcliffe Beds and Ludlow Bone Bed of Shropshire. An outline of Ludlow faunas from the Welsh Borderland and West Midlands was provided by Aldridge (1975b), who also noted an *eosteinhornensis* Zone fauna from the Pridoli Series of Capel Horeb, near Llandovery, South Wales. One other Pridoli conodont, a single specimen of *Ozarkodina remscheidensis,* was reported by Antia (1979, p. 117) from the Temeside Formation of Ludlow.

Biostratigraphical data contained in the above publications has been summarized in two previous papers (Aldridge, 1975b; Aldridge *et al.,* 1979). This chapter provides an updating of the informa-

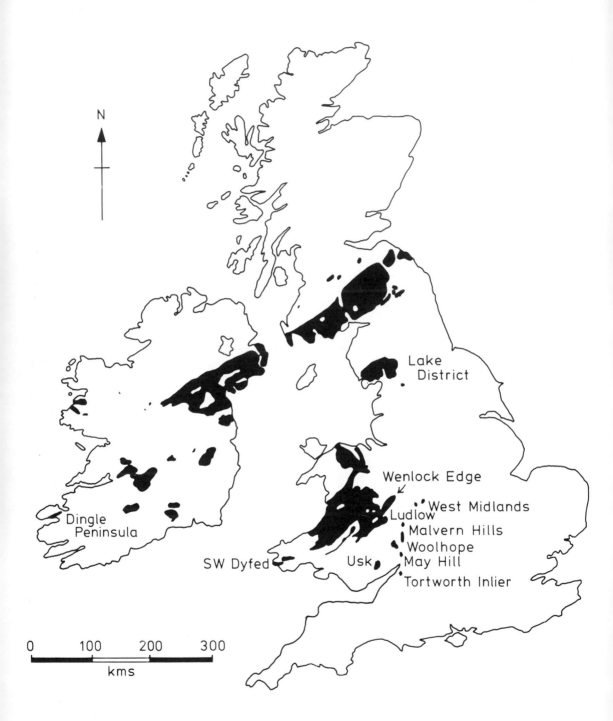

Fig. 3.1 – Distribution of Silurian outcrops in the British Isles.

tion presented in those contributions. Descriptions of all British species are currently being prepared for monographic publication and full details of sampling localities and faunas recovered will be included. An outline of the main areas sampled is given here in Fig. 3.1, and an indication of the succession of faunas and of particularly productive formations and localities is presented in Section 3.5. Locality numbers used throughout are those of the Micropalaeontology Unit, Department of Geology, University of Nottingham.

3.2 DEPOSITORY OF COLLECTIONS OF IMPORTANCE

(a) The British Museum (Natural History)
The collection at this museum includes the specimens from the Ludlow Bone Bed illustrated by Harley (1861), and figured material from the Llandovery Series (Aldridge, 1972) and the Llandovery–Wenlock boundary beds (Mabillard and Aldridge, 1983, 1985). Some of the specimens illustrated by Aldridge and Jeppsson (1984) are also housed here.

(b) The National Museum of Wales, Cardiff
This museum holds the figured specimens of Austin and Bassett (1967) from the Wenlock of Usk, and the specimens listed by Jones *et al.* (1969) from the Llandovery of the Malvern Hills.

(c) Department of Geology, University of Birmingham
The Ludlow specimens figured by Rhodes (1953) are deposited here.

(d) Department of Geology, University of Nottingham
The Micropalaeontology Unit in this department houses extensive research and reference collections; the thesis collections of Mabillard (1981) and Mohamed (1983) are included. Figured and type material includes the Wenlock specimens of Aldridge (1975a) and Aldridge *et al.* (1981), and the only recorded Silurian conodonts from Ireland (Aldridge, 1980). The specimens illustrated in a

biostratigraphical summary of British Silurian conodonts by Aldridge (1975b) are also currently held here.

(e) Department of Geology, University of Southampton
The thesis collection of Aldridge (1970) is deposited here, but is currently on extended loan to the University of Nottingham.

3.3 SILURIAN CHRONOSTRATIGRAPHY

In recent years, international agreement has been reached through the Subcommission on Silurian Stratigraphy of the International Union of Geological Sciences on the upper and lower boundaries of the Silurian System and on all internal series and stage divisions. The boundary stratotype for the base of the system is at Dob's Linn, near Moffat, Scotland, at the horizon within the lower part of the Birkhill Shale that coincides with the base of the *acuminatus* graptolite biozone (Holland *et al.*, 1984). The Silurian–Devonian boundary has its stratotype at Klonk in the Barrandian area of Czechoslovakia, at the first appearance of *Monograptus uniformis* in 'bed 20' (Martinsson, 1977).

There are four Silurian series: Llandovery, Wenlock, Ludlow and Pridoli. In a vote held in 1984, the titular members of the Subcommission on Silurian Stratigraphy accepted that the Llandovery district should be the type area for the Llandovery Series and that there should be three stages: Rhuddanian, Aeronian and Telychian (Cocks *et al.*, 1984). The type area of the Wenlock Series is around Wenlock Edge in Shropshire, with the boundary stratotype for the base in Hughley Brook, near Leasows Farm (Bassett *et al.*, 1975, Fig. 5); there are two stages, Sheinwoodian and Homerian (Bassett *et al.*, 1975; Holland, 1980). The boundary stratotype for the base of the Ludlow Series is the quarry at Pitch Coppice in the Ludlow type area (Holland *et al.*, 1963, Figs. 8 and 11) and the Ludlow Series is divided into two stages, Gorstian and Ludfordian (Holland, 1980). The Pridoli Series is defined in Czechoslovakia, where the basal boundary is at the base of the *parultimus* graptolite biozone in the Pozary section in the Barrandian area; no stages are currently recognized within the series.

3.4 CONODONT ZONATION

A conodont zonation for the Silurian System was first proposed by Walliser (1962, 1964), who based his scheme primarily on a section at Mount Cellon in the Carnic Alps of Austria. Walliser defined twelve successive-appearance zones spanning the Silurian System and lowest Devonian System (Fig. 3.2), with an additional *'Spathognathodus' snajdri* horizon identified in the Ludlow Series of Bohemia. Several of these zones have been widely recognized, but the absence of much of the Llandovery Series at Cellon (Schönlaub, 1971) and the difficulties of applying the complete scheme outside Austria have led to the development of a number of local zonations. The history of Silurian conodont biostratigraphy up to 1976 has been fully reviewed by Cooper (1980), who

SERIES	CONODONT ZONES
L. DEVONIAN	Icriodus woschmidti
PRIDOLI	O. remscheidensis eosteinhornensis
LUDLOW	Ozarkodina crispa
	Pedavis latialata
	Polygnathoides siluricus
	Ancoradella ploeckensis
	Ozarkodina? crassa
WENLOCK	Ozarkodina sagitta sagitta
	Kockelella patula
LLANDOVERY	Pterospathodus amorphognathoides
	Pterospathodus celloni
	missing interval
	Bereich I

Fig. 3.2 – Condodont zonation for the Silurian System proposed by Walliser (1964). The generic designations of several of the taxa have been revised to conform with current usage.

	CARNIC ALPS Walliser 1964	MID-WEST U.S.A Nicoll and Rexrood 1968, Pollock et al 1970	WELSH BORDER-LAND Aldridge 1972	CENTRAL APPALACH-IANS Helfrich 1975	OKLAHOMA Barrick and Klapper 1976	GUIZHOU PROVINCE, CHINA Zhou, Zhai and Xian 1981	NORTHERN EAST BALTIC Viira 1982	
							SHELF	BASIN
PRIDOLI	eosteinhornensis			S. steinhornensis eosteinhornensis		eosteinhornensis	remscheid-ensis	eosteinhornensis
							canadensis	
							eosteinhorn-ensis s.s.	
							aff.scanica	
LUDLOW	crispus			S. crispus			D. dubius – "Belodus" sp.	
	latialatus			S. tillmani				siluricus
	siluricus			S. snajdri			Ozarkodina sp.S	
	ploeckensis			unzoned interval	K. variabilis		O. confluens cornidentatus	
	crassa			S. bicornutus				
WENLOCK	sagitta			S. sagitta bohemicus	K. stauros		Ctenognathodus murchisoni	sagitta
	patula				K. amsdeni			
					K. ranuliformis			
	amorphognath-oides	P. amorph. – S. ranuliformis	P. amorpho-gnathoides		amorphognath-oides			
	celloni	N. celloni	I. inconstans			S. celloni		
			H. stauro-gnathoides					
LLANDOVERY		I. irregularis	I. discreta – I. deflecta			S. parahassi – S. guizhouensis		
						S. obesus		
	Bereich I	P. simplex						

Fig. 3.3 – Comparison of some of the local Silurian conodont zonations.

listed and provisionally correlated ten zonal schemes proposed for parts of the Silurian System of Europe, North America and Australia (some of these are shown in Fig. 3.3). Cooper advocated the use of biostratigraphical datum planes to complement the zonal schemes and to assist correlation, but few subsequent authors have adopted this approach. Moreover, additional local zonations have been published, increasing further the number of names applicable to Silurian biostratigraphical intervals (e.g. McCracken and Barnes, 1981; Zhou *et al.*, 1981; Viira, 1982).

There is thus no standard conodont zonal scheme of wide geographical applicability for the Silurian System. Cooper (1980) correctly pointed out that this is partly due to ecological factors, but we are also far from achieving a set of widely useful zonations for separate environments. It is premature, and perhaps inadvisable, to propose a zonal scheme for the British successions, and ranges documented in this chapter are related as closely as possible to Silurian chronostratigraphical divisions rather than to conodont zones. Several of the species recognized in Britain however, have been employed in various zonal schemes, and it is probably useful to indicate these here; their British ranges are illustrated in Table 2.

The index species of only four of Walliser's original zones have been unequivocally recognized in Britain (Aldridge, 1975b). Of these, *Pterospathodus celloni*, *P. amorphognathoides* and *Ozarkodina remscheidensis eosteinhornensis* are relatively numerous and widely distributed, whereas *O. sagitta sagitta*, the definitive subspecies of the *sagitta* Zone, is represented by very few specimens and the lower boundary of the zone cannot be delimited. A single broken Pa element identified as *Ozarkodina* cf. *O. crispa* has been recovered from the uppermost Ludfordian beds of Ludlow, Shropshire, but the *crispa* Zone has long been recognized to be encompassed within the *eosteinhornensis* Zone away from Cellon (Bultynck and Pelhate, 1971; Walliser, 1971; Cooper, 1980). *Ozarkodina snajdri*, regarded by Walliser (1964) as occupying a narrow horizon in the upper Ludlow Series, ranges throughout the Ludfordian Stage in Britain.

The absence at Cellon of much of the pre-*celloni* Llandovery Series posed particular problems in the early application of conodonts to Silurian stratigraphy. Within this gap, the establishment of an '*Icriodina irregularis*' (=*Distomodus kentuckyensis* of multielement nomenclature) Zone in the early Llandovery by Nicoll and Rexroad (1968) has proved widely useful; the *Icriodella discreta–I. deflecta* Zone proposed in Britain (Aldridge, 1972) may be regarded as synonymous, even though *D. kentuckyensis* is relatively uncommon in British collections. The relevant taxa are often found in the same samples (e.g. Fåhraeus and Barnes, 1981; Aldridge and Mohamed, 1982), and Nowlan (1981) has suggested that the base of the zone may be extended down into the earliest Llandovery. The proposals for a '*Panderodus simplex*' Zone (Pollock *et al.*, 1970) and a '*Paltodus dyscritus*' fauna (Thompson and Satterfield, 1975) in the early Llandovery have been less helpful, as the nominate elements, although widely recognized, have very long stratigraphical ranges. The gap between the *D. kentuckyensis* Zone and the first appearance of *P. celloni* has been filled by the *D. staurognathoides* Zone (Aldridge, 1972), in the upper part of which a characteristic *Ozarkodina aldridgei* fauna has been recognized (Uyeno and Barnes, 1983). The first appearance of *P. celloni* is stratigraphically close to that of *Icriodella inconstans* and, as the latter appears to be restricted in its distribution, the *I. inconstans* Zone (Aldridge, 1972) could be suppressed.

Local zonations of Wenlock strata include that of Barrick and Klapper (1976), who recognized five zones within the Clarita Formation of Oklahoma. The lowest is the *amorphognathoides* Zone, one of Walliser's original set and one of the most widely identified of all Silurian biozones; this zone spans the Llandovery–Wenlock boundary at the stratotype section in Shropshire (Mabillard and Aldridge, 1985). Above this in Oklahoma, four successive species of *Kockelella* form the basis for four zones: *K. ranuliformis*, *K. amsdeni*, *K. stauros* and *K. variabilis* (Barrick and Klapper, 1976). The middle two have rarely been found outside Oklahoma, but *K. ranuliformis* and *K.*

variabilis are very widely distributed. In Britain, *K. ranuliformis* is common, but its first appearance, in the Aeronian Stage, is much earlier than in America and at present it does not seem to provide a firm basis for international correlation. *K. variabilis* occurs in Ireland (Aldridge, 1980), where it may be of latest Wenlock or earliest Ludlow age, and in the Welsh Borderland, where it does not appear until the upper part of the Gorstian Stage. Another member of the *Kockelella* plexus, *K. walliseri*, which has a limited range in the Shein-woodian Stage of Britain, occurs also in North America (Helfrich, 1975; Barrick and Klapper, 1976), Germany (Walliser, 1964), Estonia (Viira, 1975) and Gotland (Jeppsson, 1983) and is a potentially useful index species.

Another North American zonation, for upper Wenlock to lowermost Devonian strata of the Central Appalachians, was proposed by Helfrich (1975). His scheme displays several similarities to Walliser's for this interval, but the lack of plat-form elements necessitated the use of additional species now referred to *Ozarkodina*, including *O. bohemica bohemica*, *O. bicornutus* and *O. tillmani*. Of these, *O. bohemica bohemica* is the only taxon found in Britain, where it is restricted to the upper Homerian Stage, a similar level to that indicated by Helfrich (1975, Fig. 10).

A succession of faunas following the *Polygnathoides siluricus* Zone was identified on Gotland by Jeppsson (1974), and most of the charac-teristic species are also recognized in the British Ludlow Series. These include *Pelekysgnathus dubius*, *Ozarkodina excavata* (Branson and Mehl), *Ozarkodina wimani* and *O. snajdri*. Jeppsson's scheme cannot be applied in Britain, however, as there is little similarity in the detailed faunal sequences in the two areas.

Few of the key species of the most recently proposed schemes, for the Llandovery Series of China (Zhou *et al.*, 1981) and the Wenlock—Pridoli rocks of Estonia (Viira, 1982), have been found in Britain. Viira (1982) however, does use the first appearance of *Distomodus dubius* to mark the base of her *Distomodus dubius—'Belodus'* sp. Zone, which precedes the *eosteinhornensis* Zone in the Estonian shelf sequence.

3.5 BRITISH SILURIAN CONODONT FAUNAS

Only a few specimens have been recovered from strata of Rhuddanian age. The best preserved are from the Woodland Formation of Girvan, Scot-land (loc. 262, NX 16889528), where broken specimens of *Distomodus kentuckyensis* are among the elements recognized (Aldridge, 1975b). This species has also been recovered from a lime-stone from low in the Bronydd Formation of the type Llandovery area (Cocks *et al.*, 1984), where it is associated with *I. discreta*, *Oulodus kentucky-ensis* (Branson and Branson) and *Panderodus unicostatus* (Branson and Mehl). All these species range into the Aeronian Stage, where a much wider diversity has been recorded. Aeronian faunas are especially well known from Shropshire and adjacent Wales, with the Pentamerus Beds of Plow-den (loc. 44, SO 39568769), the Venusbank Formation of Hope Quarry (loc. 81, SJ 35510208) and the limestone bands at Gelli Farm, Llansant-ffraid ym Mechain, Powys (loc. 204, SJ 23631941), yielding characteristic collections (see Aldridge, 1972, pp. 135—139). At Gelli Farm, *D. kentucky-ensis*, *I. discreta*, *O. kentuckyensis* and *Ozarkodina oldhamensis* are particularly distinctive, but there is an admixture of derived Ordovician species (Aldridge, 1972; Mohamed, 1983). In the Venus-bank Formation, *I. deflecta*, *K.? abrupta* and *O. oldhamensis* are characteristic (Aldridge, 1972), while *Pterospathodus? tenuis* joins the fauna in the Pentamerus Beds. This species is also abundant in collections of similar age from the top of the Skomer Volcanic Group at Marloes Bay, South-west Dyfed, Wales (loc. 244, SM 78650722).

Distomodus staurognathoides, *Oulodus? flue-geli* and *Kockelella ranuliformis* all make their first appearances in the upper Aeronian Stage and range through the Telychian Stage, which is characterized by a great variety of conodonts, including several platform-bearing species. These are particularly well represented in the Purple Shales of the Wenlock Edge area (e.g. Devil's Dingle, loc. 9, SJ 641054) and in the Wych For-mation of the Malvern Hills (e.g. Gullet Quarry, loc. 118, SO 76123811). In the Malverns, *Icriodella inconstans*, *Ozarkodina gulletensis*, *Apsidognathus tuberculatus* and *Pterospathodus celloni* are abundant, whereas the Shropshire samples contain *Aulacognathus kuehni, P. celloni* and, more rarely, *Astropentagnathus irregularis.*

Collections spanning the Llandovery—Wenlock boundary are particularly prolific in the type area below Wenlock Edge, with the sections at 'Leasows' (loc. 25, SO 56889839) and 'Domas' (loc. 24, SJ 59600075) being extremely good (Mabillard and Aldridge, 1985). Strata with *P. celloni* and *P. pennatus* are succeeded in the uppermost Llandovery Series by beds with *P. amorphognathoides,* which ranges into the lowermost Wenlock Series. Throughout the Welsh Borderland, the *amorphognathoides* interval is characterized by abundant specimens of the index species, together with *Carniodus carnulus, Johnognathus huddlei* and *Pseudooneotodus bicornis.* An atypical fauna occurs in the Coralliferous Group of Marloes Bay, Southwest Dyfed (loc. 245, SM 78720720), where these species are uncommon, but *K. ranuliformis, Apsidognathus ruginosus* and several unnamed species of *Ozarkodina* are characteristic (Mabillard and Aldridge, 1983).

Above the lowest Wenlock Series, collections show less diversity and elements are less numerous, but Sheinwoodian samples from the Woolhope Limestone Formation of Woolhope (e.g. loc. 148, SO 61223532), the Buildwas Formation of the Wenlock Edge area (e.g. loc. 28, SO 48589042) and the Barr Limestone of the West Midlands (e.g. loc. 99, SP 04929890) have all provided reasonable material, with coniform species strongly dominant. *Ozarkodina sagitta rhenana* is widespread in small numbers in the lower Sheinwoodian Stage with the best material coming from the Dolyhir and Nash Scar Limestone Formation of the Presteigne area, Powys (e.g. Nash Scar Quarry, loc. 207, SO 30276235). Relatively few conodont elements have been recovered from the Coalbrookdale Formation, with the best coming from the railway cutting at Daw End, near Walsall, West Midlands (locs. 101—104, SK 03800035—SK 03280023). A few specimens of *O. sagitta sagitta* have been recorded here (Aldridge *et al.,* 1981), and the earliest specimens of *O. confluens* occur. The Much Wenlock Limestone Formation, of late Homerian age, crops out in all the

Silurian inliers of the Welsh Borderland; collections from the Malvern Hills (e.g. Eastnor Castle Quarry, loc. 135, SO 73223629) are consistently richer than those of the other areas, with *O. confluens, O. bohemica bohemica, O. excavata* and *Panderodus* spp. abundant.

Conodont faunas of the lower Ludlow Series are poor, and only long-ranging species have been recognized outside Ireland. In the Welsh Borderland, the first rich faunas occur in the Upper Bringewood Beds (upper Gorstian Stage), where *Kockelella variabilis* is a rare but characteristic component. The highest record of this species is in the lowermost Ludfordian Stage of the Ludlow area. Limestone beds and lenses in the Ludfordian Stage of the Welsh Borderland and West Midlands commonly yield abundant conodont elements, and particularly rich collections have come from the Upper Whitcliffe Beds at Netherton, West Midlands (loc. 115, SO 93588732), and of Prior's Frome in the Woolhope Inlier (loc. 162, SO 56723901). The faunas are strongly dominated by *O. excavata, O. confluens* and *Panderodus unicostatus,* with *Distomodus? dubius* sometimes abundant. *Pelekysgnathus dubius* occurs regularly in small numbers, while *Ozarkodina snajdri, O wimani, O. remscheidensis eosteinhornensis* and *O. remscheidensis* subsp. nov. are minor components of upper Ludfordian collections.

3.6 FACIES AND CONODONT FAUNAL ASSOCIATIONS

An outline palaeogeographical map of the British area in the Silurian Period is given in Fig. 3.4. Although conodonts are known from the Lake District, Scotland and South-west Ireland, it is only in the Wales—Welsh Borderland region that sufficient material has been recovered to assess the distribution of species with respect to facies. In this area, a marine depositional basin with a variably broad shelf persisted from the early Llandovery Epoch to the late Ludlow Epoch. The distribution of conodont faunas across the shelf has been investigated and reported in several papers (Aldridge, 1976; Aldridge and Mabillard, 1981; Aldridge *et al.,* 1979; Aldridge *et al.,* 1981;

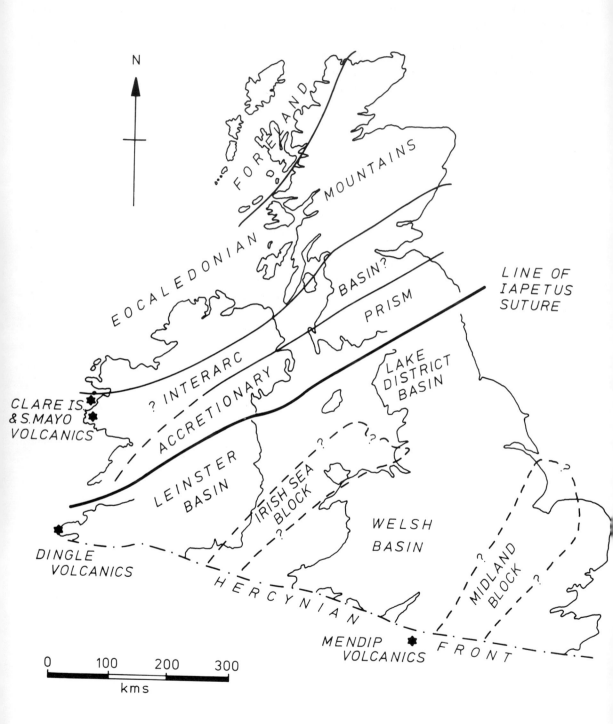

Fig. 3.4 — Outline palaeogeographic—tectonic map of the British Isles for the early Wenlock, modified from numerous sources.

Aldridge and Jeppsson, 1984), with the relationship between faunal composition and distance from shoreline receiving particular attention.

A few species appear to have had distributions virtually restricted to near-shore facies. In the Llandovery Series, this is especially true of species of *Icriodella*, which are particularly abundant in sediments of relatively shallow high-energy environments. A near-shore environment is also attributed to the Coralliferous Group of Southwest Dyfed, where the late Llandovery—early Wenlock fauna differs markedly from contemporaneous faunas elsewhere on the shelf of the Welsh Basin. The characteristic species *Apsidognathus ruginosus, Icriodella? sandersi* Mabillard and Aldridge and *Ozarkodina* spp. may reflect the difference in facies, but geographical isolation from the other areas of deposition may also have been a factor. The lower Wenlock Series of the Tortworth Inlier is also characterized by high-energy shallow-water deposits, and *Icriodella inconstans* persists here far longer than in other areas (e.g. Brinkmarsh Quarry, loc. 174, ST 67369128); the associated fauna includes *Ozarkodina hadra, O. sagitta rhenana* and *O. bohemica* subsp. nov. Near-shore environments in the later Wenlock Series and Ludlow Series of Britain have not yielded conodonts.

Environments on the outer shelf and shelf—basin margin are characterized through much of the Silurian Period by a dominance of coniform apparatuses, particularly *Dapsilodus obliquicostatus* (Branson and Mehl) and *Decoriconus fragilis* (Branson and Mehl). Other species are distributed across the shelf, but several show a preference for relatively near-shore or off-shore environments, or appear to be affected by environmental energy, with some, e.g. *Pterospathodus? tenuis,* being associated with quiet water of various depths.

PLATE 3.1

Distomodus kentuckyensis Branson and Branson 1947
Plate 3.1, Fig. 1. Table 2. Diagnosis: apparatus as known seximembrate; Pa a cruciform platform with broad lobes bearing irregular coalescing nodes; other elements robust with stout cusps and short processes that are adenticulate or carry a few discrete peg-like denticles.
Figured specimen: upper view of Pa element, NU 915/31, ×40. Woodland Formation of Woodland Point, Girvan, Ayrshire (loc. 262, NX 16889528).
Remarks: Pa element characteristic but rarely found complete, single lobes of platform relatively common.

Icriodella discreta Pollock, Rexroad and Nicoll 1970
Plate 3.1, Fig. 2. Table 2. Diagnosis: apparatus probably seximembrate; Pa element with high posterior blade bearing about four confluent fused denticles and lower anterior platform with a double row of nodes; Pb pyramidal with short cusp and large basal cavity; M dolabrate with adenticulate posterior process and weakly denticulate anterior process; S elements with tall cusps and denticulate processes.
Figured specimen: upper view of Pa element, NU 744/35, ×40. From Gelli Farm, Llansantffraid ym Mechain, Powys (loc. 204, SJ 23631941).
Remarks: Pa element characteristic, common in near-shore high-energy facies.

Icriodella deflecta Aldridge 1972
Plate 3.1, Fig. 3. Table 2. Diagnosis: apparatus probably seximembrate; Pa element with marked angle of about 45° between posterior blade and anterior platform, blade long with about seven fused denticles; remaining elements resemble those of *I discreta*.
Figured specimen: upper view of Pa element, NU 916/33, ×40. Lower part of Venusbank Formation in old quarry on North side of A488, 1.5 km NE of Hope Church, Shropshire (loc. 81, SJ 35510208).
Remarks: Pa element characteristic, common in near-shore high-energy facies.

Ozarkordina hassi (Pollock, Rexroad and Nicoll 1970)
Plate 3.1, Fig. 4. Table 2. Diagnosis: apparatus seximembrate, Pa element characteristic with prominent cusp, low short posterior process and broadly flared lips to the basal activity; Pb, M and S elements delicate with compressed denticles commonly crowded proximally.
Figured specimen: lateral view of Pa element, NU 744/38, ×40. Lower part of Pentamerus Beds of stream section 250 m SSW of New House, Marshbrook, Shropshire (loc. 40, SO 43418982).
Remarks: there is a close relationship to *O. oldhamensis,* and intermediate specimens occur.

Ozarkodina oldhamensis (Rexroad 1967)
Plate 3.1, Fig. 5. Table 2. Diagnosis: apparatus seximembrate, Pa element characteristic with broadly flared lips to the basal cavity, above which the denticles are small and commonly fused, posterior process short, both processes with even denticulation; Pb, M and S elements delicate with compressed denticles commonly crowded proximally.
Figured specimen: lateral view of Pa element, NU 915/30, ×40. Basal Venusbank Formation of old quarry on north side of A488, 1.5 km NE of Hope Church, Shropshire (loc. 81, SJ 35510208).
Remarks: this species is distinguished from *O. hassi* by the lack of a prominent cusp on the Pa element, differences in other elements are subtle.

Kockelella? abrupta (Aldridge 1972)
Plate 3.1, Figs. 6(a) and 6(b). Table 2. Diagnosis: apparatus unknown, Pa element with blade deflected inwards in posterior quarter, where denticles are low; cavity widely flared and extending to posterior tip.
Figured specimen: lateral and upper views of NU 744/36, ×40. Basal Venusbank Formation of old quarry on north side of A488, 1.5 km NE of Hope Church, Shropshire (loc. 81, SJ 35510208).
Remarks: there are close similarities to *K.? manitoulinensis* (Pollock, Rexroad and Nicoll 1970, p. 761), which characteristically has a longer posterior blade and a less widely flared cavity; it is possible that *abrupta* should be considered a subspecies of *manitoulinensis.*

Pl. 3.1] Conodonts of the Silurian System from the British Isles 79

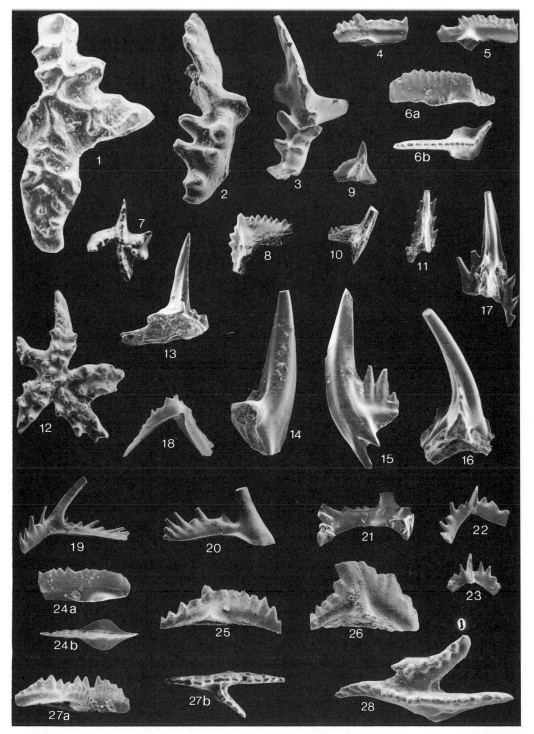

Plate 3.1

Pterospathodus? tenuis (Aldridge 1972)
Plate 3.1, Figs. 7–11. Table 2. Diagnosis: apparatus as known pentamembrate; Pa with thin, curved blade, bifurcate inner process and blade-like outer process, denticles low and discrete; Pb and intermediate Pb–M elements pyramidal with short cusps and deep basal cavities; M dolabrate with denticulate posterior process; Sa symmetrical with three denticulate processes.
Figured Specimens: Fig. 7, upper view of Pa element, NU 745/39; Fig. 8, lateral view of Pb element, NU 744/37; Fig. 9, lateral view of Pb–M intermediate, NU 5598/9; Fig. 10, inner lateral view of M element, NU 5599/11; Fig. 11, posterior view of Sa element, NU 5599/10, all × 40. Fig. 7, Pentamerus Beds of road cutting on north side of A489, 375 m W of Hillend Farm, near Plowden, Shropshire (loc. 44, SJ 39568768); Figs. 8–11, lower part of Pentamerus Beds of stream section 250 m SSW of New House, Marshbrook, Shropshire (loc. 40, SJ 43418982).
Remarks: the apparatus structure of this species compares with that of *Pterospathodus* species, but the pyramidal morphology of the Pb and Pb–M intermediate elements may warrant generic differentiation.

Distomodus staurognathoides (Walliser 1964)
Plate 3.1, Figs. 12–17. Table 2. Diagnosis: apparatus as known seximembrate; Pa a distinctive platform with five or more processes. basically one anterior, two lateral and two postero-lateral, upper surface covered by irregular nodes and ridges; other elements robust with stout cusps.
Figured specimens: Fig. 12, upper view of Pa element, NU 736/16; Fig. 13, posterior view of Pb element, NU 5600/16; Fig. 14, inner lateral view of M elment, NU 5599/14; Fig. 15, outer lateral view of Sc element, NU 5599/13; Fig. 16, posterior view of Sb element, NU 5599/12; Fig. 17, posterior view of Sa element, NU 5600/15. All × 40. All from lower part of Purple Shales in Sheinton Brook, 500 m NNW of Sheinwood Farm, Wenlock Edge area, Shropshire (loc. 14, SJ 61170307).
Remarks: distinguished from *D. kentuckyensis* mainly by the Pa element; intermediate specimens occur in the lowest part of the range.

Oulodus? fluegeli (Walliser 1964)
Plate 3.1, Figs. 18–23. Table 2. Diagnosis: apparatus seximembrate or possibly septimembrate, all elements display characteristic compression of the cusp and denticles. Pa and Pb elements with bent and twisted processes, M and Sc with flexed and variably twisted posterior processes; basal cavity in form of a narrow groove in all elements.
Figured specimens: Fig. 18, lateral view of Pa element, BM X.881; Fig. 19, lateral view of Pb element, BM X.880; Fig. 20, inner lateral view of M element, BM X.882; Fig. 21, inner lateral view of Sc element, BM X.885; Fig. 22, posterior view of Sb element, BM X.884; Fig. 23, posterior view of Sa element, BM X.883. All × 40. All from lower part of Purple Shales in Sheinton Brook, 500 m NNW of Sheinwood Farm, Wenlock Edge area, Shropshire (loc. 14, SJ 61170307).
Remarks: the compressed denticles contrast with the discrete stout denticles of typical species of *Oulodus,* and generic separation may be warranted.

Ozarkodina aldridgei Uyeno in Uyeno and Barnes 1983
Plate 3. 1, Figs. 24(a) and 24(b). Table 2. Diagnosis: apparatus seximembrate; Pa characteristic, nearly straight with widely flaring subcircular lips to basal cavity that do not extend to posterior tip, denticles of subequal size, commonly fused above cavity.
Figured specimen: lateral and upper views of Pa element, NU 1763/28, × 40. From lower part of Purple Shales in Sheinton Brook, 500 m NNW of Sheinwood Farm, Wenlock Edge area, Shropshire (loc. 14, SJ 61170307).
Remarks: this species has a very restricted stratigraphical distribution, and was used to subdivide the *Distomodus staurognathoides* Zone by Uyeno and Barnes (1983).

Pterospathodus celloni (Walliser 1964)
Plate 3.1, Figs. 25 and 26. Table 2. Diagnosis: apparatus as known pentamembrate; Pa blade-like, lacking platform ledges, with two weakly developed adenticulate offset pointed lateral lobes at about midlength; Pb arched with short offset lobes to basal cavity that do not project below lower margin; Pb–M intermediate, M and Sa elements with short, adenticulate or weakly denticulate processes.
Figured specimens: Fig. 25, lateral view of Pa element, NU 913/23, × 40; Fig. 26, lateral view of Pb element, NU 914/28, × 40. Wych Formation of Gullet Quarry, Malvern Hills, Hereford and Worcester (loc. 118, SO 76123811).
Remarks: the Pa element of this stratigraphically important species is distinctive; the denticulation is very variable, but the offset pointed adenticulate lateral lobes distinguish it from other species.

Pterospathodus pennatus pennatus (Walliser 1964)
Plate 3.1, Figs. 27(a) and 27(b). Table 2. Diagnosis: apparatus probably pentamembrate; Pa element with one lateral process elongate and denticulate, directed laterally and anteriorly, other lateral lobe offset, pointed and adenticulate; basal activity widened at junction of denticulate process with blade. Other elements resemble those of *P. celloni.*
Figured specimen: lateral and upper views of Pa element, NU 747/6, × 40. From the Wych Formation in stream on Old Storridge Common, 1.8 km S of Alfrick Church, Hereford and Worcester (loc. 124, SO 74713857).

Pl. 3.1]   **Conodonts of the Silurian System from the British Isles**   81

Remarks: forms referred to this subspecies occur together with *P. celloni*, the number increasing in stratigraphically younger samples.

Pterospathodus pennatus subsp. nov.
Plate 3.1, Fig. 28. Table 2. Diagnosis: apparatus as known pentamembrate; Pa element with one adenticulate lateral lobe and an offset lateral process bearing a curved or geniculate row of denticles, separated from the blade by an unornamented trough. Other elements similar to those of *P. celloni*.
Figured specimen: upper view of Pa element, NU 5600/18, × 40. Uppermost Purple Shales of small stream 850 m SSW of Ticklerton, Shropshire (loc. 23, SO 48109006).
Remarks: the lack of platform ledges distinguishes this subspecies from *P. amorphognathoides;* it occurs with *P. celloni* in the uppermost *P. celloni* Zone.

Repository of specimens on this plate: NU, Micropalaeontology Unit, Department of Geology, University of Nottingham; BM, Palaeontology Department, British Museum (Natural History).

PLATE 3.2

Astropentagnathus irregularis Mostler 1967

Plate 3.2, Figs. 1 and 2. Table 2. Diagnosis: apparatus probably septimembrate; Pa_1 with platform-like lateral processes, the inner bearing a single row of nodes and directed anteriorly, the outer bifurcate; Pa_2 a platform with a single laterally directed denticulate lateral process; Pb arched, broad and deeply excavated; M pyramidal with small recurved cusp; S elements with deep cavities.

Figured specimens: Fig. 1, upper view of Pa_1 element, NU 737/22, × 40; Fig. 2, upper view of Pa_2 element, NU 5601/20, × 40. Fig. 2, Purple Shales of Sheinton Brook, 500 m NNW of Sheinwood Farm, Wenlock Edge area, Shropshire (loc. 15, SJ 61250302).

Remarks: rather rare in British collections, mostly represented by broken processes only; occurs in lower part of *P. celloni* Zone.

Aulacognathus kuehni Mostler 1967

Plate 3.2, Figs. 3 and 4. Table 2. Diagnosis: apparatus probably seximembrate; Pa characteristic with platform-like processes, posterior process deflected inwards, inner lateral process straight and at about 45° to free blade, outer lateral process tri-lobed and separated from carina by an unornamented trough. Pb with prominent cusp and short pointed, weakly ornamented lateral processes, M and Sa–Sc elements with prominent cusps and high processes bearing confluent denticles, Sa palmate.

Figured specimens: Fig. 3, upper view of Pb element, NU 941/26, × 40; Fig. 4, upper view of Pa element, NU 746/0, × 40. Purple Shales of ash-disposal reservoir 730 m NNE of Buildwas Church, Shropshire (loc. 9, SJ 641054).

Remarks: a fairly common and very distinctive species of the *P. celloni* Zone, but not recognized in the upper part of the zone.

Ozarkodina polinclinata subsp. nov.

Plate 3.2, Fig. 5. Table 2. Diagnosis: apparatus seximembrate; Pa characteristic, a straight blade with erect slender denticles of subequal height and slit-like cavity with narrow lips along posterior half. All elements delicate, M planate.

Figured specimen: lateral view of Pa element, NU 4228/3, × 40. Purple Shales of Sheinton Brook, 500 m NNW of Sheinwood Farm, Wenlock Edge area, Shropshire (loc. 15, SJ 61250302).

Remarks: British specimens differ from the typical subspecies in the regularity of the denticulation and in the relatively greater length of the flared basal cavity; the new subspecies occurs regularly but in small numbers in the *celloni* Zone.

Icriodella inconstans Aldridge 1972

Plate 3.2, Fig. 6. Table 2. Diagnosis: apparatus unknown; Pa straight, blade short with tall cusp, platform lanceolate bearing two parallel rows of nodes that are laterally elongated in the central portion; outer lateral lobe strong but unornamented, inner lateral lobe weak.

Figured specimen: upper view of BM X.870, × 40. Wych Formation of Gullet Quarry, Malvern Hills, Hereford and Worcester (loc. 118, SO 76123811).

Remarks: common in near-shore high-energy facies.

Icriodella malvernensis Aldridge 1972

Plate 3.2, Fig. 7. Table 2. Diagnosis: apparatus unknown; Pa sigmoidal in upper view, with curved blade and platform, outer lateral lobe strongly developed and bearing one to three laterally elongated ridges.

Figured specimen: upper view of NU 745/41, × 40. Wych Formation of 'Sycamore Tree Quarry', Malvern Hills, Hereford and Worcester (loc. 119, SO 76464594).

Remarks: typical specimens known from only the one locality.

Kockelella ranuliformis (Walliser 1964)

Plate 3.2, Fig. 8. Table 2. Diagnosis: apparatus seximembrate; Pa characteristic with straight or slightly curved blade and rounded basal cavity; cavity lips flare from midpoint of unit and extend beyond posterior of blade; there are no lateral processes. Other elements with small basal cavities; denticles and cusps of M and Sa–Sc elements compressed with sharp edges.

Figured specimen: upper view of Pa element, NU 5606/24, × 40. Acidaspis Limestone, 75 m SE of Trecoed Farm, S of Llandrindod Wells, Powys (loc. 214, SO 05255520).

Remarks: occurs regularly in small numbers in the *D. staurognathoides, P. celloni* and *P. amorphognathoides* zones.

Ozarkodina gulletensis (Aldridge 1972)

Plate 3.2, Fig. 9, Table 2. Diagnosis: apparatus seximembrate; Pa with straight blade lower at posterior, denticles subequal in size with free tips; cusp broad, not always prominent, white matter forms conspicuous roots to denticles. Pb element arched and bowed with prominent cusp and flared cavity lips; Pb, M and Sa–Sc elements with broad denticles.

Figured specimen: lateral view of Pa element, NU 745/42, × 40. Wych Formation of Gullet Quarry, Malvern Hills, Hereford and Worcester (loc. 118, SO 76123811).

Remarks: Pa element rather generalized in morphology, lacking extreme features, but readily distinguishable from other coeval species.

Pl. 3.2] Conodonts of the Silurian System from the British Isles 83

Plate 3.2

Carniodus carnulus Walliser 1964

Plate 3.2, Figs. 10–18. Table 2. Diagnosis: apparatus structure uncertain; most elements have prominent cusps, all have compressed processes bearing small erect, often crowded denticles; the processes may be thickened below the denticle row. There is a considerable range of morphology, with intergradations apparent between several elements.

Figured specimens: lateral views of NU 743/34, NU 743/31, NU 5601/24, NU 5602/26, NU 916/34, NU 743/33, NU 742/29, NU 5601/22, NU 742/30. All × 40. Uppermost Wych Formation, Birches Farm Lane, West Malvern, Hereford and Worcester (loc. 127, SO 76034685).

Remarks: present in relatively small numbers in the *P. celloni* Zone, abundant in the *P. amorphognathoides* Zone.

Pseudoonoeotodus tricornis Drygant 1974

Plate 3.2, Fig. 19. Table 2. Diagnosis: apparatus of squat conical elements, deeply excavated with thin walls; elements with a single tip or with three discrete denticles arranged in a triangular pattern at the apex.

Figured specimen: upper view of three-tipped element, BM X.1060, × 40. Uppermost Purple Shales of Hughley Brook, 200 m SE of 'Leasows', Hughley, Shropshire (loc. 25, SO 56889839).

Remarks: occurs regularly in small numbers from within the *D. staurognathoides* Zone to within the *P. amorphognathoides* Zone.

Apsidognathus tuberculatus Walliser 1964

Plate 3.2, Figs. 20–24. Table 2. Diagnosis: apparatus comprises a broad platform element with short free blade, prominent curved carina and upper surface ornament of radial and concentric nodes; a lenticular compressed element with a nodose ornament; an arched element with prominent cusp and nodose flared lateral faces; a lyriform element with a short free blade, central carina extended posteriorly and nodose lateral ridges; and a cruciform element with compressed processes. All but the lenticular and cruciform elements with broad shallow basal cavities.

Figured specimens: Fig. 20, upper view of platform element, NU 737/21; Fig. 21, outer lateral view of lenticular element, NU 920/3; Fig. 22, oblique upper view of cruciform element, NU 911/16; Fig. 23, lateral view of arched element, NU 5600/17; Fig. 24, upper view of lyriform element, NU 737/20. All × 40. All from Wych Formation of Gullet Quarry, Malvern Hills, Hereford and Worcester (loc. 118, SO 76123811).

Remarks: all elements are distinctive, but the species is particularly characterized by the nodose ridges of the platform element, which radiate from the centre of the unit.

Repository of specimens on this plate: NU, Micropalaeontology Unit, Department of Geology, University of Nottingham; BM, Palaeontology Department, British Museum (Natural History).

PLATE 3.3

Apsidognathus ruginosus Mabillard and Aldridge 1983

Plate 3.3, Figs. 1–6. Table 2. Diagnosis: Apparatus similar to that of *A. tuberculatus,* but possibly also contains squat and slender conical elements; all elements characterized by an ornamentation of short narrow ridges. Posterior portion of carina on platform element curved strongly inwards to produce markedly asymmetrical development of platform; arched element pyramidal and widely flared; cruciform element with short lateral processes; lyriform element with broad free blade and conspicuous transverse rugae on platform.

Figured specimens: Fig. 1, upper view of platform element, BM X773; Fig. 2 lateral view of arched pyramidal element, BM X778; Fig. 3, outer lateral view of lenticular element, BM X775; Fig. 4, upper view of lyriform element, BM X779; Fig. 5, lateral view of squat conical element, BM X780: Fig. 6, lateral view of slender conical element, BM X782. All × 40. All from Coralliferous Group of Marloes Bay, Dyfed (loc. 245, SM 787072).

Remarks: currently known only from South-west Dyfed, where it is a characteristic member of the *P. amorphognathoides* Zone fauna.

Pl. 3.3]   Conodonts of the Silurian System from the British Isles   85

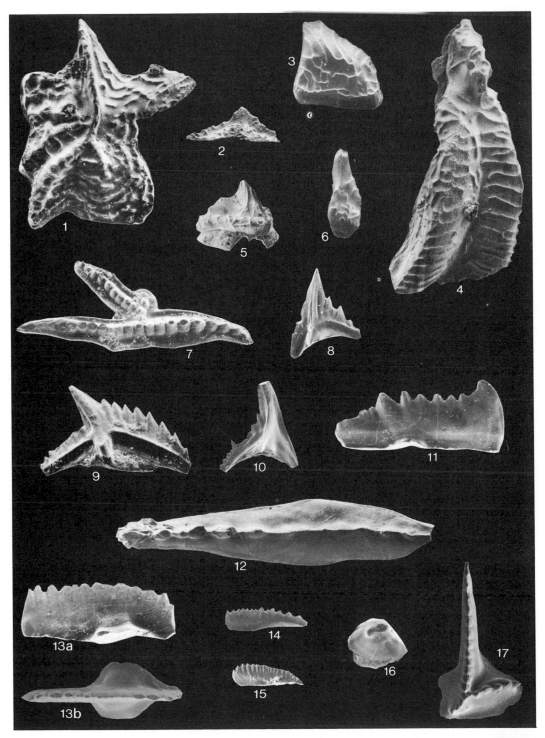

Plate 3.3

Pterospathodus amorphognathoides Walliser 1964
Plate 3.3, Figs. 7–10. Table 2. Diagnosis: apparatus as known pentamembrate; Pa element with denticulate bifurcated lateral process on one side of carina and narrow platform ledge round entire unit; Pb element arched with narrow platform ledge at base of denticle row and one or two downwardly projecting lips to basal cavity; Pb–M intermediate element with prominent cusp, denticulated anticusp and posterior process and adenticulate lateral costa; M element with adenticulate anticusp and denticulate posterior process; Sa element with denticulate lateral processes.
Figured specimens: Fig. 7, upper view of Pa element, NU 5163/24; Fig. 8, lateral view of Pb–M intermediate element, NU 5165/34; Fig. 9, lateral view of Pb element, NU 742/28; Fig. 10, inner lateral view of M element, NU 5165/32. All × 40. All from uppermost Wych Formation, Birches Farm Lane, West Malvern, Hereford and Worcester (loc. 127, SO 76034685).
Remarks: abundant, widespread and distinctive through its short stratigraphical range.

Ozarkodina hadra (Nicoll and Rexroad 1968)
Plate 3.3, Fig. 11. Table 2. Diagnosis: only Pa element currently known; characteristically arched blade with a small basal cavity situated posterior of midlength, blade height decreases rapidly posterior of cavity; cusp on mature specimens usually small, anterior denticle may be large.
Figured specimen: lateral view of NU 2944/36, × 40. Lower part of Brinkmarsh Formation in Brinkmarsh Quarry, Whitfield, Gloucestershire (loc. 174, ST 67369128).
Remarks: currently known in Britain from a single locality, where all specimens are broken.

Johnognathus huddlei Mashkova 1977
Plate 3.3, Fig. 12. Table 2. Diagnosis: the only element currently recognized is a long slender platform, bilaterally symmetrical, narrower anteriorly, with smooth or marginally serrate upper surface traversed by straight medial carina that comprises high discrete denticles anteriorly, fading posteriorly; basal cavity wide and deep.
Figured specimen: upper view of BM X799, × 40. Coralliferous Group of Marloes Bay, Dyfed (loc. 245, SM 787072).
Remarks: of regular occurrence in small numbers in the *P. amorphognathoides* Zone; normally represented by broken or fragmentary specimens.

Ozarkodina bohemica subsp. nov.
Plate 3.3, Figs. 13(a) and 13(b). Table 2. Diagnosis: apparatus seximembrate; Pa a straight blade, robust and high with denticles of even height, becoming fused above cavity often to extent of forming a linear ridge; cavity with wide subcircular lips, flaring from midpoint and not extending to posterior lip. Pb arched with prominent triangular cusp and flaring cavity lips, ramiform M and Sa–Sc elements with long processes and slender denticles, crowded proximally.
Figured specimen: lateral and upper views of Pa element, NU 1428/36, × 40. Lower part of Brinkmarsh Formation, Brinkmarsh Quarry, Whitfield, Gloucestershire (loc. 174, ST 67369128).
Remarks: currently known from only the one locality; distinguished from *O. bohemica bohemica* by the high blade and strong denticle fusion shown by the Pa element.

Ozarkodina sagitta rhenana (Walliser 1964)
Plate 3.3, Fig. 14. Table 2. Diagnosis: apparatus seximembrate; Pa a straight blade with erect slender anterior denticles and broad discrete posterior denticles; blade decreases steadily in height posteriorly from midpoint, basal cavity with arrow-shaped lips occupying posterior part of unit. Pb, M and Sa–Sc elements delicate with slender closely packed denticles that become crowded proximally; processes of Sb element of unequal length.
Figured specimen: lateral view of Pa element, NU 1763/29, × 40. Dolyhir and Nash Scar Limestone Formation of quarry 850 m W of Burlingjobb, Powys (loc. 209, SO 244583).
Remarks: Pa element distinguished from that of *O. sagitta sagitta* by the relatively small number of denticles (nine to seventeen).

Ozarkodina sagitta sagitta (Walliser 1964)
Plate 3.3, Fig. 15. Table 2. Diagnosis: apparatus seximembrate; Pa a straight blade with erect slender denticles; blade height decreases steadily in height posteriorly from midpoint, basal cavity with arrow-shaped lips occupying posterior part of unit. Pb, M and Sa–Sc elements delicate, similar to those of *O. s. rhenana,* but with more slender cusps; processes of Sb element of subequal length.
Figured specimen: lateral view of Pa element, NU 3214/42, × 40. Coalbrookdale Formation of Daw End railway cutting, near Walsall, West Midlands (loc. 103, SK 036003).
Remarks: very rare in British collections; distinguished from *O. sagitta rhenana* by relatively large number (fourteen to twenty-two) of denticles on Pa element.

Pseudooneotodus bicornis Drygant 1974
Plate 3.3, Fig. 16. Table 2. Diagnosis: apparatus of squat conical elements, deeply excavated with thin walls; elements with single tip or with two denticles at apex.

Pl. 3.3]   **Conodonts of the Silurian System from the British Isles**   87

Figured specimen: upper view of two-tipped element, BM X1059, × 40. Buildwas Formation of Hughley Brook, 200 m SE of 'Leasows', Hughley, Shropshire (loc. 25, SO 56889839).

Remarks: only apparatuses including specimens with two distinct denticle tips are referred to this species; earlier Llandovery specimens occur in which the apex is occupied by two denticles fused to form a concave linear ridge.

Kockelella walliseri (Helfrich 1975)
Plate 3.3, Fig. 17. Table 2. Diagnosis: apparatus seximembrate; Pa with blade long and straight anterior of cusp, posterior blade comprises two or three denticles and is strongly incurved; basal cavity flares widely from posterior of midpoint to beyond posterior tip of blade and supports a long straight denticulate outer lateral process. Other elements with prominent compressed cusps and deep processes bearing discrete compressed denticles.

Figured specimen: upper view of Pa element, NU 3213/4, × 40. Barr Limestone from trackside 300 m NE of Hayhead Farm, Great Barr, West Midlands (loc. 98, SP 04859879).

Remarks: a short-ranging widespread species with a distinctive Pa element.

Repository of specimens on this plate: NU, Micropalaeontology Unit, Department of Geology, University of Nottingham; BM, Palaeontology Department, British Museum (Natural History).

PLATE 3.4

Ozarkodina confluens (Branson and Mehl 1933)
Plate 3.4, Fig. 1. Table 2. Diagnosis: apparatus seximembrate; Pa element a straight or slightly curved blade with flared basal cavity at about midlength beneath inconspicuous cusp; one to four denticles at anterior end larger then remainder. All elements with confluent denticles and extensive white matter forming clear denticle 'roots'.
Figured specimen: lateral view of Pa element, NU 1338/37, × 40. Upper Whitcliffe Beds, tramway section, Netherton, West Midlands (loc. 115, SO 93588732).
Remarks: a common and widespread constituent of Wenlock and Ludlow faunas.

Ozarkodina? sp. nov.
Plate 3.4, Fig. 2. Table 2. Diagnosis: apparatus probably seximembrate; all elements tiny and delicate with confluent slender denticles. Pa element with short high blade, central cavity below inconspicuous cusp; anterior denticles slender and tall, posterior denticles slender, lower and gently inclined posteriorly.
Figured specimen: lateral view of Pa element, NU 3213/2, × 40. Nodular beds, Much Wenlock Limestone Formation, west side of Wren's Nest Hill, Dudley, West Midlands (loc. 109, SO 93569195).
Remarks: occurs sporadically and in small numbers in the Much Wenlock Limestone Formation.

Ozarkodina bohemica bohemica (Walliser 1964)
Plate 3.4, Figs. 3(a) and 3(b). Table 2. Diagnosis: apparatus seximembrate; Pa a relatively long blade with steep posterior termination; denticles commonly fused above subcircular basal cavity, cavity lips in mature specimens extend to, or nearly to, posterior tip of blade. Pb element arched with prominent triangular cusp and flaring cavity lips, ramiform M and Sa−Sc elements with long processes and slender denticles, crowded proximally.
Figured specimen: lateral and upper views of Pa element, NU 1021/12, × 40. Much Wenlock Limestone Formation of Eastnor Castle Quarry, Eastnor, Herford and Worcester (loc. 135, SO 73223629).
Remarks: a common constituent of faunas from the Much Wenlock Limestone Formation.

Kockelella variabilis Walliser 1957
Plate 3.4, Figs. 4−9. Table 2. Diagnosis: apparatus seximembrate; Pa element with straight or slightly curved denticulate blade, a denticulate bifurcated lateral process on one side and a denticulate single or bifurcated lateral process on the other; cavity not widely flared beyond processes. Pb element arched with confluent denticles, ramiform M and Sa−Sc elements with tall cusps and discrete denticles, all of subcircular or elliptical cross-section.
Figured specimens: Fig. 4, lateral view of Pb element, NU 2652/22; Fig. 5, upper view of Pa element, NU 2652/20; Fig. 6, inner lateral view of M element, NU 2653/26; Fig. 7, posterior view of Sa element, NU 2652/21; Fig. 8, posterior view of Sb element, NU 2653/24; Fig. 9, inner lateral view of Sc element, NU 2652/23. All × 40. All from Annascaul Formation of W face of Caherconree Mountain, 15 km NE of Annascaul, Co. Kerry, Ireland.
Remarks: Pa element distinctive; the Irish specimens may be as old as late Wenlock but are more likely to be early Ludlow; in England the species is not recorded before the mid-Gorstian.

Distomodus? dubius (Rhodes 1953)
Plate 3.4, Figs. 10−15. Table 2. Diagnosis: apparatus structure uncertain, possibly seximembrate; elements robust with tall stout cusps, processes short and adenticulate or with a few discrete peg-like denticles; white matter fills distal portion of cusps but narrows proximally to a point at cavity tip, producing a triangle of hyaline matter at cusp base.
Figured specimens: Figs. 10 and 11, lateral views of P? elements, NU 5602/13 and 5602/14; Fig. 12, inner lateral view of M element, NU 5602/2; Fig. 13, lateral view of Sc element, NU 5607/26; Fig. 14, posterior view of Sa element, NU 5605/15; Fig. 15, posterior view of Sb element, NU 5603/32. All × 40. All from Upper Whitcliffe Beds of old quarry 50 m S of lane junction at Perton, Woolhope area, Hereford and Worcester (loc. 160, SO 59694031).
Remarks: the lack of a platform element renders the generic assignment uncertain; a common constituent of upper Ludlow faunas.

Pelekysgnathus dubius Jeppsson 1972
Plate 3.4, Fig. 16. Table 2. Diagnosis: apparatus with an element displaying a linear row of few broad discrete denticles and a terminal cusp; basal cavity deep and widely flared with a marginal fold on the inner side; associated small erect or suberect coniform elements may be from the same apparatus.
Figured specimen: lateral view of NU 910/11. × 40. Whitcliffe Beds from foreshore at Tite's Point, Gloucestershire (loc. 187, SO 68820460).
Remarks: normally occurs with *D? dubius,* but in small numbers.

Pl. 3.4]   **Conodonts of the Silurian System from the British Isles**   89

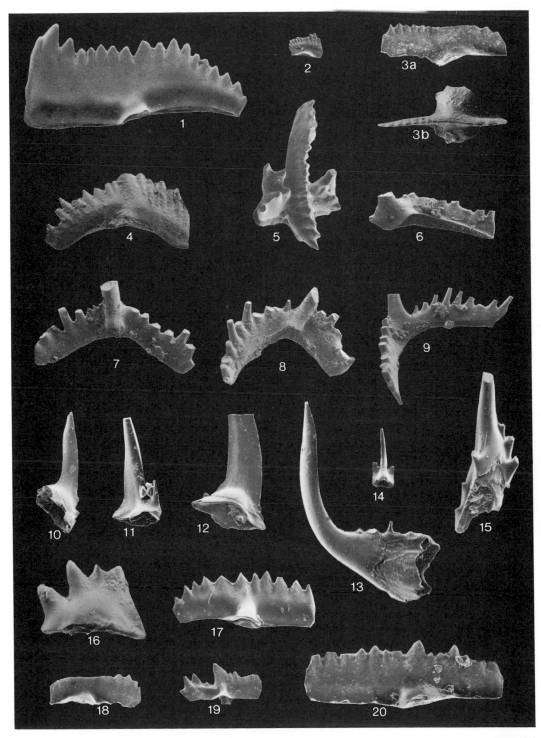

Plate 3.4

Ozarkodina remscheidensis subsp. nov.

Plate 3.4, Fig. 17. Table 2. Diagnosis: apparatus probably seximembrate; Pa element a straight compact blade bearing irregular but mostly broad denticles; cusp inconspicuous, cavity at midlength with broadly flared lips.

Figured specimen: lateral view of Pa element, NU 5603/30, × 40. Upper Whitcliffe Beds opposite Yew Tree Inn, Prior's Frome, Hereford and Worcester (loc. 162, SO 56723901).

Remarks: other elements of apparatus uncertain, but Pa is associated with ramiform elements bearing crowded denticles of alternating size.

Ozarkodina snajdri (Walliser 1964)

Plate 3.4, Fig. 18. Table 2. Diagnosis: apparatus not completely known, but probably seximembrate; Pa a long blade with vertical or steeply curved posterior termination, basal cavity with widely flared lips that extend to, or almost to, posterior tip of unit; upper surface of blade above cavity straight, with denticles commonly fused.

Figured specimen: lateral view of Pa element, NU 3036/1, × 40. Uppermost Upper Whitcliffe Beds, 'Ludford Lane' 130 m SW of Ludford Bridge, Ludlow, Shropshire (loc. 77, SO 51157413).

Remarks: distinguished from *O. bohemica* by more even denticle height and more broadly flared cavity; in *O. crispa* (Walliser 1964) the flared lips of the cavity extend posteriorly beyond the blade.

Ozarkodina wimani (Jeppsson 1974)

Plate 3.4, Fig. 19. Table 2. Diagnosis: apparatus not completely known, but probably seximembrate; Pa a short straight blade with prominent cusp, immediately posterior to which the process is very low; basal cavity central, flaring laterally. Associated elements, which may belong to the apparatus, include an Sa with a denticulated posterior process.

Figured specimen: lateral view of Pa element, NU 5603/31, × 40. Upper Whitcliffe Beds of old quarry 50 m S of lane junction at Perton, Hereford and Worcester (loc. 160, SO 59694031).

Remarks: typical specimens of Pa element show distinctive denticulation, but there are some specimens intermediate with *O. remscheidensis*; ramiforms associated with *O. wimani* lack alternating denticulation.

Ozarkodina remscheidensis eosteinhornensis (Walliser 1964)

Plate 3.4, Fig. 20. Table 2. Diagnosis: apparatus seximembrate; Pa a long blade with relatively even denticulation and an inconspicuous cusp; cavity slightly posterior of midlength with widely flaring lips, commonly pinched; Pb arched with slender confluent denticles on processes. ramiform M and Sa–Sc elements with alternating denticulation on the processes; Sa without posterior process.

Figured specimen: lateral view of Pa element, NU 5605/18, × 40. Upper Whitcliffe Beds of road cutting at Diddlebury, Shropshire (collected by L. Jeppsson, SO 503858).

Remarks: widespread in small numbers in the Upper Whitcliffe Beds of the Welsh Borderland.

Repository of specimens on this plate: Micropalaeontology Unit, Department of Geology, University of Nottingham.

3.7 REFERENCES

Aldridge, R. J. 1970. Llandovery conodonts from Wales and the Welsh Borderland. *Unpublished Ph.D. Thesis.* University of Southampton.

Aldridge, R. J. 1972. Llandovery conodonts from the Welsh Borderland. *Bull. Brit. Mus. (Nat. Hist.), Geol.*, **22**, 125–231, 9 plates.

Aldridge, R. J. 1975a. The Silurian conodont *Ozarkodina sagitta* and its value in correlation. *Palaeontology*, **18**, 323–332, 1 plate.

Aldridge, R. J. 1975b. The stratigraphic distribution of conodonts in the British Silurian. *J. Geol. Soc. London*, **131**, 607–618, 3 plates.

Aldridge, R. J. 1976. Comparison of macrofossil communities and conodont distribution in the British Silurian. In C.R. Barnes (Ed.) *Conodont Paleoecology, Geol. Assoc. Can. Special Paper.* **15**, 91–104.

Aldridge, R. J. 1980. Notes on some Silurian conodonts from Ireland. *J. Earth Sci. R. Dublin Soc.*, **3**, 127–132, 1 plate.

Aldridge, R. J., Dorning, K. J., Hill, P. J. and Siveter, D. J. 1979. Microfossil distribution in the Silurian of Britain and Ireland. In A. L. Harris, C. H. Holland and B. E. Leake (Eds.): *The Caledonides of the British Isles – reviewed, Geol. Soc. London Spec. Pub.*, **8**, 433–438.

Aldridge, R. J., Dorning, K. J. and Siveter, D. J. 1981. Distribution of microfossil groups across the Wenlock Shelf of the Welsh Basin. In J. W. Neale and M. D. Brasier, (Eds.): *Microfossils from Recent and Fossil Shelf Seas,* Ellis Horwood, Chichester, Sussex. 18–30, 3 plates.

Aldridge, R. J. and Jeppsson, L. 1984. Ecological specialists among Silurian conodonts. *Spec. Paper Palaeontol.*, **32**, 141–149.

Aldridge, R. J. and Mabillard, J. E. 1981. Local variations in the distribution of Silurian conodonts: an example from the *amorphognathoides* interval of the Welsh Basin. In J. W. Neale and M. D. Brasier (Eds.): *Microfossils from Recent and Fossil Shelf Seas,* Ellis Horwood, Chichester, Sussex. 10–17.

Aldridge, R. J. and Mohamed, I. 1982. Conodont biostratigraphy of the early Silurian of the Oslo region. In: *IUGS Subcommission on Silurian Stratigraphy Field Meeting, Oslo Region, 1982,* in *Paleontol. Contr. Univ. Oslo,* **278**, 109–120, 2 plates.

Antia, D. D. J. 1979. Bone beds: A review of their classification, occurrence, genesis, diagenesis, geochemistry, palaeoecology, weathering and microbiotas. *Mercian Geol.*, **7**, 93–175, 19 plates.

Austin, R. L. and Bassett, M. G. 1967. A *Sagitta* Zone conodont fauna from the Wenlockian of the Usk Inlier, Monmouthshire. *Geol. Mag.*, **104**, 274–283, 1 plate.

Barrick, J. E. and Klapper, G. 1976. Multielement Silurian (late Llandoverian–Wenlockian) conodonts of the Clarita Formation, Arbuckle Mountains, Oklahoma, and phylogeny of *Kockelella*. *Geol. Palaeontol.*, **10**, 59–100, 4 plates.

Bassett, M. G. 1974. Review of the stratigraphy of the Wenlock Series in the Welsh Borderland and South Wales. *Palaeontology*, **17**, 745–777.

Bassett, M. G., Cocks, L. R. M., Holland, C. H., Rickards, R. B. and Warren, P. T. 1975. The type Wenlock Series. *Annu. Rep. Inst. Geol. Sci.*, **75/13**, 1–19.

Branson, E. B. and Branson, C. C. 1947. Lower Silurian conodonts from Kentucky. *J. Paleontol.*, **21**, 549–556, 2 plates.

Branson, E. B. and Mehl, M. G. 1933. Conodonts from the Bainbridge (Silurian) of Missouri. *Univ. Mo. Stud.*, **8**, 39–52, 1 plate.

Brooks, M. and Druce, E. C. 1965. A Llandovery conglomeratic limestone in Gullet Quarry, Malvern Hills, and its conodont fauna. *Geol. Mag.*, **102**, 370–382, 1 plate.

Bultynck, P. and Pelhate, A. 1971. Découverte de la Zone a *eosteinhornensis* (Conodontes) dans le synclinorium médian du Massif Armoricain. *Colloq. Ordovicien–Silurien Brest, 1971* in *Mém. BRGM*, **73**, 189–198.

Cocks, L. R. M., Woodcock, N. H., Rickards, R. B., Temple, J. T. and Lane, P. D. 1984. The Llandovery Series of the type area. *Bull. Brit. Mus. (Nat. Hist.), Geol.*, **38**, 131–182.

Collinson, C. and Druce, E. C. 1966. Upper Silurian conodonts from Welsh Borderland (abstract). *Am. Assoc. Pet. Geol. Bull.*, **50**, 608.

Cooper, B. J. 1980. Toward an improved Silurian conodont biostratigraphy. *Lethaia*, **13**, 209–227.

Davis, R. A. 1974. Conodonts from across the Llandoverian–Wenlockian boundary at Woolhope (Silurian, Great Britain). *Abstracts Geol. Soc. Am.*, **6**, 505.

Druce, E. C. 1967. Conodont faunas from the Silurian of the Welsh Borderland and the Carboniferous of Ireland. *Unpublished M.Sc. Thesis,* University of Wales.

Drygant, D. M. 1974. [Simple conodonts from the Silurian and Lowermost Devonian of the Volyno-Podolian.] *Paleontol. Sb. Lvov.*, **10**, 64–70, 2 plates (in Russian).

Eccleston, B. L. 1958. Conodont faunas from the Silurian rocks of the Welsh Borders, with particular reference to the Ludlovian. *Unpublished M.Sc. Thesis,* University of London.

Fåhraeus, L. E. and Barnes, C. R. 1981. Conodonts from the Becscie and Gun River Formations (Lower Silurian) of Anticosti Island, Quebec. In P. J. Lesperance (Ed.): *Subcommission on Silurian Stratigraphy (Ordovician–Silurian Boundary Working Group) Field Meet., Anticosti-Gaspé, Quebec, 1981, Vol. II: Stratigraphy and Paleontology,* 167–172.

Harley, J. 1861. On the Ludlow Bone Bed and its Crustacean remains. *Q. J. Geol. Soc. London,* **17**, 542–552, 1 plate.

Helfrich, C. T. 1975. Silurian conodonts from Wills Mountain Anticline, Virginia, West Virginia, and Maryland. *Spec. Paper Geol. Soc. Am.*, **161**, v + 82 pp., 86 pp. appendix on microfiche, 16 plates.

Holland, C. H. 1980. Silurian series and stages: decisions concerning chrono-stratigraphy. *Lethaia*, **13**, 238.

Holland, C. H., Lawson, J. D. and Walmsley, V. G. 1963. The Silurian rocks of the Ludlow district, Shropshire. *Bull. Brit. Mus. (Nat. Hist.) Geol.*, **8**, 93–171,

7 plates.

Holland, C. H., Ross, R. J. and Cocks, L. R. M. 1984. Ordovician–Silurian boundary. *Lethaia*, **17**, 184.

Jeppsson, L. 1972. Some Silurian conodont apparatuses and possible conodont dimorphism. *Geol. Palaeontol.*, **6**, 51–69, 2 plates.

Jeppsson, L. 1974. Aspects of Late Silurian conodonts. *Foss. Strata*, **6**, 1–54, 12 plates.

Jeppsson, L. 1983. Silurian conodont faunas from Gotland. *Foss. Strata*, **15**, 121–144.

Jones, R. K., Brooks, M., Bassett, M. G., Austin, R. L. and Aldridge, R. J. 1969. An upper Llandovery limestone overying Hollybush Sandstone (Cambrian) in Hollybush, Malvern Hills. *Geol. Mag.*, **106**, 457–469.

Mabillard, J. E. 1981. Micropalaeontology and correlation of the Llandovery–Wenlock boundary beds in Wales and the Welsh Borderland. *Unpublished Ph.D. Thesis*, University of Nottingham.

Mabillard, J. E. and Aldridge, R. J. 1983. Conodonts from the Coralliferous Group (Silurian) of Marloes Bay, South-west Dyfed, Wales. *Geol. Palaeontol.*, **17**, 29–36, 4 plates.

Mabillard, J. E. and Aldridge, R. J. 1985. Microfossil distribution across the base of the Wenlock Series in the type area. *Palaeontology*, **28**, 89–100.

Martinsson, A. (Ed.) 1977. *The Silurian–Devonian Boundary*, International Union of Geological Sciences Ser. A, **5**, Schweizerbart'sche, Stuttgart, 1–345.

Mashkova, T. V. 1977. [New conodonts of the *amorphognathoides* Zone from the Lower Silurian of Podolia.] *Paleontol. Zh. Akad. Nauk SSSR*, **1977** (4), 127–131 (in Russian).

McCracken, A. D. and Barnes, C. R. 1981. Conodont biostratigraphy and paleoecology of the Ellis Bay Formation, Anticosti Island, Quebec, with special reference, to late Ordovician–early Silurian chronostratigraphy and the systemic boundary. *Bull. Geol. Surv. Can.*, **329**, 51–134, 7 plates.

Mohamed, I. 1983. Palaeontology and biostratigraphy of early Silurian conodonts of the Oslo region, Norway and of Wales. *Unpublished Ph.D. Thesis*, University of Nottingham.

Mostler, H. 1967. Conodonten aus dem tieferen Silur der Kitzbühler Alpen (Tirol). *Ann. Naturhist. Mus. Wien*, **71**, 295–303, 1 plate.

Nicoll, R. S. and Rexroad, C. B. 1968. Stratigraphy and conodont paleontology of the Salamonie Dolomite and Lee Creek Member of the Brassfield Limestone (Silurian) in Southeastern Indiana and adjacent Kentucky. *Bull. Indiana Geol. Surv.*, **40**, 1–73, 7 plates.

Nowlan, G. S. 1981. Late Ordovician–early Silurian conodont biostratigraphy of the Gaspé Peninsula – a preliminary report. In P. J. Lesperance (Ed.) *Subcommission on Silurian Stratigraphy (Ordovician–Silurian Boundary Working Group) Field Meet. Anticosti-Gaspé, Quebec, 1981, Vol. II: Stratigraphy and Paleontology*, 257–291, 7 plates.

Pander, C. H. 1856. *Monographie der fossilen Fische des Silurischen Systems der Russisch-Baltischen Gouvernements*, Akademie der Wissenschaften, St. Petersburg, 1–91, 7 plates.

Pollock, C. A., Rexroad, C. B. and Nicoll, R. S. 1970. Lower Silurian conodonts from Northern Michigan and Ontario. *J. Paleontol.*, **44**, 743–764, 4 plates.

Rexroad, C. B. 1967. Stratigraphy and conodont paleontology of the Brassfield (Silurian) in the Cincinnati Arch area. *Bull. Indiana Geol. Surv.*, **36**, 1–64, 4 plates.

Rhodes, F. H. T. 1953. Some British Lower Palaeozoic conodont faunas. *Philos. Trans. R. Soc. London, Ser. B*, **237**, 261–334, 4 plates.

Rhodes, F. H. T. and Newall, G. 1963. Occurrence of *Kockelella variabilis* Walliser in the Aymestry Limestone of Shropshire. *Nature (London)*, **199** (4889), 166–167.

Schönlaub, H. P. 1971. Zur Problematik der Conodonten-Chronologie an der Wende Ordoviz–Silur mit besonderer Berucksichtigung der Verhältnisse im Llandovery. *Geol. Palaeontol.*, **5**, 35–57, 3 plates.

Smith, J. and Jones, T. R. 1881. Notes on a collection of bivalved Entomostraca and other microzoa from the Upper Silurian strata of the Shropshire district. *Geol. Mag.*, **8**, 70–75.

Thompson, T. L. and Satterfield, I. R. 1975. Stratigraphy and conodont biostratigraphy of strata contiguous to the Ordovician–Silurian boundary in Eastern Missouri. *Missouri Geol. Surv. Rep. Invest.*, **57**, 61–108.

Uyeno, T. T. and Barnes, C. R. 1983. Conodonts of the Jupiter and Chicotte Formations (Lower Silurian), Anticosti Island, Quebec. *Bull. Geol. Surv. Can.*, **355**, vii + 49 pp., 9 plates.

Viira, V. 1975. A new species of *Spathognathodus* from the Jaani Stage of the East Baltic. *Izv. Akad. Nauk. Est. SSR, Khim. Geol.*, **24**, 233–236, 2 plates (in Russian with English summary).

Viira, V. 1982. Late Silurian shallow and deep water conodonts of the East Baltic. In D. Kaljo and E. Klaamann (Eds.): *Ecostratigraphy of the East Baltic Silurian*, Institute of Geology, Academy of Sciences of the Estonian SSR, Tallinn, 79–87.

Walliser, O. H. 1957. Conodonten aus dem oberen Gotlandium Deutschlands und der Karnischen Alpen. *Notizbl. Hess. Landesamtes Bodenforsch. Wiesbaden*, **85**, 28–52, 3 plates.

Walliser, O. H. 1962. Conodont Chronologie des Silurs (Gotlandium) und des tieferen Devons mit besonderer Berücksichtigung der Formations Grenze. *Symp. Silur–Devon-Grenze, Bonn, Bruxelles, 1960*, 281–287.

Walliser, O H. 1964. Conodonten des Silurs. *Abh. Hess. Landesamtes Bodenforsch*, **41**, 1–106, 32 plates.

Walliser, O. H. 1966. Die Silur–Devon-Grenze. *Neues Jahrb. Geol. Paläontol., Abh.*, **125**, 235–246.

Walliser, O. H. 1971. Conodont biostratigraphy of the Silurian of Europe. In W. C. Sweet and S. M. Bergström (Eds.): *Symp. on Conodont Biostratigraphy*, in *Mem. Geol. Soc. Am.*, **127**, 195–206.

Whittard, W. F. 1928. The stratigraphy of the Valentian rocks of Shropshire. The main outcrop. *Q. J. Geol. Soc. London*, **83**, 737–759.

Young, J. 1881. Specimens exhibited. *Proc. Nat. Hist. Soc. Glasgow*, **4**, 78–79.

Zhou, X.-Y., Zhai, Z.-Q. and Xian, S.-Y. 1981. On the Silurian conodont biostratigraphy, new genera and species in Guixhou Province. *Oil Gas Geol.*, **2**, 123–140, 2 plates (in Chinese with English summary).

4

Conodonts of the Devonian System from Great Britain

R. L. Austin, M. J. Orchard and I. J. Stewart
with contributions from
R. P. Barnes, C. Castle, M. Drummond, W. T. Kirchgasser, P. M. Sadler and E. B. Selwood

4.1 HISTORY OF CONODONT STUDIES

Conodonts from the marine sequences of Devon and Cornwall have in the past thirty years proved to be invaluable aids for correlating British strata of Devonian age with the standard reference sections of Europe. Most of the conodont investigations in Britain have been related to the solving of stratigraphic or tectonic problems and there have been relatively few publications describing conodonts systematically. British conodonts of Devonian age, however, were amongst the first described, since Hinde (1879) worked extensively in Southwest England and Young (1880) recorded conodonts of this age from limestones near Newton Abbot, South Devon. Over seventy years elapsed before the next publication when Dineley and Rhodes (1956), in their paper, reported conodonts from Devonian horizons in the West and Southwest of Britain. Later, Rhodes and Dineley (1957a, 1957b) described and illustrated cono-

donts retrieved from a borehole at Bishopsteignton, near Newton Abbot. A Middle Devonian conodont fauna from the Tamar Valley was reported by Matthews (1962). Harvey (1967) mentioned conodonts of Lower Devonian age from Veryan Bay, Cornwall. Austin (1967) recorded *Icriodus* from the Hope's Nose Limestone, Devon. Conodonts from near the Middle–Upper Devonian boundary in North Cornwall were described and illustrated by Kirchgasser (1970). Additional information was provided by Tucker (1969). Tucker and Straaten (1970a) documented Upper Devonian faunas from the Chudleigh area. The same researchers (Tucker and Straaten, 1970b; Straaten and Tucker, 1972) listed Upper Devonian conodonts from the Saltern Cove–Elberry Cove region of Devon. Middle Devonian conodonts were described and illustrated by Matthews (1970) from the Lummaton Shell Bed, near Torquay; Austin *et al.* (1970) mentioned and illustrated Upper Devonian conodonts from the

Baggy and Lower Pilton Beds of North Devon, and Upper Devonian (Famennian) faunas were reported by Riddolls (1970a) from near Newton Abbot. Hendriks *et al.* (1971) reported finds of further conodonts from South Cornwall. The conodont fauna of the Plymouth Limestone was described and illustrated by Orchard (1972, 1974, 1977, 1978a, 1978b). Smythe (1973) reported icriodids from the Brixham area. Sadler (1973a) presented detailed conodont information to support his interpretation of the stratigraphy in the Roseland area of South Cornwall (see also Barnes, 1983). Rhodes *et al.* (1973) commented on conodont faunas from the Chudleigh and Barnstable areas of Devon. Additional conodonts from near the Middle–Upper Devonian boundary in North Devon were reported by Mouravieff (1977) (see also House *et al.*, in Scrutton, 1978). Conodonts discovered from near Torquay, of Middle–Upper Devonian age, were documented by Castle (1977, 1978). Orchard (1979) described and illustrated Middle Devonian conodont faunas from the Ilfracombe Slates of North Devon. Late Devonian conodonts from North Cornwall were reported by Stewart (1981a), and Whiteley (1981) recorded conodonts of Upper Devonian age from Southeast Cornwall. Selwood *et al.* (1982) presented details of the conodont sequence within a borehole from Chillaton, West Devon. There are further records of Devonian conodonts in Isaac *et al.* (1982). A detailed illustrated report of the work of the Exeter group is included in Selwood *et al.* (1984). Further information regarding Devonian conodont occurrence is contained in the unpublished theses of Riddolls (1970b), Waters (1974), Williams (1970), Barnes (1982), Drummond (1982), Castle (1982), Sadler (1973a), Leveridge (1974), Stewart (1981b) and Orchard (1975). Reworked Devonian conodonts are mentioned in a number of publications (Matthews, 1969; Matthews *et al.*, 1972; Matthews and Thomas, 1974). Previous summaries of Devonian

conodont occurrences are contained in House *et al.* (1977) and Scrutton (1978). The sequence at Marble Cliff has been updated by House and Dineley (in press).

Outside Devon and Cornwall, Owens *et al.* (in Poole, 1977) have reported Famennian conodonts from the Steeple Aston Borehole of Oxfordshire. There is also the possibility that conodonts recovered from Pembrokeshire (Bassett and Jenkins, 1977) may be of uppermost Devonian age.

The stratigraphic range (in relation to the former standard conodont zones) of conodonts referred to in the more important references, previously cited, are indicated in Fig. 4.1. The geographical distribution of conodont-bearing localities relative to the publications mentioned above is summarized in Fig. 4.2. A detailed description of conodont localities and their faunas is contained in the guidebook for a field excursion to be held during the summer of 1985 (Austin *et al.*, in press).

4.2 CONODONT LOCALITIES

In the British Isles, with the notable exception of the North Sea (Pennington, 1975), marine rocks of Devonian age are confined to an area south of a line from Bristol to London (Fig. 4.3). Devonian rocks outcrop at the surface in Southwest England (in the counties of Cornwall, Devon and Somerset) and have been assigned to a variety of marine environments (Goldring *et al.*, 1968). House *et al.* (1977) comprehensively reviewed and correlated the sequences (see also House, 1963; House and Selwood, 1966, and Selwood, 1960). Outside Southwest England there is a single borehole record of Devonian conodonts retrieved at depths of between 786.69 and 790.96 m below the surface in Oxfordshire. Conodont-bearing horizons are located within seven well-defined areas (Fig. 4.2).

Fig. 4.1 – The stratigraphic range of published records of conodonts related to a subdivision of the Devonian System. The latter published by House *et al.* (1977) contains a sequence of conodont zones, which subsequently have been updated (see Tables 3–6 of this volume). Note in particular the change in position of the Middle–Upper Devonian boundary (−○−) following the redefinition of the base of the Upper Devonian (see p. 121). The numerals on the columns refer to the areas as outlined on Fig. 4.2.

Selwood, Stewart, Turner and Whiteley (1982) — 7

Rhodes, Williams and Robinson (1973) — 5

Austin, Druce, Rhodes and Williams (1970) — 5

Whiteley (1981) — 7

Stewart (1981) — 7

Riddolls (1970) — 3

Orchard (1974) — 2

Straaten and Tucker (1972) — 3

Tucker and Straaten (1970) — 3

Rhodes, Williams and Robinson (1973) — 3

Kirchgasser (1970) — 4

Mouravieff (1977) — 4

Orchard (1979) — 5

Matthews (1970) — 3

Matthews (1962) — ? 2 ?

Drummond (1982) — 3

Selwood et al. (1984) — 3

Castle (1977,1978,"1982) — 3

Orchard 1972,1978 — 2

Sadler (1973; Hendriks, House and Rhodes (1971) — 1

CONODONT ZONES / AMMONOID ZONES		
DEVONIAN — UPPER — FAMENNIAN		
Protognathodus		Wocklumeria Stufe
Spathognathodus costatus		
Polygnathus styriacus		Clymenia Stufe
Scaphignathus velifer		Platyclymenia Stufe
Palmatolepis marginifera		
Palmatolepis rhomboidea		Cheiloceras Stufe
Palmatolepis marginifera		
Palmatolepis triangularis		
FRASNIAN		
Palmatolepis gigas		Crickites holzapfeli
Ancyrognathus triangularis		Manticoceras cordatum
Polygnathus asymmetricus		Pharciceras lunulicosta
Schm. hermani Poly. cristatus		
MID. DEVONIAN — GIVETIAN		
Polygnathus varcus		Maenioceras terebratum
		Maenioceras molarium
EIFELIAN — COUVINIAN		
Icriodus obliquimarginatus		Cabrieroceras crispiforme
Polygnathus kockelianus		Pinacites jugleri ?
Spathognathodus bidentatus		Anarcestes lateseptatus
Icriodus corniger		Sellanarcestes wenkenbachi
Non-latericrescid Icriodus-Poly.		
LOWER DEVONIAN — EMSIAN		
i.c.,b. bilatericrescens Steinhornensis Polygnathus		Mimagoniatites zorgensis ?
Ic. huddlei curvicauda - ic.h. huddlei		Anetoceras hunsrueckianum
SIEGENIAN		
i.c.h. curvicauda rectangularis si augustidens		
Ancyrodelloides Ic. pesavis		
GEDINNIAN		
Icriodus w postwoschmidti		
Icriodus w woschmidti		

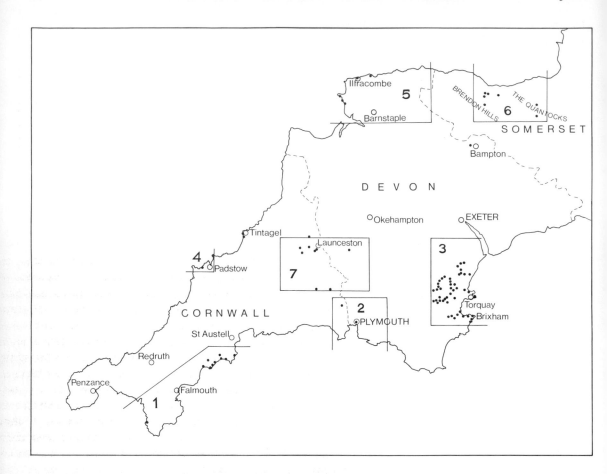

Fig. 4.2 – The geographical distribution of conodont localities in South-west England. Information based on the following. Area 1 (South Cornwall): Harvey, 1967; Hendriks *et al.*, 1971; Sadler, 1973a; Barnes, 1983. Area 2 (Plymouth region): Orchard, 1972, 1974, 1975, 1978a. Orchard, in Scrutton, 1978. Area 3 (Southeast Devon): Rhodes and Dineley, 1957a; Austin, 1967; Tucker and Straaten, 1970a; Riddolls, 1970a; Matthews, 1970; Straaten and Tucker, 1972. Rhodes *et al.*, 1973; Castle, 1977, 1978, 1982; Castle, in Scrutton, 1978; Drummond, 1982; Selwood *et al.* 1984. Area 4 (North Cornwall): Tucker, 1969; Kirch-gasser, 1970; Mouravieff, 1977; House *et al.*, in Scrutton, 1978; House and Dineley, in press. Area 5 (North Devon): Dineley and Rhodes, 1956; Austin *et al.*, 1970; Rhodes *et al.*, 1973; Sandberg and Dreesen, 1984. Area 6 (West Somerset): Orchard, herein. Area 7 (East Cornwall and West Devon): Stewart, 1981a; Whiteley, 1981; Isaac *et al.*, 1982; Selwood *et al.*, 1982.

(a) South Cornwall.	**(a) South Cornwall (area 1)**
(b) Plymouth Region.	Barnes (1983) has revised the stratigraphy and
(c) Southeast Devon.	tectonic setting of this region (Figs. 4.4 and 4.5).
(d) North Cornwall.	The pioneer investigations were undertaken by
(e) North Devon.	Sadler (1973a) who was able to suggest that Lower
(f) West Somerset.	Devonian conodonts from his 'Roseland Vol-
(g) East Cornwall and West Devon.	canics' sequence (now incorporated into the

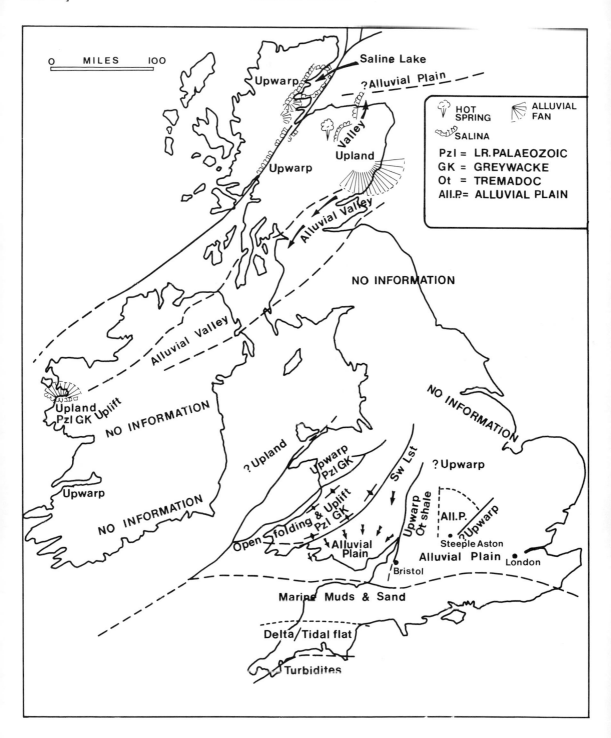

Fig. 4.3 – The palaeogeography of Britain during part of the Devonian Period (Emsian Stage). Map compiled by Dr. D. Moore.

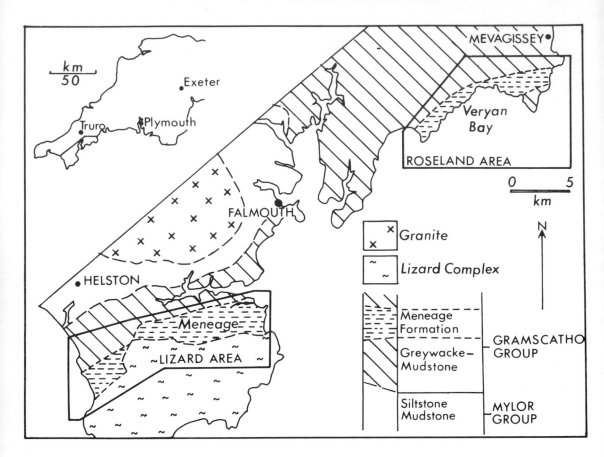

Fig. 4.4 – Geological map of part of area 1 (South Cornwall). Modified from Barnes (1983).

Middle–Upper Devonian Meneage Formation (Barnes, 1983)) represented one of five distinct faunas (see p.119 and Table 3). Harvey (1967), Hendriks *et al*. (1971) and Leveridge (1974) also reported Lower Devonian and some Middle Devonian conodonts from this sequence. Barnes and Bultynck (in prep.) question some of the Middle Devonian age assignments. The Meneage Formation stratigraphically overlies the Veryan (Limestone) Formation from which Sadler reported conodonts representing the *Polygnathus costatus patulus; Polygnathus costatus costatus* and *Tortodus kockelianus kockelianus* Zones of Middle Devonian (Eifelian) age. Middle Devonian conodonts have also been reported from Neal Point (Matthews, 1962; Orchard, 1978a) and from

Botus Fleming (Orchard, 1978a). Orchard (1978a) has also recorded Upper Devonian conodonts from the Neal Point limestones.

(b) Plymouth Region (area 2)

In Southwest Devon, the Devonian succession is best exposed (Fig. 4.6) on the east side of Plymouth Sound and beneath the City of Plymouth (Orchard, in House *et al.*, 1977). The oldest strata, outcropping in the south, are the Dartmouth Beds, which are predominantly continental in origin. Northward, the overlying Meadfoot Beds consists of a sequence of shallow marine, transgressive clastic sediments that contain Upper Siegenian to Upper Emsian shelly faunas (Evans, 1981).These beds are in turn succeeded by predominantly argillaceous sediments, the Jenny-

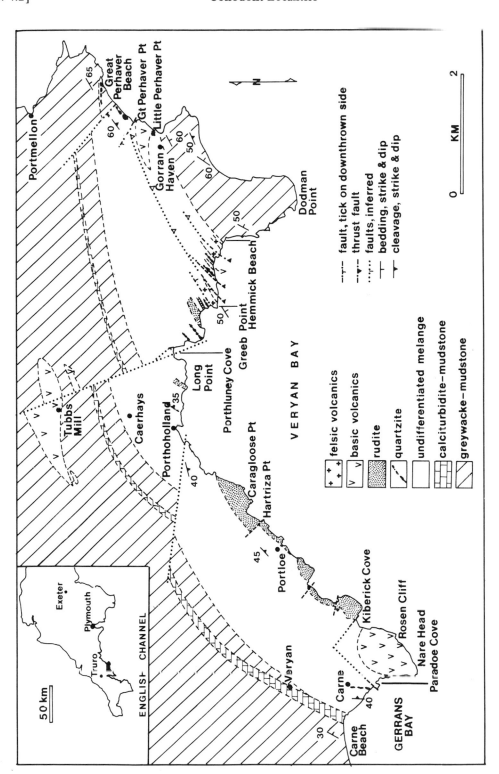

Fig. 4.5 — Geological map of the Roseland area. Modified from Barnes (1983).

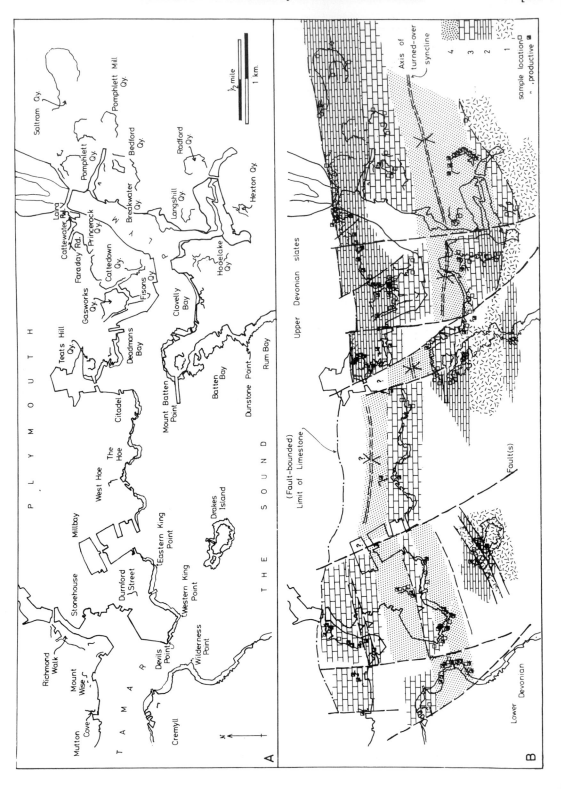

cliff Slates. Towards the top of the slates, thin beds of crinoidal limestone become more frequent and northwards they pass into the basal beds of the Plymouth Limestone, a carbonate complex that yields Eifelian to Frasnian, and locally Famennian conodonts (Orchard, in Scrutton, 1978). The pelagic 'purple and green slates' outcrop north and west of the Plymouth Limestone. Fossils, particularly ostracods (Gooday, 1975), show that the slates are both contemporaneous and younger than the Plymouth Limestone.

The oldest conodonts from the Plymouth area, from the Meadfoot Beds are poorly preserved icriodids. They resemble *Icriodus corniger* and *I. culicellus,* which in combination range from mid-Emsian (*inversus* Zone) through early Eifelian (*c. costatus* Zone).

Icriodus also dominates the faunules (fauna 1, Orchard, 1978a) from the Jennycliff Slates— Plymouth Limestone transition beds at Dunstone Point (SX 488526), where rare *Polygnathus linguiformis* and *Belodella* also occur. *Icriodus c. corniger* and *I. retrodepressus* are identified, implying an age close to the Lower—Middle Devonian boundary.

Younger and more diverse conodont faunules (Orchard 1978b; faunas 3 and 4 and in part fauna 5, Orchard, 1978a) occur at the northern margin of the Plymouth Limestone in Princerock (SX 499543). There, platy argillaceous limestones interbedded with volcaniclastics contain *Polygnathus pseudofoliatus* and *Ozarkodina bidentata* accompanied by ubiquitous coniform elements and *Polygnathus linguiformis linguiformis* and sparse specimens of *Polygnathus angustipennatus* sensu lato. *Icriodus* is also common and includes forms that resemble *I. struvei* and *I. difficilis.* These beds are collectively regarded as late Eifelian in age. Beds outcropping along strike to the west in Coxside (SX 486541) are characterized by *Polygnathus xylus ensensis* and *I. regularicrescens,* and are thought to approximate the Eifelian— Givetian boundary.

The thicker-bedded limestones of Northern Cattedown yield a conodont fauna (fauna 6, Orchard, 1978a) regarded as early Givetian. It includes *Tortodus?* n. sp. (=*Polygnathus* aff. *P. variabilis* sensu Orchard, 1978a), *P. latus?, P. linguiformis* subsp. b sensu Weddige, 1977, *Ozarkodina brevis, Icriodus obliquimarginatus* and the *I. expansus* group of Orchard (1978a). The latter group often occurs alone within the main body of the carbonate complex in Plymouth, as at Coxside and on Drakes Island (SX 468529). In contrast, *Icriodus* is virtually absent in polygnathid-dominated faunules from the western outcrops, such as at Richmond Walk (SX 461545), where *Ozarkodina brevis* and *Polygnathus timorensis* are succeeded by *P. ansatus, P. linguiformis weddigei* and *Icriodus latericrescens latericrescens.* These faunules (faunas 7 and 8, Orchard 1978a) represent the Lower and Middle *varcus* Subzones.

The Middle *varcus* Subzone fauna from Mount Wise (fauna 9, Orchard, 1978a) includes abundant *Polygnathus linguiformis linguiformis* and *P. ansatus* accompanied by *P. linguiformis mucronatus.* This locality is remarkable in providing the only record of *P. tuberculatus* outside North America, and the only one from within the *varcus* Zone.

The interval Upper *varcus* Subzone through the Lowermost *asymmetricus* Zone is sparsely represented in Plymouth. Rare broad-plated fragments resembling *Polygnathus cristatus* and *Palmatolepis disparilis* occur in the massive, coral-stromatoporoid limestones of Plymouth Hoe (fauna 10, Orchard, 1978a) and indicate an uppermost Middle Devonian 'reef' maxima correlative with beds best exposed in southern Cattedown.

Lower *asymmetricus* Zone faunas containing *Ancyrodella rotundiloba, Polygnathus asymmetricus* and *P. dengleri* (fauna 11, Orchard 1978a) occur in red thin-bedded crinoidal limestones at both Western and Eastern King, and to the east in dark micrites in Radford Quarry (SX 505530),

Fig. 4.6 — (A) Locality map of area 2 (Plymouth region). (B) Age and structure of the Plymouth Limestone: minor faults omitted: 1, volcanics and argillites, Eifelian; 2, limestones, Eifelian to Givetian, pre-*varcus* Zone; 3, limestones, *varcus* Zone to pre-*asymmetricus* Zone; 4, limestones and calcareous shales, *asymmetricus* Zone and younger (Orchard, 1978a). Reproduced by kind permission of the author.

where the fauna is dominated by *Icriodus symmetricus*.

Younger conodonts occur both in bedded carbonates and in the fillings of fissures and solution cavities within older limestones (Orchard, 1974). One tectonized fauna (fauna 12, Orchard, 1978a) of probable Middle *asymmetricus* Zone age occurs in bedded limestones in Durnford Street (SX 464536) where *Polygnathus asymmetricus unilabius* Huddle (=*P. a.* n. subsp. A of Orchard, 1978a), *Palmatolepis* aff. *P. disparalvea* and *Ancyrodella africana* Garcia-Lopez (= *A.* aff. *A. gigas* sensu Orchard) are recorded.

Higher beds in this inverted sequence carry the mid-Frasnian *Ancyrognathus triangularis,* as do bedded limestones in Radford Quarry to the east, and the red calcareous matrix of a conglomerate interpreted as a fissure-fill within Givetian limestones in Cattedown (SX 493538). *Ancyrodella curvata, Palmatolepis subrecta* and *Icriodus symmetricus* (fauna 14, Orchard, 1978a) also occur at Cattedown, and *Ancyrodella nodosa* is known from Western King.

The youngest faunules from the Plymouth Limestone are to be found in carbonate and argillaceous pockets at Western King, where common *Palamatolepis triangularis, P. delicatula, P. subperlobata* and *I. alternatus* (fauna 15, Orchard, 1978a) indicate the Upper *P. triangularis* Zone of early Famennian age.

To the north and west of the Plymouth Limestone, the red and green argillites contain rare limestone beds which have produced conodonts of both Givetian and Famennian ages. Those near Botus Fleming (Orchard, 1978a, Fig. 5f) are correlatives of the Lower *varcus* Subzone at Richmond Walk, whereas others at Neal Point on the Tamar include both Middle Devonian (Matthews, 1962) and mid-Famennian carbonates, tectonically juxtaposed. The Famennian fauna is abundant and includes *Palmatolepis glabra lepta, P. g. pectinata, P. distorta, P. quadrantinodosa, P. minuta, P. inflexoidea, P. stoppeli* and *P. marginifera,* a Lower *marginifera* Zone association.

To the east of Plymouth, Middle Devonian conodonts are poorly known from small isolated outcrops of limestone at Cofflete Creek (SX

545500), Brixton (SX 557524), Ugborough (SX 682556) and Yealmpton (SX 575513). The last locality has yielded only indeterminate conodonts, thermally metamorphosed to a colour alteration index of 7. Each of the others contains faunules dominated by *Icriodus* with rare *Polygnathus linguiformis* and the *P. costatus* group.

Southeast Devon (area 3)

In the region of Newton Abbot the Devonian sequences fall into two groups, the northern and the southern successions, separated by the Bickington Thrust. Conodont faunas, ranging from the *patulus* to the *costatus* zones, have been reported from the southern successions (Selwood *et al.,* 1984). The southern successions lie in an area of complex tectonics and rapid facies change. The Middle and earliest Upper Devonian rocks consist of limestones set in a slate succession and range in age from the Eifelian to early Frasnian stages (Fig. 4.7). Additional records of conodonts from the area are contained in earlier papers (Rhodes and Dineley 1957a, 1957b; Riddolls, 1970a). Conodonts (representative of the *asymmetricus–marginifera* zones and the *styriacus* Zone) retrieved from the Upper Devonian limestones of the Chudleigh area have been listed by Tucker and Straaten (1970a) and Rhodes *et al.* (1973).

All the Devonian sequences of the Torquay–Brixham area (Fig. 4.8) occur in thrust slices or nappes displaced northwards. In order to restore the geographic relationships of the rocks the uppermost slices must be repositioned southwards with respect to the underlying slices. The rocks which were originally southernmost are contained in the Torbay Nappe; northwards of those lay the rocks now preserved in the Brixham–Totnes Nappe. The northernmost facies are now preserved in the Dartington, or Dartington–Maldon, Nappe (see also Coward and McClay, 1983). The general stratigraphy of this area has been described by House *et al.* (1977, pp. 19 and 20). Matthews (1970) recorded a *varcus* Zone conodont fauna from the Lummaton Shell Bed. Tucker and Straaten (1970a) and Straaten and Tucker (1972) assigned conodonts from the Saltern

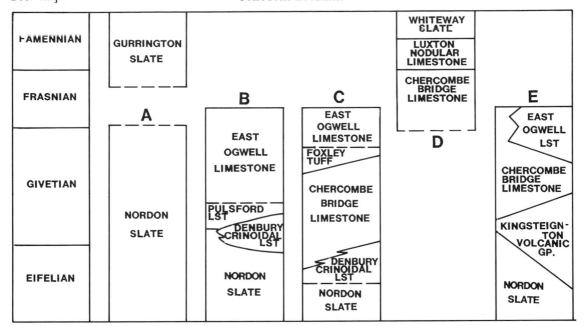

Fig. 4.7 – Generalized stratigraphical successions of Devonian rocks in the Newton Abbot district: A, Bick-ington–Beacon Hill succession; B, Torbryan succession; C, D, E, Ugbrooke, East Ogwell successions (modi-fied after Selwood et al. (1984); Formations, conodont localities and zones of the Newton Abbot region (Selwood et al., 1984) are as follows:

Nordon Slate
1. Small pit (SX 79896669) 201 m SSW of Lee Farm, near Broadhempston. Early Givetian.
2. Disused quarry (SX 80516649) 410 m NE of Broadhempston church. Upper hermanni cristatus Zone or lowermost asymmetricus Zone.
3. Small pit (SX 80836682) at Waterford Cross, 457 m SW of Coppa Dolla, asymmetricus Zone.
4. In woodland (SX 81026746) 90 m W of Collacombe Bridge. Probably varcus Zone.
5. At (SX 81376699) 320 m SE of Coppa Dolla, kockelianus (unrestricted) Zone–late ensensis Zone.
6. Road cutting (SX 81606925) near Heathfield Farm. No worthwhile age estimate possible.
7. Exposure in field (SX 81856993) 183 m S of West Ogwell Convent. Probably varcus Zone.
8. Dainton Quarry (SX 85106597) 732 m S of Dainton, varcus Zone.
9. Disused quarry (SX 87536698) at junction of Huxner Road and Whilborough Road. Probably varcus Zone

Kingsteignton Volcanic Group
10. Pit (SX 88717315) NE of Ware Barton, kockelianus (unrestricted) Zone.
11. Quarry (SX 89687375) N of Forder Cross. Upper patulus to C. costatus Zone.

Denbury Crinoidal Limestone.
12. Disused quarry (SX 82036912) 366 m NW of Denbury Post Office. No worthwhile age estimate possible.
13. At (SX 82086691) 119 m NE of Torbryan church. No worthwhile age estimate possible.
14. Deer park (SX 82407040) SW of Chercombe Bridge. No worthwhile age estimate possible.
15. Temporary exposure at Chercombe Bridge (SX 83317113). No worthwhile age estimate possible.

Pulsford Limestone
16. Disused quarry (SX 80776795) 247 m SSE of Pulsford. Probably varcus Zone.
17. Exposure (SX 80786790) 6 m above footpath, 293 mm SSE of Pulsford, varcus Zone.
18. At (SX81326738) 320 m NE of Coppa Dolla. Probably varcus Zone.
19. At (SX 81496727) 411 m E of Coppa Dolla. Probably varcus Zone.
20. Pit (SX 81586690) 400 m W of Torbryan church. Possibly varcus Zone.

Chercombe Bridge Limestone
21. Exposure (SX 83217089) 210 m SW of Chercombe Bridge. Possibly late Eifelian.
22. Wood House Quarry (SX 89037384) W of Bishopsteignton. varcus Zone.

(Continued next page)

Fig. 4.7 (*continued from previous page*)

East Ogwell Limestone
23. Emblett Hill Borehole (SX 83997065) at 12.5 m depth, *asymmetricus* Zone.
24. Disused quarry (SX 84137002) 366 m E of East Ogwell. Probably *varcus* Zone.
25. Disused Ransley Quarry (SX 84437018), *triangularis* Zone–Lower *gigas* Zone.
26. N. of Ransley Quarry (SX 84487036). Lower *gigas* Zone.
27. Small disused quarry (SX 85186971) NW of Abbotskerswell. Probably *varcus* Zone.
28. Disused Grange Quarry (SX 85206860) near Abbotskerswell. Probably *varcus* Zone.

29. East face of Wolborough Quarry (SX 85247041). Probably *varcus* Zone.
30. Disused quarry (SX 85606755) in Gotemhill Wood, *varcus* Zone.
31. Exposure (SX 85856835) in Slade Lane, 329 m SE of Court Grange. Probably *varcus* Zone.
32. Thinly bedded limestones in Stoneycombe Quarry (SX 86206704). Late *ensensis* Zone.
33. Kerswell Down Quarry (SX 87356768), *varcus* Zone.
34. Quarry (SX 87777473) S of Torhill Cottages. Probably *varcus* Zone.
35. Quarry (SX 88207500) SW of Whiteway Barton. Possibly *asymmetricus* Zone.
36. Strongs Cover (SX 88807519) E of Whiteway Barton. No worthwhile age estimate possible.

Luxton Nodular Limestone
37. Emblett Hill Borehole (SX 83997065) at 3.76–4.57 m depth, *marginifera* Zone.
38. Rydon Ball Farm Borehole (SX 84366929) at 97.23–98.45 m depth. Lower or Middle *velifer* Zone.
39. Rydon Ball Farm Borehole (SX 84366929) at 151.49 m depth. The youngest forms present indicate the lower *marginifera* Zone. Note; The fauna appears to be a mixed one. It includes forms which indicate the *crepida* and *rhomboidea* Zones.
40. Rydon Ball Farm Borehole (SX 84366929) at 156.97–157.07 m depth, *marginifera* Zone.
41. Rydon Ball Farm Borehole (SX 84366929) at 191.16 m depth, *marginifera* Zone.
42. Temporary exposure in a trench (SX 84836895) NW of Abbotskerswell. Lower *marginifera* Zone of Sandberg and Ziegler (1973).
43. Exposure (SX 85086942) 0.8 km S of Newton Abbot Hospital. Kiln Wood Beds. The youngest forms present indicate the Middle and Upper *Palmatolepis triangularis* Zone. The fauna is a mixed one. It includes forms which indicate the *Ancyrognathus triangularis* or Lower *gigas* Zone.
44. Exposure (SX 85266985) 270 m S of Newton Abbot Hospital. *Ancyrognathus triangularis* Zone or Lower *gigas*.
45. Trench (SX 87637712) at Well Farm. Probably *styriacus* Zone. Some indication of reworking.
46. Trench (SX 87647711) at Well Farm. Lower and Middle *styriacus* Zone. Some indication of reworking.
47. Trench (SX 87647710) at Well Farm. Near the *styriacus* Zone–*costatus* Zone boundary. Some of the conodonts in this fauna have been reworked.
48. Trench (SX 87657710) at Well Farm. Middle–Upper *velifer* Zone.
49. Trench (SX 87667709) at Well Farm. Lower *marginifera* Zone.
50. Trench (SX (87677708) at Well Farm. Lower *marginifera* Zone.
51. Field exposure (SX 87667470) N of Lyndridge Hill Cottages. Upper *crepida* Zone.
52. Field exposure (SX 87677468) N of Lyndridge Hill Cottages. Kiln Wood beds. Upper *gigas* Zone.
53. Roadside exposure (SX 87767704) near Well Farm, Kiln Wood beds, *Ancyrognathus triangularis* Zone.
54. Borehole (SX 87767704) near Well Farm. Probably *gigas* Zone.
55. Track (SX 88017699) adjoining Well farmyard, *rhomboidea* or Lower *marginifera* Zone.
56. Track (SX 88017699) adjoining Well farmyard, *rhomboidea* Zone.
57. Track (SX 88017699) adjoining Well farmyard, *rhomboidea* Zone.
58. Track (SX 88037697) near Well Farm. Lower *marginifera* Zone.
59. Track (SX 88037697) near Well Farm. Upper *marginifera* Zone.
60. Quarry (SX 88207500) SW of Whiteway Barton. Lower *marginifera* Zone.
61. Quarry (SX 88207500) SW of Whiteway Barton. Middle *velifer* Zone.
62. Most northerly crag (SX 88217502) in field SW of Whiteway Barton, *crepida* Zone.
63. Most southerly crag (SX 88217502) in field SW Whiteway Barton. Upper *crepida* Zone.
64. Quarry (SX 88807520) in Strongs Cover, E of Whiteway Barton, *crepida* Zone, with condensed or reworked forms.
65. Cliff (SX 90007288) W of Luxton's Steps. Probably in range *crepida* Zone–*marginifera* Zone.
66. Stream section (SX 90047313–SX 90057308) near Bishopsteignton. Upper *marginifera* or Lower *velifer* Zone.
67. Cliff (SX 90157306) NW of Luxton's Steps. Upper *marginifera* Zone.
68. Road cutting (SX 90956714) at Barton, *velifer* Zone.

Whiteway Slate
69. Rydon Ball Farm Borehole (SX 84366929) at 89.61–90.83 m depth. Upper *costatus* Zone.

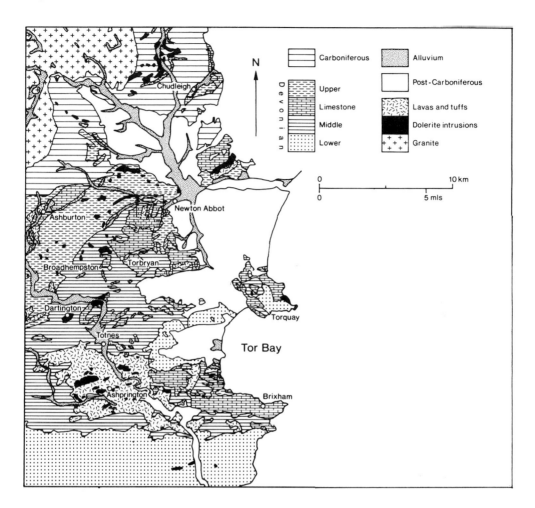

Fig. 4.8 – Geological map of area 3, (Southeast Devon). Modified from Scrutton, 1978.

Cove–Elberry Cove region to the *asymmetricus* Zone through to the Upper *velifer* Zone. Conodonts from the Torquay area have been investigated in detail by Castle (1977, 1978, 1982; in Scrutton, 1978). The Torquay Limestone Group may be divided into three lithostratigraphical units, which are in ascending order the Daddyhole Limestone, the Walls Hill Limestone and the Barton Limestone. A correlation chart for the successions in the Torquay area has been provided by Dr. Castle (Fig. 4.9). Conodonts representative of the *partitus* Zone through to the *An. triangularis* Zone are reported from collections at eight separate

locations. The Middle–Upper Devonian boundary is present at Barton Quarry (see Fig. 4.17). The stratigraphic units of Southern Torbay have been investigated for conodonts by Drummond (1982), who provides a summary (Fig. 4.9). The conodonts present range from the *costatus costatus* Zone through to the *marginifera* Zone.

The earliest Devonian rocks seen in the Torquay promontory are the shallow-marine clastic Meadfoot Beds. These are of Emsian age and are exposed at Hope's Nose (SX 947635) and Meadfoot Bay (SX 933633). By earliest Eifelian times this facies had given way to develop-

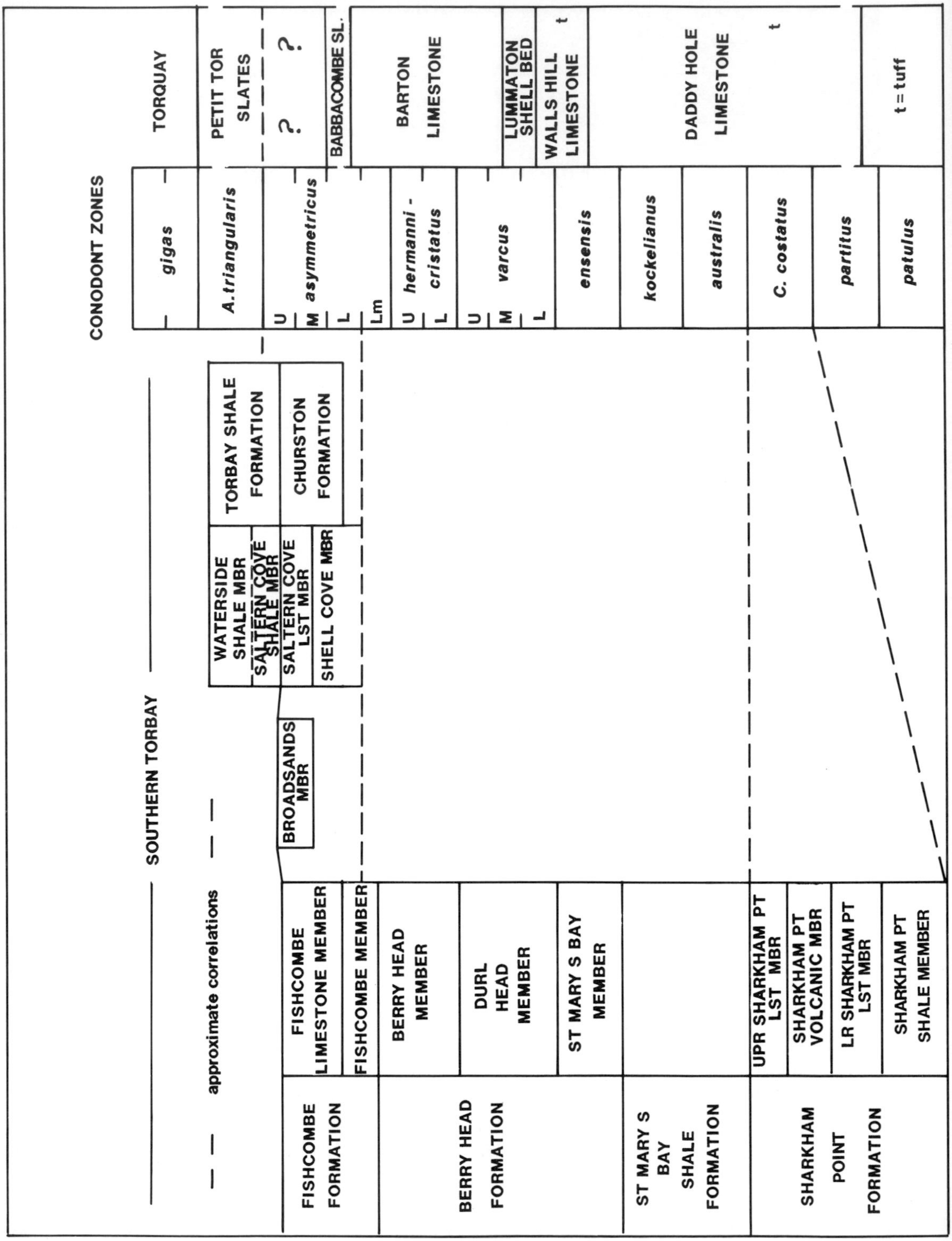

CONODONT ZONES

SOUTHERN TORBAY --- approximate correlations

Conodont Zone		TORQUAY	SOUTHERN TORBAY
gigas			
A. triangularis		PETIT TOR SLATES	
asymmetricus	U	? ?	
	M	?	
	L	BABBACOMBE SL.	TORBAY SHALE FORMATION
Lm			CHURSTON FORMATION
hermanni-cristatus	U	BARTON LIMESTONE	WATERSIDE SHALE MBR / SALTERN COVE SHALE MBR / SALTERN COVE LST MBR / SHELL COVE MBR
	L		
varcus	U	LUMMATON SHELL BED	
	M	WALLS HILL LIMESTONE t	
	L		BROADSANDS MBR
ensensis			FISHCOMBE LIMESTONE MEMBER / FISHCOMBE MEMBER — FISHCOMBE FORMATION
kockelianus		DADDY HOLE LIMESTONE	BERRY HEAD MEMBER / DURL HEAD MEMBER — BERRY HEAD FORMATION
australis		t	ST MARY S BAY MEMBER — ST MARY S BAY SHALE FORMATION
C. costatus			UPR SHARKHAM PT LST MBR / SHARKHAM PT VOLCANIC MBR / LR SHARKHAM PT LST MBR — SHARKHAM POINT FORMATION
partitus			
patulus			SHARKHAM PT SHALE MEMBER

t = tuff

◀

Fig. 4.9 – Conodont zones and stratigraphic units (informal), Southern Torbay–Torquay region. The vertical intervals have no significance. The localities and conodont zones recognised by Dr. Drummond in the Southern Torbay (Brixham) areas follows:

(i) BRIXHAM TOTNES NAPPE REGION

Sharkham Point Formation (Eifelian)
Lower Sharkham Point Limestone Member
Sharkham Point (SX 930544), *costatus costatus* Zone.
Upper Sharkham Point Limestone Member
Sharkham Point (SX 934548) and Stoke Gabriel (SX 844567), *costatus costatus* Zone.
St. Mary's Bay Shale Formation (Eifelian)
St. Mary's Bay (SX 932552 and SX 932551) and Galmpton Creek, Waddeton Boathouse (SX 873562), *kockelianus* Zone.
Berry Head Formation (Givetian)
St. Mary's Bay Member (Eifelian–Givetian boundary)
St. Mary's Bay (SX 933554 and SX 935555), *ensensis* Zone.
Durl Head Member
Durl Head Quarry (SX 939558) and Durl Rock (SX 939557), *ensensis* Zone.
Berry Head Member
Durl Head, Old Quarry (SX 945564), Berry Head (SX 945564), Lower Well Farm (SX 862569) and White Rocks (SX 879579), *ensensis–varcus* zones.
Fishcombe Formation (Givetian–Frasnian)
Fishcombe Member
Fishcombe Cove (SX 919570). Lowermost–Lower *asymmetricus* Zone.
Fishcombe Limestone Member
Fishcombe Cove (SX 919569), Fishcombe Point (SX 918569) and Fishcombe (SX 918569). Lower *asymmetricus* Zone.
Broadsands Member
Elberry Cove (SX 903572) and Churston Point (SX 901573). Middle–Upper *asymmetricus-? triangularis* Zone.
Transition to Torbay Shale Formation *(Frasnian)*
Ivy Cove (SX 908571) and Elberry Cove (SX 904569). Middle–Upper *asymmetricus* Zone–*triangularis* Zone.
Churston Formation
Shell Cove Member
Shell Cove (SX 896582 and SX 896583). Lower–Middle *asymmetricus* Zone.
Shell to Saltern Coves (SX 896584). Middle *asymmetricus* Zone.
Saltern Cove Limestone Member
Saltern Cove (SX 895585). Middle *asymmetricus* Zone.
Transition to Torbay Shale Formation
Saltern Cove (SX 895586), *An. triangularis* Zone.
Saltern Cove (SX 895586) sample equivalent to sample 1 of Straaten and Tucker (1972)).
Saltern–Waterside Coves (SX 895586), equivalent to sample 6 of Straaten and Tucker (1972), *marginifera* Zone.

(ii) DARTINGTON–MALDON NAPPE REGION

Bourton Limestone Formation (?Eifelian)
Berry Castle Lodge (SX 838616).
Marldon Limestone Formation
Culverton Copse (SX 857627), Marldon (SX 866633), Afton Tor Quarry (SX 838632), Shadrack Farm, Newground Copse (SX 828627) and Sandland Copse Quarry (SX 824620), *ensensis* Zone.
Dartington Limestone Formation
Mount Barton Quarries (SX 806640), Shinners Bridge Quarry (SX 789622), Blacklers Copse (SX 802627), Dartington Driveway (SX 800623 and 800622), Chacegrove Copse (SX 794632), Littlehempstone Quarry (SX 813625 and SX 813624), Lane E of Littlehempstone Quarry (SX 813625), Scrattons Farm (SX 810623) and quarry, (SX 809628), *varcus* Zone.
Pennies Wood Limestone Member
Pennies Wood (SX 818635), ? *disparilis* Zone.

(*Continued next page*)

ment of the Torquay Limestone Group, which is essentially a shallow-water carbonate complex. According to Dr. Castle the following information is available.

The Daddyhole Limestone, the oldest member of the Torquay Limestone Group, comprises dark, well-bedded and often fossilferous limestones. The fauna includes corals and stromatoporoids with brachiopods, gastropods and bryozoa and, as at Triangle Point and Dyer's Quarry, may be prolific. The base of the Daddyhole Limestone is placed at the base of the first limestone bed of a 4.5 m sequence of alternating shales and limestones seen on the western side of Daddyhole Cove (SX 92666277) (Scrutton, 1977), and its lower horizons are of early to mid-Eifelian age (*partitus* and lower part of *c. costatus* zones at Daddyhole Cove (SX 926628) and Triangle Point (SX 921628). The top of the unit is represented Dyer's Quarry (SX 922628) and Peaked Tor Cove (SX 921628). The top of the unit is represented by about 10 m of dark limestones at the base of

the sea cliffs at the northern end of Redgate Beach (SX 93576497), which is referred to the early Givetian upper *ensensis* Zone. A continuous sequence of Đaddyhole Limestone is not recognized.

Thin-bedded, shaly and crinoidal limestones cropping out inland (Parkfield Road and Teignmouth Road (SX 909653–909654)) date from the lower part of the *ensensis* Zone. These horizons may belong to the second of two deeper-water episodes which interrupted deposition of the Daddyhole Limestone. The same episode, which at least in its later part is of low to mid-*ensensis* Zone age, led to the formation of shaly intercalations in the highest levels of the Daddyhole Limestone and in the base of the succeeding Walls Hill Limestone (seen in the northern cliffs at Redgate Beach), while the first, which occurred during the *c. costatus* Zone, brought shales, shaly limestones and thin-bedded limestones into successions exposed, for example, in the cliffs above Triangle Point (around SX 92856284) and in

Fig. 4.9 (*continued from previous page*)

The localities and conodont zones recognised by Dr. Castle in the Torquay area (see also Castle, in Scrutton, 1978) are as follows
Daddyhole Limestone
Daddyhole Cove (SX 926627) and Triangle Point (SX 928628), *partitus* Zone.
Triangle Point (SX 928628), Dyers Quarry (SX 922628) and Peaked Tor Cove (SX 921628), *c. costatus* Zone.
? Daddyhole Limestone
Parkfield Road–Teignmouth Road (SX 909653–SX 909654), *ensensis* Zone.
Walls Hill Limestone
Redgate Beach (SX 93576497), Long Quarry Point (SX 937650), Babbacombe Road (SX 931649) and New Quarry (SX 933653), *ensensis* Zone.
Lummaton Quarry (SX 913665), Trumlands Quarry (SX 915662), Waldon Hill (SX 915635), Castle Road (SX 914642) and St. James Road (SX 912650). Lower *varcus* Zone.
Lummaton Quarry (SX 913665) and Trumlands Quarry (SX 915662). Lower *varcus* Zone.
Petit Tor Beach (SX 927663). Middle *varcus* Subzone.
? Wall Hill Limestone
Waldon Hill (SX 915635), Castle Road (SX 914642) and St. James Road (SX 912650). Lower *varcus* Subzone.
Madrepore Road (SX 917639) and Waldon Hill (SX 916636). Middle *varcus* Subzone.
Barton Limestone
Lummaton Quarry (SX 913665) and Babbacombe Cliff (SX 926656). Middle *varcus* Subzone.
Barton Quarry (SX 912671). Upper *hermanni–cristatus* Zone.
Barton Quarry (SX 912671). Lowermost *asymmetricus* Zone.
Barton Quarry (SX 912671) and Babbacombe Cliff (SX 926656). Lower *asymmetricus* Zone.
Babbacombe Slates
Footbridge at Half Tide Rock (SX 928655). Lower *asymmetricus* Zone.
Petit Tor Slates
Petit Tor Beach (SX 927663). Middle *asymmetricus* Zone (probably reworked).
Petit Tor Beach (SX 927663) and Petit Tor Quarry (SX 927662). *An. triangularis* Zone.

Peaked Tor Cove. There was intermittent volcanic activity during early to mid-Eifelian times, associated with the first period of deepening. This is illustrated by the presence of thin tuff beds at Triangle Point and Dyer's Quarry.

The base of the Walls Hill Limestone is defined as the base of the bed (about 8 m thick) of massive pale-grey limestone overlying the Daddyhole Limestone low in the sea cliffs at the northern end of Redgate Beach (SX 93576497) (Scrutton 1977). The Walls Hill Limestone is typically a massive pale- to medium-grey limestone, in which the fauna is dominated by stromatoporoids in a crinoidal, micritic or sparry matrix. Its development began in early Givetian times, during the upper part of the *ensensis* Zone (Redgate Beach–Long Quarry Point (SX 935649–937650); Babbacombe Road (around SX 931649); New Quarry (SX 933653)) and, as indicated by the lower parts of the 146 m (aaprox.) thick succession on Long Quarry Point, stromatoporoid growth was prolific. The resulting reefal structure is thought to have produced some degree of facies differentiation, and the higher levels at Long Quarry Point, as well as certain horizons at New Quarry and Withy Point (SX 931654), have been interpreted as having formed in a rather restricted, lagoonal or back-reef environment (Scrutton, 1977). Conodonts are sparse or absent from these limestones, consistent with this interpretation.

The highest levels of the Walls Hill Limestone are represented by about 50 m of typically massive, pale, stromatoporoidal and often dolomitized limestones in the southern part of Lummaton Quarry (SX 913665), which are of Lower *varcus* Subzone age. Irregular lenses of the famous Lummaton Shell Bed are developed at the northern end of the quarry, with their particularly rich fauna of brachiopods with bivalves, gastropods, trilobites, crinoids, ostracods, algae and conodonts; bryozoa also occur and are dominant in the matrix (Scrutton, 1977). The Lummaton Shell Bed Member is the basal division of the Barton Limestone, which directly succeeds the Walls Hill Limestone and is represented at Lummaton by about 30 m of medium-grey, massive, bioclastic and fossiliferous limestones. The Barton Limestone here dates from the Middle *varcus* Subzone, the Shell Bed straddling the Lower to Middle *varcus* Subzone boundary in age.

A continuous succession in the Walls Hill Limestone is not recognized, and it is believed that the Walls Hill Limestone at Lummaton represents a second cycle of reef development rather than growth having been continuous from the Upper *ensensis* Zone to the Lower *varcus* Subzone. It is thought that growth was interrupted in the Lower *varcus* Subzone by an episode of deepening, during which darker limestones (sometimes bedded), shaly limestones, shales and tuffs variously accumulated in the region of St. James Road (SX 912650), Stentiford Hill (SX 917641) and Trumlands Quarry (SX 915662).

Tectonically isolated outcrops of grey-red, bedded and massive, crinoidal and bioclastic limestones date from the Lower *varcus* Subzone at Castle Road (SX 914642) and Waldon Hill–Royal Terrace Gardens (SX 91546354) and from the Middle *varcus* Subzone at Madrepore Road (SX 91776394) and Waldon Hill–Warren Road (SX 91646368). These horizons are coeval with successions at Lummaton and may be back-reef equivalents, indicating that the second cycle of reef growth also resulted in some extent of facies differentiation.

The Barton Limestone, the basal division of which is taken at the Lummaton Shell Bed Member (Scrutton, 1977), is typified at Barton Quarry (SX 912671) by a medium-grey, massive, often coarsely bioclastic and fossiliferous limestone.

As observed above, the basal part of the Barton Limestone at Lummaton is of Middle *varcus* Subzone age, whereas at Barton Quarry the *varcus,* Upper *hermanni–cristatus,* Lowermost and Lower *asymmetricus* zones are recognized. This indicates that deposition of the unit continued from mid-Givetian to earliest Upper Devonian times. (It should be noted that diagnostic faunas are scattered at Barton, and zonal boundaries have not yet been identified.) The Middle *varcus* Subzone and the Lower *asymmetricus* Zone are represented in the Barton Limestone at Babbacombe Cliff (SX 926656), although here the limestone is bedded, darker, finer grained and sometimes less fossiliferous than at Barton.

Intercalations of dark-grey slate are present in stratigraphically higher levels of the Barton Limestone at Babbacombe Cliff, and the formation passes upwards into the Babbacombe Slates (the transition is exposed in a roadside outcrop at the top of Oddicombe Beach Hill (SX 92456566–SX 92406572)). The Babbacombe Slates are dark grey to black in colour and contain thin (1–7 cm), dark, pyritic and often impersistent limestone bands. Conodont faunas from the Babbacombe Slates near the footbridge at Half Tide Rock (SX 92816551) are of Lower *asymmetricus* Zone age, indicating that the deepening of the environment which brought about the change from the Barton Limestone to the Babbacombe Slates occurred in the early Upper Devonian. This event effectively marked the end of major carbonate development in the Torquay region.

Younger Upper Devonian strata occur in the Petit Tor area, where red Petit Tor Slates are associated with pale-grey, massive Walls Hill Limestone. The Petit Tor Slates comprise various red sediments including slates and slaty, sometimes crinoidal limestones (seen in Petit Tor Quarry (SX 927662) and in ledges overlooking the southern end of Petit Tor Beach (around SX 92706636)) and calcareous mudstones and nodular limestones (exposed in the vertical wall behind the lowest ledge (SX 92686637)). The red lithologies yield conodonts referable to the *An. triangularis* Zone, together with probably reworked elements indicative of the Middle *asymmetricus* Zone, whereas the Walls Hill Limestone is of early Middle *varcus* Subzone age.

The red Upper Devonian sediments in the Petit Tor Quarry and higher ledges form irregular areas within the Middle Devonian limestones and have been interpreted as the infillings of solution cavities (Scrutton, 1978; Castle, 1982). The mudstones and nodular limestones in the wall behind the lowest ledge, and probably also the red slates seen in the combe behind Petit Tor Beach (SX 926664), may have originally overlain the Walls Hill Limestone, but there is much tectonic complexity in this area and field relationships are not clear.

The youngest-dated Devonian horizons in the Torquay promontory are developed at Anstey's Cove (SX 935646), where ostracod evidence has demonstrated that the deep-water ostracod-slate facies was well established by late Fammenian *Clymenia* or *Wocklumeria* Stufen age (House *et al.*, 1977, p. 20). Ash beds in the slates indicate that there was volcanic activity at this time.

(d) North Cornwall (area 4)

The Marble Cliff Beds (Tucker, 1969), a succession of limestone turbidities, with interstratified shales are well exposed in cliff sections on the North Devon coast, near Padstow (Fig. 4.10). The Marble Cliff Beds succeed the Trevone Slates, a thick sequence of laminated dark-grey shales with many light-graded beds, the latter probably of tuffaceous origin. Above the Marble Cliff Beds there is another sequence of banded shales, the Longcarrow Cove Beds, which contain graded tuff beds and agglomerates. The Longcarrow Cove Beds, of the western succession are partly equivalent to the Pentire Pillow Lavas of the eastern succession. At the type locality the Marble Cliff Beds are separated from the underlying Trevose Slates by a prominent sill.

Conodonts from limestone beds within the Trevose Slates at Trevone Bay and Rock have been referred to the *varcus* Zone (Kirchgasser, 1970). Conodonts from the Marble Cliff Beds and Longcarrow Cove Tuffs and Slates were described by Kirchgasser (1970) from the section at Marble Cliff, which consists of approximately 70 m of alternating limestone and shale, which are overturned. The Marble Cliff Beds were referred to the lower part of the Lower *asymmetricus* Zone and the Longcarrow Cove Tuffs and Slates were assigned to the upper part of the Lower *asymmetricus* Zone. The presence of *S. hermanni* within the Trevose Slates and the Marble Cliff Beds is of particular interest as it is a zonal fossil. Mouravieff (1977) provided additional details of conodonts within the Marble Cliff Beds. Tucker (1969) reported that conodonts of the *varcus* Zone occur in the Rumps Point Limestones, north of Polzeath. Further information in North Corn-

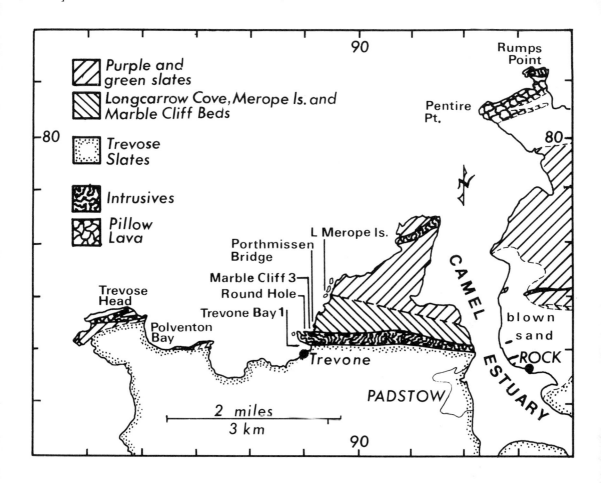

Fig. 4.10 — Simplified geological map of part of area 4 (North Cornwall), with conodont localities. Modified from Kirchgasser (1970).

wall was provided by House *et al.* (in Scrutton, 1978).

The succession of beds at Marble Cliff has been intensively studied and it represents one of the best known and most detailed of all British conodont sequences (Fig. 4.11). The importance of this section with regard to the change in the definition of the Middle—Upper Devonian boundary has been stressed by House and Dineley (in press). It is probably the thickest well-documented conodont sequence in Europe relevant to the boundary. The boundary between the Middle and Upper Devonian is taken in the Marble Cliff sec-

tion below bed 151 at the first appearance of *Ancyrodella rotundiloba*. Kirchgasser (in House and Dineley, in press) provides an update of zonal assignments. The base of the *disparilis* Zone is placed at the base of bed 55. The entry of *Polygnathus dengleri*, in the upper part of the *disparilis* Zone, commences in bed 91. The base of the Lowermost *asymmetricus* Zone, marked by the entry of *P. norrisi*, lies about 8 m below bed 151 where the Lower *asymmetricus* Zone begins. Reference is also made to the presence of Upper *asymmetricus* Zone equivalents in the Harbour Cove Slates.

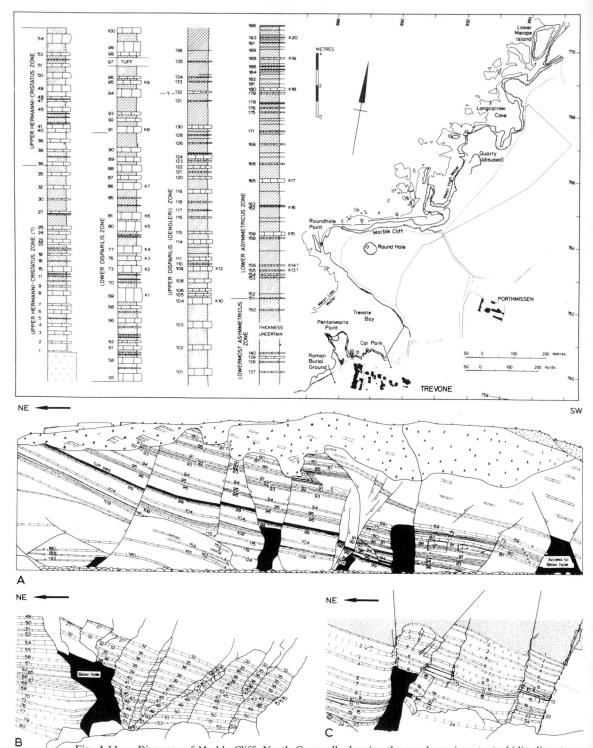

Fig. 4.11 – Diagrams of Marble Cliff, North Cornwall, showing the numbers given to turbidite limestones. Diagram modified after House *et al.* in Scrutton, 1978. Based on the work of W. T. Kirchgasser, N. A. Moura-vieff and R. de Cartier de Marchienne.

(e) North Devon (area 5)

The Devonian sequences of the North Devon coast (Fig. 4.12) have been described by House et al. (1977). Orchard (1979) described a varcus Zone conodont fauna from the Ilfracombe Slates near Ilfracombe. Four of his samples came from the Rillage Limestone, near the top of the Lester Shales. His fifth sample, with the most prolific fauna, came from a thin limestone about 50 m below the top of the Kentisbury Slates, a horizon close to the base of the Morte Slates. Specimens of poorly preserved Icriodus and rare Polygnathus are now reported (M. J. Orchard) from the following new localities.

Sandy Bay (SS 569474); David's Stone Limestone.
Combe Martin Beach (SS 577474); Combe Martin Beach Limestone.
Hagginton Beach (SS 540482); Combe Martin Beach Limestone.

Conodonts from the Baggy and Pilton Beds of North Devon were reported by Rhodes et al. (1973). Williams (1970), recognized in the Lower Pilton Beds an Icriodus and a Polygnathus Subzone within the Spathognathodus (bischoffi) costatus Zone. Pseudopolygnathus and Pelekysgnathus were other genera present in the Lower Pilton Beds. The Pilton Beds were collected from Fremington Pill, from south of Croyde Bay and from a roadside section near Bampton. The Baggy Beds were sampled from the cliff sections north of Croyde Bay (see Scrutton, 1978, for locality maps). Sandberg and Dreesen (1984) illustrated the apparatus of 'Icriodus' pectinatus from the Pilton Beds at Saunton Down.

(f) West Somerset (area 6)

Several new collections are reported (M.J.O.) with Icriodus and sparse Polygnathus from the Ilfracombe Beds at outcrops in the Quantock Hills

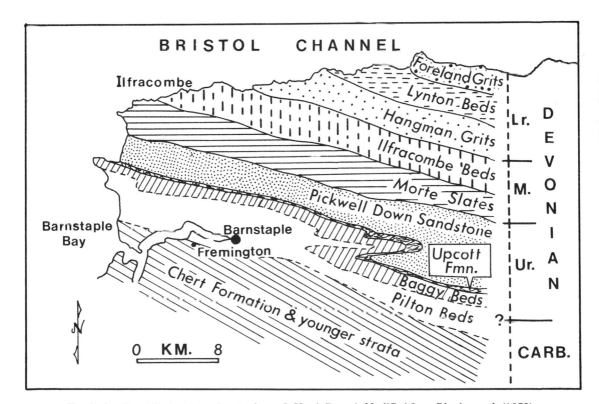

Fig. 4.12 – Simplified geological map of area 5 (North Devon). Modified from Rhodes et al. (1973).

and Brendon Hills of West Somerset. The localities are as follows.

1. Quarry S of Parsons Lane, NNW of Aisholt (ST 192361). Roadwater Limestone.
2. Quarry, ESE of Tudballs Farm (ST 212236). Lower Aisholt Limestone.
3. Quarry at Badger Copse, E. of Cothelstone (ST 189318). Leigh Barton Limestone.
4. Quarry NE of Stiles Farms, Rodhuish (ST 013396). Rodhuish Limestone.
5. NNE of Hill Farm, S of Withycombe (ST 015408). Rodhuish Limestone.
6. Quarry E of road, NE of Treborough (ST 015367). Roadwater Limestone.
7. S of Sandhill Farm, near Withycombe (ST 020405). Roadwater Limestone.
8. Unnamed limestone from a quarry at Stream (ST 065397).

(g) East Cornwall and West Devon (area 7)

An overview of the geology of this region is contained in Isaac et al. (1982). Sediments of Devonian and Carboniferous age were assigned to seven facies, which occur within five main tectonic units bounded by major thrusts. Stewart (1981a) has documented the conodonts from the Launceston area, which range from the Famennian *marginifera* Zone through to the *nodosus* Zone of the Dinantian Subsystem. The Upper *styriacus* Zone and the Lower *B. costatus* Zone have been recognized at Viverdon Down (Whiteley, 1981). Selwood et al. (1982) described conodonts from beds transitional in age between the Devonian and Carboniferous Systems; included were *B. costatus, Siphonodella praesulcala* and protognathodids. Detailed description of Upper Devonian conodont sequences from this region are given later in this chapter (see 4.5c).

The pattern of Devonian outcrops in this area lying south of the Culm Synclinorium is now recognized as being controlled by a thrust and nappe regime in which allochthonous and parautochthonous successions are overriden by nappes derived from the south (Isaac et al., 1982; Coward and McClay, 1983). Upper Devonian strata are developed at all tectonic levels, but most conodont faunas are derived from the allochthon. As palinspastic reconstructions are impracticable, only the broad setting of late Devonian sedimentation can currently be assessed.

Overall, it appears that deposition was concentrated towards the edge of a broad continental shelf on which thick sequences of monotonous greyish-green muds accumulated (Tredorn Slate, Delabole Slate and Kate Brook Slate). Conodont faunas indicate a stratigraphic range for these sequences from at least the *marginifera* Zone into the *costatus* (now *aculeatus ultimus*) Zone. These were only rarely disturbed by incursions of distal turbidites. Differential subsidence, probably fault related, which was inherited from mid-Devonian times, permitted the development of local basins and rises. The latter supported reef complexes through Givetian and early Frasnian times, and their morphologies were to influence late Devonian sedimentation profoundly during a sustained period of deepening associated with northward marine transgression. Basinal mudrocks show gradation into rise-slope (slates with nodular limestones) and condensed rise deposits (thin-bedded flaser and nodular limestones) towards and on the sites of the former reef complexes. The latter are exemplified by certain facies of the Petherwin Formation (*marginifera* Zone to early Carboniferous). Only in the latest *costatus* Zone does the polarity of lithofacies become less discernible.

Successions vary upwards through the nappe pile, but it is not appropriate to detail these here. Instead, the formations, the locality details and their stratigraphical ranges are included in Fig. 4.13 where they are grouped according to depositional environment determined by facies analysis. No attempt is made to show structural relations, although it is worth noting that the Buckator Formation (column 16) occurs in the structurally highest and farthest travelled nappe, Boscastle Nappe (Selwood et al., 1985) which compromises near-shore and deltaic facies. This is consistent with the northward migration of the Variscan deformation front in the late Devonian with a corresponding activation and filling of basins from south to north. At Trenault (SX

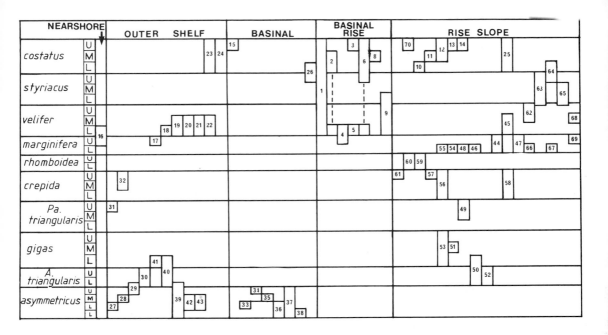

Fig. 4.13 – Upper Devonian conodont localities related to Upper Devonian formations and the range of conodont zones identified at each locality. The localities are placed in their environmental setting, but there is no significance as to relative placement within each environment. The localities are as follows:

Petherwin Formation
1. Trenault Main Quarry (SX 26258292), near Launceston.
2. Trenault, Quarry B (SX 26548260), near Launceston.
3. Trenault, Quarry C (SX 26468274), near Launceston.
4. West Petherwin Quarry (SX 30578231), near Launceston.
5. Petherwin Water Quarry (SX 31468251), near Launceston.
6. Landlake Mill Quarry (SX 32838235), near Launceston.
7. Landlake Quarry (SX 32718228).
8. Cephalopod Limestone Quarry, Landlake (SX 32868229), near Launceston.
9. Landerslake Quarry (SX 26428111), near Launceston.

Stourscombe Formation
10. Strayerpark Plantation (SX 26558122), near Launceston.
11. Trial Pit A.30 (SX 26618120), near Launceston.

Liddaton Formation
12. Overwood Quarry (SX 30258722), near Yeolmbridge.
13. River Tamar section, Dutson (SX 34158590), Launceston.
14. Lea Cottage Quarry (SX 43678180), near Chillaton.

Yeolmbridge Formation
15. Treguddick Mill (SX 27578142), near Launceston.

Buckator Formation
16. Trenault (SX 26318303), near Launceston.

Tredorn Slate
17. Strayerpark Quarry (SX 26538102), near Launceston.
18. Blackhill Quarry (SX 29638180), near Launceston.

Delabole Slate
19. West Quarry (SX 05108695), Trebarwith Strand.
20. Lanterdan Quarry (SX 05108708), Trebarwith Strand.

(Continued next page)

Fig. 4.13 (*continued from previous page*)

21. Between Lanterdan Quarry and Caroline Quarry (SX 05138721), Trebarwith Strand.
22. Hole Beach (SX 05098703), Trebarwith Strand.

Kate Brook Slate
23. Keason (SX 32416785), near Callington.
24. Railway cutting, Tavistock (SX 47407432).

South Brentor Formation
25. Borehole (SX 44148193), Chillaton.

Bealbury Formation
26. Viverdon Down (SX 37466754), near Callington.

Plymouth Limestone
27. Western King (SX 46065331), Plymouth.
28. Durnford Street road cutting (SX 46395369), Plymouth.
29. Western King (SX 46085329), Plymouth.
30. Fisons Quarry (SX 49315377), Plymouth.
31. Western King (SX 46145326), Plymouth.
32. Radford Quarry (SX 50405314), Plymouth.

Longcarrow Cove Slate Formation
33. Longcarrow Cove (SW 891765), Marble Cliff, Trevone.

Harbour Cove Slate Formation
34. Gun Point (SW 91877679), Padstow.
35. Lower Merope Island (SW 89467699), Trevone.

Marble Cliff Limestone Formation
36. Marble Cliff (SW 891765), Trevone.

Nordon Slate
37. Small pit (SX 80836682), Waterford Cross, Coppa Dolla.
38. Quarry (SX 80516649), Broadhempston.

East Ogwell Limestone
39. Emblett Hill Borehole (SX 83997065) at 12.5 m depth.
40. Ransley Quarry (SX 84437018), near East Ogwell.
41. N of Ransley Quarry (SX 84487036), near East Ogwell.
42. Quarry (SX 87777473), Torhill Cottages, Near Kingsteignton.
43. Quarry (SX 88207500), Whiteway Barton, near Kingsteignton.

Luxton Nodular Limestone
44. Emblett Hill Borehole (SX 83997065), near East Ogwell at 3.76–4.57 m depth.
45. Rydon Ball Farm Borehole (SX 84366929), near East Ogwell at 97.23–98.45 m depth.
46. Rydon Ball Farm Borehole (SX 84366929), 151.49 m depth.
47. Rydon Ball Farm Borehole (SX 84366929), 156.97–157.07 m depth.
48. Trench (SX 84836895), NW of Abbotskerswell.
49. Exposure (SX 85086942), S of Newton Abbot Hospital.
50. Exposure (SX 85266985), S of Newton Abbot Hospital.
51. Field Exposure (SX 87677468), Lyndridge Hill Cottages, near Kingsteignton.
52. Well Farm (SX 87767704), near Ideford.
53. Borehole (SX 87767704), Well Farm, near Ideford.
54. Track (SX 88037697), Well Farm, near Ideford.
55. Quarry (SX 88207500), Whiteway Barton, near Kingsteignton.
56. Field exposure (SX 88217502), Whiteway Barton, near Kingsteignton.
57. Field Exposure (SX 88217502), Whiteway Barton, near Kingsteignton.
58. Quarry (SX 88807520), Strongs Cover, Whiteway Barton, near Kingsteignton.
59. Track (SX 88017699), Well Farm, near Ideford.
60. Track (SX 88017699), Well Farm, near Ideford.
61. Field Exposure (SX 87667470), Lyndridge Hill Cottages, near Kingsteignton.
62. Trench (SX 87657710), Well Farm, near Ideford.
63. Trench (SX 87637712), Well Farm, near Ideford.

(Continued next page)

263830) the Buckator Formation yields a Lower *velifer* Zone fauna dominated by *'Icriodus'* pectinatus and *Pandorinellina* cf. *insita*.

The occurrences detailed in Fig. 4.13 broadly reflect the abundance of conodonts; the richest faunas occur in rise and rise-slope deposits associated with the sites of earlier reefs. The low level of information about the Frasnian–Famennian boundary in the carbonate-rich facies may reflect the fact that these 'dead' reefs stood exposed for a considerable period in the late Devonian (Orchard, 1974) and even following submergence accumulated mainly condensed sequences which suffered extensive reworking of faunas. There is no evidence for sedimentary breaks in the Luxton Nodular Limestone; the reworked faunas characteristic of the formation were almost certainly transported down-slope from the former reefal areas. Conodonts have yet to be documented from 'basinal' successions including the Frasnian–Famennian boundary.

Available information on conodonts from the Upper Devonian of Cornwall and West Devon shows that the established zonal scheme works well, although the relationship of the ammonoid and conodont chronologies can only be determined locally. Adjustments to the relative ranges of significant species (Klapper and Ziegler, 1979) and the relative ranges of some 'shallow-water' species that abound in Cornwall, but are rare in the type sections of Germany, are indicated in Tables 5 and 5a. The earlier appearances noted are probably significant, although the upward extension of ranges shown are possibly a consequence of reworking. The proposal (Paproth, 1980) to place the base of the Carboniferous System at the first appearance of *Siphonodella sulcata* in the evolutionary lineage from *S. praesulcata* proves entirely satisfactory in West Devon where Selwood *et al.*

(1982) have described the transition in a section corroborated by several faunal groups.

4.3 DEPOSITORY OF COLLECTIONS OF IMPORTANCE

Collections of British Devonian conodonts are housed as follows.

(a) The Geology Departments of Universities

Recent research on Devonian conodonts has been concentrated in Britain at two centres, the University of Exeter and the University of Hull. At Exeter under the guidance of Dr. E. B. Selwood and Dr. J. M. Thomas and often in association with the British Geological Survey (formerly the Institute of Geological Sciences) a number of students have completed Ph.D. Theses. They include I. J. Stewart, M. J. Whiteley, R. A. Waters and B. W. Riddolls. Parts of their collections are at the University of Exeter, but the bulk is at the British Geological Survey, Keyworth. The collections of Rhodes and Dineley (1957a) were housed at the University of Exeter, but their current location is unknown. Professor M. R. House, University of Hull, has supervised a number of postgraduate and postdoctoral studies including those of C. Castle, M. J. Orchard and W. T. Kirchgasser. Some of their material is located at Hull; the remainder is either at the British Geological Survey or at the Sedgwick Museum. The University of Newcastle (with Dr. C. T. Scrutton and Dr. H. A. Armstrong) has a strong interest in the Devonian System and the B. E. Leveridge and M. Drummond collections are located there. The R. P. Barnes Collection is at the University of Southampton. The University of Bristol has long been associated with research on the Devonian System of Southwest England. E. J. Loeffler reports that parts of the S. C.

Fig. 4.13 (*continued from previous page*)
64.   Trench (SX 87647710), Well Farm, near Ideford.
65.   Trench (SX 87647710), Well Farm, near Ideford.
66.   Trench (SX 87667709), Well Farm, near Ideford.
67.   Trench (SX 87677708), Well Farm, near Ideford.
68.   Quarry (SX 88207500), SW of Whiteway Barton, near Kingsteignton.
69.   Track (SX 88037697), near Well Farm, Ideford.

Whiteway Slate
70.   Rydon Ball Farm Borehole (SX 84366929), near East Ogwell at 89.61–90.83 m depth.

Matthews and P. M. Sadler collections are at Bristol University with the remainder deposited at the British Geological Survey and at the British Museum. Material from the studies of J. A. Williams and J. C. Robinson, supervised by F. H. T. Rhodes when at the University College of Swansea, is now located at the University of Cornell. Dr. R. Goldring, University of Reading, was closely connected with the work of M. E. Tucker and P. van Straaten. Their material is deposited at the University of Reading. The Sedgwick Museum, Cambridge, houses the Kirchgasser collection from North Cornwall (SM H 9330–H 9379) and most of the Orchard collection from the Plymouth Limestone (which bear the prefix SM).

(b) British Geological Survey, Keyworth, Nottingham

According to David Butler (British Geological Survey, London), conodont studies at the former Institute of Geological Sciences were undertaken by M. J. Reynolds. The British Geological Survey collections include conodonts from the Steeple Aston Borehole (Poole, 1977) and specimens illustrated from the Ilfracombe Slates (Orchard, 1979), which bear the prefix SAD. There are also a few conodonts (registered as DEA 3749) from the Pilton Shales locality on the *Taunton 1:50 00 Geological Sheet.* Conodont collections associated with the Survey remapping of the Newton Abbot and Tavistock sheets, undertaken as a contract with Exeter University (Selwood *et al.,* 1984), are also located at the Survey (registration numbers AD 3769–97). The Riddolls (1970a) collection from a borehole at Rydon Ball Farm, Newton Abbot, is registered as AD 801–841. The Sadler collection from Cornwall was destined for deposition at the Survey (prefixed by the letters SAQ) but the collection has yet to be deposited and is currently with Dr. Sadler at the University of California.

(c) British Museum (Natural History), London

R. L. Hodgkinson reports that the British Museum conodont collections contain only a few British specimens from the Lower Frasnian rocks at Lower Dunscombe Farm, Chudleigh, Devon

(Dineley and Rhodes, 1956, register numbers X 9–11). However, there are a number of conodonts from Devonian localities overseas, which include a G. J. Hinde collection described by Branson and Mehl (1934) from a variety of localities in North America and Canada.

4.4 DEVONIAN CHRONOSTRATIGRAPHY

The Silurian–Devonian boundary in Britain is represented by non-marine rocks and therefore comment concerning the definition of the base of the Devonian System can be avoided. Internationally the base of the Devonian System (defined by the appearance of *Monograptus uniformis*) is taken at the appearance of the *Icriodus woschmidti woschmidti* fauna. This fauna also may be used to recognize the base of the Gedinnian (Lochkovian?) Stage. The base of the Siegenian (Pragian?) Stage approximates to the appearance of the *Icriodus huddlei-curvicauda– I. rectangularis* s.1–*I. angustoides angustoides* fauna, whilst the base of the Emsian Stage occurs within the range of the *Icriodus huddlei curvicauda–I. huddlei huddlei* fauna. The base of the Middle Devonian Series and of the Eifelian Stage formerly was recognized at the base of the *Icriodus corniger* Zone with the *Icriodus obliquimarginatus* Zone representing the base of the Givetian Stage. Now the base of the *partitus* Zone defines the base of the Middle Devonian (Eifelian Stage) and the *ensensis* Zone is taken as the base of the Givetian Stage. The base of the Upper Devonian Series is herein taken at the base of the Lower (not Lowermost) *Polygnathus asymmetricus* Zone (see also House and Ziegler, 1977; House, 1982; Ziegler, 1982; Ziegler and Klapper, 1982a). The base of the Frasnian Stage formerly was located within the upper part of the *Polygnathus varcus* Zone. The base of the Fammenian Stage is taken at the base of the Middle *Palmatolepis triangularis* Zone. The Devonian–Carboniferous boundary is defined and recognized by the appearance of *Siphonodella sulcata* (Paproth, 1980).

Ziegler (1979) has reviewed the historical subdivision of the Devonian System and has documented details of conodont biostratigraphy within the European Devonian rocks (Ziegler, 1971). An update of Devonian conodont biostratigraphy is provided by Klapper and Ziegler (1979) and Ziegler and Klapper (1982b). Summaries of the conodont zonation and of the boundaries and divisions recognized within the Devonian System of Britain are to be found in Tables 3–5a (see also House and Dineley, in press).

4.5 CONODONT ZONATION

(a) Lower Devonian Series
The best known Lower Devonian conodont faunas in Europe occur in Spain and have been reported from the Celtiberian Ranges of Aragon (Carls and Gandl, 1969) and the Eastern Guadarrama (Carls, 1969; Bultynck, 1971, 1976a). Further records for Northern Spain are given by Boersma (1973). Uncertainty exists concerning the ranges given for taxa from these sections, often as a result of the different opinions of the different researchers concerning conodont taxonomy.

Klapper and Ziegler (1979) reported ten conodont zones for the Lower Devonian sequence of Nevada. These were based on the first appearance and range of the following species and subspecies.

10. *Polygnathus serotinus.*
 9. *Polygnathus inversus.*
 8. *Polygnathus gronbergi.*
 7. *Polygnathus dehiscens.*
 6. *Eognathodus sulcatus* n. subsp.
 5. *Eognathodus sulcatus sulcatus.*
 4. *Pedavis pesavis pesavis.*
 3. *Ozarkodina* n. sp. D.
 2. *Ozarkodina eurekaensis.*
 1. *Icriodus woschmidti hesperius.*

The upper four zones can be recognized and applied in Spain but, of the remainder, only zone 3 can be recognized with any degree of confidence within the Spanish sequences. Consequent to the re-definition of the base of the Middle Devonian Series the *Polygnathus costatus patulus* Zone is now included at the top of the Lower Devonian Series.

Ziegler (1971) recognized the following conodont zones within the Lower Devonian.

7. Non-latericrescid *Icriodus–Polygnathus* (partim).
6. *Icriodus bilatericrescens–Pandorinellina (Spathognathodus) steinhornensis steinhornensis–Polygnathus.*
5. *Icriodus huddlei curvicauda–I. huddlei huddlei.*
4. *Icriodus huddlei curvicauda–I rectangularis* s. 1–*I. angustoides angustoides.*
3. *Ancyrodelloides–Icriodus pesavis.*
2. *Icriodus woschmidti postwoschmidti.*
1. *Icriodus woschmidti woschmidti.*

Sadler (1973a) reported details of Lower Devonian conodont occurrences in Britain. The conodonts were recovered from limestones found as small discontinuous lenses within the Meneage Formation of South Cornwall. Each record has to be taken individually since there can be no certainty as to the true stratigraphic sequence in the sections from which the samples were collected. It should be noted also that no attempt is made here to revise Lower Devonian zonation, nor to revise the taxonomic nomenclature used by Sadler. The latter is beyond the scope of this volume (and was impossible, since the specimens have only recently been located). The former is undesirable as the original sequence of zones suggested by Ziegler (1971) provides the most convenient scheme with which to compare the British records. The following sequence of Lower Devonian faunas may be recognized in Britain, based on the work of Sadler (1973a, 1973b).

5. *Polygnathus* fauna.
4. *Icriodus bilatericrescens–Pandorinellina steinhornensis* fauna.
3. *Icriodus huddlei curvicauda–Icriodus huddlei huddlei* fauna.
2. *Icriodus huddlei curvicauda–Icriodus angustoides* fauna.
1. *Icriodus woschmidti* fauna.

The distribution of conodonts in Cornwall, as shown in Table 3 is based on the work Sadler (1973b). A number of the Cornish specimens show distortion and some are broken, which often hinders precise taxonomic assignment. For comparison the range of species reported from Cornwall is also shown (Table 3), with reference to the zones proposed by Ziegler (1971) and Klapper and Ziegler (1979). The conodonts illustrated in Plate 4.1 are those illustrated by Sadler (1973b) and have not been published previously. Previously recorded Lower Devonian localities are listed in the appendix to this chapter.

(b) Middle Devonian Series

The boundary between the Lower and Middle Devonian Series has been under discussion by the Subcommission on Devonian Stratigraphy (Ziegler and Klapper, 1982a). The base of the Eifelian Stage, which corresponds in biostratigraphic terms to the base of the *partitus* Zone is herein taken to represent the base of the Middle Devonian Series (Weddige, 1982).

The zonation currently adopted for the Eifelian Stage is that proposed by Weddige (1977), and modified by Klapper (1977). The Eifelian Stage consists of five zones based on the first appearance of subspecies as follows.

5. *Polygnathus xylus ensensis* (partim).
4. *Tortodus kockelianus kockelianus.*
3. *Tortodus kockelianus australis.*
2. *Polygnathus costatus costatus.*
1. *Polygnathus costatus patulus.*

The *patulus* Zone may be further divided into two portions with *P. costatus partitus* appearing in the upper part (Klapper *et al.,* 1978).

This scheme replaces the earlier threefold subdivision of the Eifelian Stage (which is retained for Cornwall in this study) into the *corniger, bidentata* and *kockelianus* zones, a proposal made by Wittekindt (1966) based on a study of conodonts in sections within the Eastern Rhenish Slate Mountains. In the Couvinian sections of Belgium (Bultynck, 1970) and in the type Eifelian (Weddige, 1977) of Germany *O. bidentata* appears above the *kockelianus* Zone. In the type Eifelian section the upper part of the sequence contains a Lower *ensensis* Zone fauna. The *ensensis* Zone is also represented in the upper part of the type Cou-

vinian and ranges into the Lower Givetian Stage (Weddige, 1977).

The following conodont zones are recognized within the Givetian Stage.

5. Lowermost *Polygnathus asymmetricus.*
4. *Palmatolepis disparilis.*
3. *Schmidtognathus hermanni—Polygnathus cristatus* (Lower and Upper).
2. *Polygnathus varcus* (Lower, Middle and Upper).
1. *Polygnathus ensensis* (partim).

The lowermost *ensensis* zone was introduced by Weddige (1977). It replaced the *Polygnathus obliquimarginatus* Zone of Ziegler (1971). The *Polygnathus varcus* Zone can be subdivided into Lower, Middle and Upper *varcus* based on the first occurrence of *P. timorensis; P. ansatus* and *P. latifossatus* respectively (Ziegler *et al.,* 1976). The *varcus* Zone was introduced by Bischoff and Ziegler (1957) and redefined by Ziegler *et al.* (1976). Ziegler *et al.* (1976) described the associated fauna of the *Schmidtognathus hermanni— Polygnathus cristatus* Zone and of the Lowermost *asymmetricus* Zone. The conodonts of the *disparilis* Zone have been described by Ziegler and Klapper (1982a).

The sequence of Middle Devonian conodonts in Britain, as seen in the Plymouth, Torquay and North Cornwall regions, has been described previously in this chapter. The stratigraphical range of diagnostic Middle Devonian species is shown in Table 4. Previously documented records are contained in the appendix to this chapter.

(c) Upper Devonian Series

Ziegler (1962) proposed a zonation for the Upper Devonian Series based on sections in Germany, which until very recently had been modified slightly in subsequent years. Sandberg and Ziegler (1973) inserted a Lower *rhomboidea* Zone between the *Upper crepida* Zone and the former (now Upper) *rhomboidea* Zone, *Pa. poolei* being restricted to the new zone. The same publication saw the former *quadrantinodosa* Zone renamed as the *marginifera* Zone. The Lower *marginifera* Zone is recognized by the first appearance of *Pa. margini-*

fera marginifera, *Pa. quadrantinodosa quadranti-*
nodosa and *Pa. q. inflexoidea*. The last two are
restricted to the Lower *marginifera* Zone. *Pa.*
stoppeli, which first appears in the Upper *rhom-*
boidea Zone does not range above the *marginifera*
Zone. The Upper *marginifera* Zone is difficult to
recognize; its upper limit coincides with the first
appearance of *Sc. velifer*, whereas its lower limit
is marked by the disappearance of species characteristic of the Lower *marginifera* Zone. Ziegler
et al. (1974) revised the taxonomy of the *Bis-*
pathodus Group. Sandberg *et al.* (1978) established
and documented the *S. praesulcata* fauna. This
conodont zonation scheme is summarized by
Klapper and Ziegler (1979) and the nominate
species are listed below.

11. *Siphonodella praesulcata.*
10. *Bispathodus costatus.*
9. *Polygnathus styriacus.*
8. *Scaphignathus velifer.*
7. *Palmatolepis marginifera.*
6. *Palmatolepis rhomboidea.*
5. *Palmatolepis crepida.*
4. *Palmatolepis triangularis.*
3. *Palmatolepis gigas.*
2. *Ancyrognathus triangularis.*
1. *Polygnathus asymmetricus* (partim).

A revised taxonomy of important conodonts
from the *styriacus* Zone and adjacent zones is
given by Sandberg and Ziegler (1979). These
reasearchers recorded the biofacies of significant
elements and implied that diagnostic indices did
not extend into shallow-water biofacies. The
degree of refinement, which has now been achieved
is well illustrated by Sandberg *et al.* (1983), who
indicated that the Upper Devonian spans an
interval of some 14 million years and, within this
interval of time, twenty-eight conodont faunas
may be recognized. Each subdivision of the conodont biostratigraphic scheme thus averages approximately half a million years of geological time.

Sandberg and Dreesen (1983, 1984) have
suggested ten conodont zones for near-shore
environments. They are in ascending sequence as
follows: *Icriodus symmetricus* (equivalent to
Lower *asymmetricus* to *An. triangularis*); Lower,

Middle and Upper *Pelekysgnathus planus* (equivalent to Lower *gigas* to lower part of Middle *Pa.*
triangularis); Lower, Middle and Upper *'Icriodus'*
cornutus (equivalent to upper part of Middle *Pa.*
triangularis to Upper *marginifera*) and Lower,
Middle and Upper *'I' costatus* (equivalent to
Uppermost *marginifera* to Upper *praesulcata*).

Ziegler and Sandberg (1983, 1984) have
recently proposed a major revision of the late
Devonian conodont zonation for the interval
between the top of the Upper *marginifera* Zone
to the top of the *S. praesulcata* Zone. The following new zones were proposed on the first appearance of species as indicated within the brackets:
Uppermost *marginifera (Sc. velifer)*, Lower *trachy-*
tera (Pa. rugosa trachytera), Upper *trachytera (Ps.*
granulosus), Lower *postera (Pa. perlobata postera)*,
Upper *postera (Pa. gracilis manca)*, Lower *expansa*
(Pa. gracilis expansa), Middle *expansa (B. aculeatus)*,
Upper *expansa (B. ultimus)*, Lower *S. praesul-*
cata, (Pa. gracilis gonioclymeniae), Middle *S.*
praesulcata (without *Pa. gracilis goniocylmenae*
and *Pr. kockeli*) and Upper *S. praesulcata (Pr.*
kockeli). The relationship between the shallow-
water and pelagic zonations is shown in Fig. 4.14.
The present knowledge of Upper Devonian conodont element range in Britain is shown in Tables
5 and 5a (the diagnostic forms in Table 5 and
the associated fauna in Table 5a).

The British conodont sequence in the lower
part of the Upper Devonian Series as seen in the
Plymouth, Torquay and North Cornwall successions has been described previously in this chapter.
Upper Devonian conodont sequences also are well
developed in the region of Newton Abbot. A virtually complete sequence of faunas from the
former Upper *marginifera* Zone through to the
former Upper *costatus* Zone has been recognized
in Cornwall. These are summarized below together
with a discussion of the relationships of Ziegler
and Sandberg's (1984) scheme.

(i) The Upper *marginifera* Zone (Klapper and
Ziegler, 1979; Sandberg and Ziegler, 1973);
the Upper *marginifera* Zone (Ziegler and
Sandberg, 1984)
This zone is characterized by the range of *Pa.*

SERIES	STAGE	FORMER ZONATION		STANDARD CONODONT ZONES (PELAGIC BIOFACIES)	DEFINITION OF LOWER LIMIT BY APPEARANCE OF:		NEARSHORE CONODONT ZONES	DEFINITION OF LOWER LIMIT BY APPEARANCE OF
UPPER DEVONIAN	FAMENNIAN	Protognathodus	L	praesulcata	U	Pr. kockeli		NO FIRST APPEARANCE (EXTINCTION OF "I." raymondi)
			U	praesulcata	M	No. Pr. kockeli-No Pa. g. gonioclymeniae		
		costatus	M	praesulcata	L	S. praesulcata		
			L	expansa	U	B. ultimus		
				expansa	M	B. aculeatus	"Icriodus" costatus	"I." costatus darbyensis
		styriacus	U	expansa	L	Pa. gracilis expansa		
			M	postera	U	Pa. gracilis manca		
			L	postera	L	Pa. perlobata postera		"I." costatus costatus Morphotype 1
		velifer	U	trachytera	U	Ps. granulosus		
			M	trachytera	L	Pa. rugosa trachytera		
			L	trachytera	Um	Sc. velifer velifer		
		marginifera	U	marginifera	U	Pa. marginifera utahensis		
			L	marginifera	L	Pa. m. marginifera		"I." chojnicensis
				rhomboidea	U	Pa. rhomboidea		
				rhomboidea	L	Pa. poolei	"Icriodus" cornutus	
				crepida	U	Pa. glabra glabra		Pelekysgnathus inclinatus
				crepida	M	Pa. termini		
				crepida	L	Pa. crepida		
				triangularis	U	Pa. tenuipunctata		"I." cornutus
				triangularis	M	Pa. delicatula clarki		
	FRASNIAN			triangularis	L	Pa. triangularis	Pelekysgnathus planus	I. alternatus alternatus
				gigas	Um	Pa. linguiformis		
				gigas	U	An. asymmetricus		
				gigas	L	Pa. gigas		P. planus
				An. triangularis		An. triangularis	Icriodus symmetricus	I. symmetricus
				asymmetricus	U	A. curvata		
				asymmetricus	M	Pa. punctata		
				asymmetricus	L	A. rotundilobata		

Key to Genera

An. = Ancyrognathus
A. = Ancyrodella
B. = Bispathodus
I. = Icriodus
"I." = taxa of the genus Pelekysgnathus that have triple-row platform (I) elements
P. = Pelekysgnathus
Pa. = Palmatolepis
Pr. = Protognathodus
Ps. = Pseudopolygnathus
S. = Siphonodella
Sc. = Scaphignathus
No formal Zone

Fig. 4.14 — Conodont zonations for the Upper Devonian Series, incorporating near-shore and pelagic (off-shore) biofacies. Based on Ziegler and Sandberg (1984) and Sandberg and Dreeson (1984).

marginifera marginifera between the last occurrence of *Pa. quadrantinodosa quadrantinodosa* and the first occurrence of *Sc. velifer*. The range of *Pa. m. marginifera* with *P. glaber bilobatus* in the absence of scaphignathids is here also taken to identify this zone. The most common association is composed of *Pa. m. marginifera, Pa. glabra distorta, Pa. perlobata schindewolfi, Pa. rugosa* cf. *ampla, P. diversus* and *'I.' cornutus*. All these forms range upwards into the overlying zone.

(ii) The *velifer* Zone (Ziegler, 1962; Klapper and Ziegler, 1979); the Uppermost *marginifera* Zone and the *trachytera* Zone (Ziegler and Sandberg, 1984)

The former Lower *velifer* Zone in Cornwall is recognized by the explosive first appearance and range of *Sc. velifer* before the first occurrence of *Pa. rugosa trachytera*. As *velifer* is interpreted as a shallow-water species, its use as a cosmopolitan indice is precluded. *Pa. m. marginifera* is recognized in the lower part of this zone and *'Sp.' bohlenanus* and *Pe. inclinatus* appear above the base of this zone. *Sc. velifer, Sc. pseudostrigosus. Sc. subserratus, P. diversus* and *'Sp.' amplus*, with subordinate palmatolepids, notably *Pa. glabra lepta, Pa. glabra distorta* and *Pa. perlobata schindewolfi*, are the most common forms recovered. *B. stabilis* and *P. semicostatus* first appear in this zone. Infrequent specimens of *'Icriodus' cornutus* are last recorded within this zone in Cornwall which correlates the top of the *'I.' cornutus* Zone with the new Uppermost *marginifera* Zone. *'Icriodus' pectinatus* is apparently restricted to the former Lower *velifer* Zone.

The base of the former Middle *velifer* Zone is defined as the first occurrence of the proposed zonal index *Pa. rugosa trachytera. P. perplexus* first appears at the base of this zone and ranges higher. The upper limit of the former Middle *velifer* Zone, however, has proved difficult to define, *Ps. granulosus* having not been recovered from Cornish faunas. Thus the Upper *trachytera* Zone is not identified. Associated Middle *velifer* or *trachytera* Zone forms include *Pa. glabra lepta, Pa. glabra distorta, Pa. perlobata schindewolfi, Pa. perlobata helmsi, P. nodocostatus* s.1., *P. semi-*costatus, *P. diversus, Sc. pseudostrigosus, Sc. subserratus, 'Sp.' amplus* and *'Sp.' bohlenanus*.

The occurrence of *Sc. velifer* in the absence of *Pa. rugosa trachytera, P. glabra distorta, P. nodocostatus* s.1. and *'Sp.' amplus* before the first appearance of *P. styriacus* is taken to identify a position in the former Upper *velifer* Zone. As noted, the nominate species of the Upper *trachytera* Zone has not been recovered. *Pa. glabra lepta* is last recorded in the Upper *velifer* Zone; higher occurrences in the *costatus* Zone are taken to indicate reworking.

(iii) The *styriacus* Zone (Ziegler, 1962); the *perlobata postera* Zone, *gracilis expansa* Zone (Ziegler and Sandberg, 1984).

The former Lower *styriacus* Zone has proved difficult to define. In part this is because *Ps. granulosus* has not been recorded in Cornish faunas, although more important is the high degree of condensation of this and adjacent zones in Cornwall. Faunal elements of this zone, including *Sc. subserratus*, occur in reworked associations with elements of the former Middle and Upper *styriacus* zones. The Lower *styriacus* Zone equates to the lower part of the *perlobata postera* Zone. The Middle *styriacus* Zone in Cornwall cannot be based on the first appearance of *Pa. gracilis manca*, as this subspecies has only been recorded from the lower part of the former Upper *styriacus* Zone. As with the Lower *styriacus* Zone, faunal admixture due to condensation denies confident recognition of this zone and thus the significance of the late appearance of *Pa. g. manca* is probably only local.

Faunas from the former Upper *styriacus* Zone are among the most rich and diverse faunas recovered. The zone is characterized by the range of *P. styriacus, Ps. brevipennatus, Pa. rugosa rugosa* and the proposed indice *Pa. gracilis expansa* before the first appearance of *B. costatus*. Double-rowed bispathodids, notably *B. jugosus* and advanced forms of *B. stabilis*, close to *B. aculeatus*, with incipient accessory dextral denticles first appear within this zone and are locally associated with representatives of *Cl. ormistoni. P. homoirregularis, P. subirregularis, P. margaritatus* and *Pa. gracilis manca* are only recorded from this zone in Cornwall, although Sandberg and Ziegler (1979) indicate more extensive ranges for these species. 'Sp.' bohlenanus, 'Sp.' werneri, Pa. perlobata maxima and P. semicostatus are here last recorded within the Upper styriacus Zone.

(iv) The costatus Zone (Ziegler, 1962); the expansa Zone (pars) and praesulcata Zone (Zielger and Sandberg, 1984)

The Lower costatus Zone is characterized in Cornwall and Devon by the sudden appearance of abundant B. costatus which occurs with subordinate Ps. brevipennatus before the first appearance of Pa. gracilis gonioclymeniae and Ps. marburgensis trigonicus. The associated fauna is dominated by Pa. gracilis gracilis and B. stabilis. The Bispathodus aculeatus group appears slightly above the base of this zone (Ziegler et al., 1974) and marks the base of the Middle expansa Zone.

The base of the former Middle costatus Zone is defined as the first occurrence of Pa. gracilis gonioclymeniae (Ziegler, 1962). The first appearance of Ps. marburgensis trigonicus is taken as an additional aid in the recognition of the base of this zone. B. costatus, the B. aculeatus group and Pa. gracilis gracilis remain as abundant elements but the upper limit, however, of the former Middle costatus Zone cannot be so readily defined. Sandberg and Ziegler (1979) discovered that Pa. gracilis gonioclymeniae ranges up into the lowermost part of the Upper costatus Zone and that Pa. g. sigmoidalis occurs as low as the Upper styriacus Zone, so that the disappearance of the former and the appearance of the latter can no longer be used to mark the base of the former Upper costatus Zone. In Cornwall the upper limit of the former Middle costatus Zone has been based on the first appearance of Ps. graulichi in the absence of Pa. g. gonioclymeniae. 'Sp.' supremus appears at the base of this zone and is followed by B. ultimus slightly above this level. The use of P. znepolensis as an indicator of the Middle costatus Zone (Klapper and Ziegler, 1979) is here refuted as the species has been recovered from faunas as low as the velifer Zone (see also Klapper, in Ziegler, 1975).

In Cornwall, Pa. gracilis sigmoidalis does not appear until after the first occurrence of Bispathodus ultimus which corresponds to the original German material of Ziegler (1962) rather than the American faunas described by Sandberg and Ziegler (1979). P. vogesi is first recorded close to the upper limits of the Upper costatus Zone. In Cornwall, S. praesculata appears to have a biostratigraphic range concurrent with the lower range of Bispathodus ultimus.

(v) The praesulcata Zone

The praesulcata Zone was established by Sandberg et al. (1978) as the lowest zone of the essentially Lower Carboniferous Siphonodella zonation. S. praesulcata first appears in faunas associated with Ps. marburgensis trigonicus and B. costatus apparently above the last occurrence of Pa. gracilis gonioclymeniae in Cornwall. Ziegler and Sandberg (1984) recognize a Lower praesulcata Zone in which S. praesulcata and Pa. g. gonioclymeniae both occur. On this basis the Lower praesulcata Zone has yet to be confirmed in Southwest England. Associated fauna includes the B. aculeatus group, B. ultimus, Ps. graulichi and Pa. gracilis gracilis. At higher levels, protognathodids appear before the first occurrence of S. sulcata.

4.5 CONODONT ZONATION OF THE BOUNDARY OF THE DEVONIAN–CARBONIFEROUS SYSTEMS

(a) Introduction

The precise position of the Devonian–Carboniferous boundary has long been the subject of research and debate (Paproth and Streel, 1984). Paproth (1964) described the history of research which led to the placement of the boundary at the base of the Gattendorfia Limestone above the last of the clymenids (2nd Heerlen Congress, 1935) in the proposed type section in the Hönne Valley. This boundary is readily identifiable in areas of cephalopod-bearing strata, but much of the European and American Lower Carboniferous is lacking in cepahlopods. To resolve this problem, microfossils have been utilized in both the definition and recognition of the boundary.

Austin *et al.* (1970) discussed the usage of conodonts in the recognition of the Devonian–Carboniferous boundary in Great Britain and made particular reference to the Upper Devonian Baggy and Lower Pilton Beds of North Devon and the basal K Zone of the Avonian. They correlated their lowest Avonian conodont Zone (*Patrognathus variabilis–'Spathognathodus' plumulus assemblage Zone*) with the *kockeli–dentilineatus* Zone of Voges (1959) and the *sulcata* Zone of Collinson *et al.* (1962), although they did not recognize standard zonal indices, and their faunas from the Lower Pilton Beds, which they considered younger than uppermost *Wocklumeria* faunas of the German type section, are no younger than the Lower *costatus* Zone (see also House and Sevastopulo, 1984).

There have been more precise correlations, however, between the North American and German conodont sequences (Collinson *et al.*, 1971) where the evolutionary development of *Protognathodus* and *Siphonodella* has been established.

(b) The *Protognathodus* fauna

The first described species of *Protognathodus*, *Pr. kockeli* was considered by Bischoff (1957) to be an important zonal element of the Lower Carboniferous. Ziegler (1969) recovered abundant protognathodids from lenses of Stockum Limestone from which Schmidt (1924) had described his *Imitoceras* fauna and, in the absence of other diagnostic, indices placed the fauna in the uppermost Upper Devonian. Alberti *et al.* (1974) summarized the occurrence of protognathodids and recognized two faunas. A younger *Protognathodus* fauna with *Pr. kockeli*, *Pr. collinsoni*, *Pr. meischneri* and *Pr. kuehni*, and an older fauna which lacks *Pr. kuehni*. Sandberg *et al.* (1972) placed faunas with *Pr. kuehni* in the *sulcata* Zone, and faunas which lack *Pr. kuehni* in the Upper Devonian *praesulcata* Zone.

Protognathodids appear in Cornwall in the uppermost part of the Upper *costatus* Zone and are associated with *Polygnathus communis communis*, *P. communis dentatus*, *P. vogesi*, *P. inornatus*, *S. praesulcata*, *Ps. graulichi*, *B. aculeatus aculeatus* and rare *B. costatus* and *Pa. gracilis*

gracilis. *Pr. kuehni* has not been recovered from Cornwall and denies the use here of protognathodids as accurate indicators of the Devonian–Carboniferous boundary. However, a slightly younger fauna with *Pr. kockeli*, *Pr. collinsoni*, *Pr. meischneri*, *S. sulcata*, *B. a. aculeatus*, *B. stabilis*, *P. c. Communis*, *P. longiposticus* and extremely rare *Pa. gracilis gracilis* must on the basis of the presence of *S. sulcata*, be placed in the Lower Carboniferous.

Sandberg *et al.* (1978) and Klapper and Ziegler (1979) regard the *Protognathodus* fauna as representing a particular biofacies of the *praesulcata* and *sulcata* Zones and, because of the more widespread occurrence of siphonodellids, the latter are considered as more useful indices of the Devonian–Carboniferous boundary.

(c) The *praesulcata–sulcata* boundary

The working Group on the Devonian–Carboniferous Boundary have designated that the base of the Carboniferous System be based on the first occurrence of *S. sulcata* within the evolutionary lineage from *S. praesulcata* (Paproth, 1980). The lowest occurrence of *S. sulcata* is in the base of the *Gattendorfia* Limestone at Hönnetal, and nearby in lenses of Stockum Limestone in the uppermost part of the immediately underlying Hangenberg Shale (Sandberg *et al.*, 1978). Although *Gattendorfia* has not been recorded from Stockum, the *stratum typicum* for *G. subinvoluta* yields a conodont and trilobite fauna equivalent to that of the Stockum Limestone horizon (Alberti *et al.*, 1974).

The Belgian type sections have not yielded *Siphonodella praesulcata–sulcata* (Bouckaert and Groessens, 1976), although they contain abundant *Ps. graulichi*, an apparent homeomorph of *S. praesulcata*. Both *Ps. graulichi* and *S. praesulcata* occur in Cornwall before the lowest occurrence of *S. sulcata* and are taken to represent a transitional fauna between the uppermost Upper Devonian Belgian and German faunas. The appearance of *S. sulcata* after *S. praesulcata* has been noted at several localities in Devon and Cornwall.

Ziegler and Sandberg (1984a) have recently reviewed important candidate sections for the

stratotype of the Devonian–Carboniferous boundary related to conodont sequences from North
America, Europe and China.

4.7 FACIES AND ITS CONTROL ON
DEVONIAN CONODONT DISTRIBUTION

Increasingly the effect of facies on the distribution
of Devonian conodont genera is being appreciated
(Sandberg *et al.*, 1983). Environmental and palaeogeographic factors affect the occurrence of particular genera, and recent studies have attempted
to distinguish between palaeoecological differences
and differences due to provincialism (see Klapper
and Ziegler, 1979, for a detailed discussion).

In the lower part of the Lower Devonian
Series, provincialism was marked; the distinct
aspect of Lower Devonian faunas from Nevada
and Spain has been mentioned previously. In the
upper part of the Lower Devonian Series, differences between conodont sequences become less
pronounced and are more subtle, involving differences in terms of species. Study of the distribution
of species of the genera *Icriodus*, *Polygnathus* and
Sannemannia indicate that, in the upper part of
the Lower Devonian Series and in the Middle
Devonian Series, species of *Polygnathus* tend to
have a widespread geographical distribution,
whereas species of *Icriodus* and *Sannemannia* tend
to have a restricted distribution. Klapper and
Ziegler (1979) postulated that species of *Polygnathus* were capable of widespread distribution, via
major oceanic currents, whereas *Icriodus* and other
icriodontids, which developed endemic species,
were probably not capable of distribution and
survival via oceanic currents. Weddige and Ziegler
(1976) discussed the ratios of *Icriodus* to *Polygnathus* from limestones of the type Eifelian Stage.
A positive correlation was noted between *Icriodus*
and the carbonate content of the limestone. It
was suggested that *Polygnathus* and *Icriodus*
were differentiated vertically in quiet waters and
that the *Icriodus* habitat was more extensive
vertically and more densely populated in energy-
rich shallow water. Davis (1975), from a study of
the Middle Devonian Tully Limestone of New
York State, noted a *Polygnathus–Icriodus* distri-

bution consistent with a depth-stratification model
(Seddon and Sweet, 1971). *Icriodus* was more
abundant nearer shore. A major exception was an
abundance of *Icriodus* within a deep-water environment, normally populated by *Polygnathus*.
Davies suggested that this resulted from a reduction of *Polygnathus* species within a stagnating
environment transitional to the anoxic environment. Here the oxygen-poor deeper water left
elements of the surface water life zone, i.e. *Icriodus*, predominating in the sediment. In the Middle
Devonian Series, according to Dr. Mouravieff (in
Klapper and Ziegler, 1979), species of *Palmatolepis* did not live in the relatively shallow areas in
and around reefs, a habitat which was occupied by
species of *Ancyrognathus*. *Icriodus* likewise had a
restricted distribution; Chatterton (1976) recognized four distinct associations of conodont taxa,
or biofacies, which were represented in Eifelian
and lower Givetian strata of Canada. Chatterton
recognized these four associations on the basis of
the percentage composition of the included
genera, namely *Panderodus*, *Coelocerodontus*,
Belodella, *Polygnathus*, *Icriodus*, *Pelekysgnathus*,
'*Acodina*' and '*Spathognathodus*'. The four biofacies recognized by Chatterton were as follows.

Biofacies I was dominated by *Panderodus* and
Coelocerodontus often with *Belodella* and *Polygnathus*. This was similar to biofacies I of Druce
(1973). Chatterton suggested that conodonts of
biofacies I lived in shallow shelf areas of moderate
to low energy at the sea floor with slightly higher
temperatures and salinities than those of the open
oceans.

Biofacies IA was dominated by species of
Belodella and *Polygnathus* with sparse specimens
of *Coelocerodontus*, *Icriodus* and *Panderodus*.
Chatterton suggested that this biofacies represented
shoal shelf seas slightly nearer the shelf margin
than biofacies I, but with salinities and temperatures that were slightly above those normal for the
surface waters of the open ocean at similar palaeo-
latitudes.

Biofacies II was dominated by species of
Polygnathus and *Icriodus* with smaller numbers of
Pelekysgnathus, *Belodella*, *Coelocerodontus* and
Panderodus. This was similar to biofacies II of

Druce (1973). The diverse macrofauna found with this conodont biofacies suggested to Chatterton an open marine environment. There was also evidence to suggest that the sea was of shallow to moderate depth in this environment. Thus the salinities and temperatures (at the surface) of the sea may have been lower in the environment characterized by biofacies II than those of biofacies I and IA even if the depths were no greater.

Biofacies III was dominated by species of *Polygnathus* and contains rare specimens of *Icriodus* and simple cone elements together with a few specimens of '*Spathognathodus*'. This was similar to biofacies II of Druce (1973). This biofacies appeared to be representative of more open marine and deeper-water conditions than either biofacies I or biofacies II.

A suggested relationship between these biofacies and their environments is indicated in Fig. 4.15. However, not all the differences between Middle Devonian conodont faunas can be explained by ecological factors. Bultynck (1976b) suggested that differences in abundance and occurrence of conodonts in faunas from rocks of a similar environmental setting in Michigan and in Belgium may be due to provincialism.

Schumacher (1977) recognized three distinctive and recurring conodont facies spanning the Givetian–Frasnian boundary in Central Missouri. An *Icriodus*-dominated biofacies was restricted to the shallow subtidal facies. A biofacies characterized by species of *Polygnathus* with narrow platforms and simple ornamentation occurred in both shallow and deep subtidal facies with a preference for the former. An *Ancyrodella–Polygnathus asymmetricus* biofacies composed chiefly of taxa with wide platforms was restricted to a deep subtidal facies. Each of the conodont biofacies retained their ecological integrity over the time interval studied, but the taxonomic composition changed in response to evolution within the biofacies.

The polygnathid stock of the Middle Devonian Series evolved in relatively deep water as also did the palmatolepid stock of the Upper Devonian Series. Thus these genera are best for biostratigraphic investigations according to Klapper and Ziegler (1979). Sandberg (1977) grouped conodont faunas of the *Polygnathus styriacus* Zone in the Western United States into five major conodont biofacies, the geographic boundaries of which correspond approximately to the five recognized

CONODONT BIOFACIES	BIOFACIES III	BIOFACIES II	BIOFACIES I A	BIOFACIES I	
CHARACTERISTIC FORMS	*Polygnathus*	*Polygnathus and Icriodus and/or Pelekysgnathus and/or Belodella*	*Polygnathus and Belodella and/or Coelocerodontus*	*Panderodus and /or Coelocerodontus*	
ENVIRONMENT	Basin or Slope	Shallow open marine	Shallow slightly restricted	Semi-restricted	Restricted
TEMPERATURE	Normal marine	Normal marine	Sl. above normal	Above normal	Above normal
SALINITY	Normal marine	Normal marine	Sl. above normal	Above normal	Above normal
LITHOLOGY	Calc. shale	Limestone and Calc. shale	Limestone	Limestone & Dolomite	Dolomite & Evaporite
ENERGY AT SUBSTRATE	Low	Low to high	Moderate to Low	Low	Low
ABUNDANCE	Low to high	Moderate to high	Low	Very low	Absent
DIVERSITY OF MACROFAUNAS	Low	High	Moderate	Low	Very low
DIVERSITY OF CONODONT FAUNAS	Moderate to low	High	Moderate	Low	– – – – – –

Fig. 4.15 – Middle Devonian conodont biofacies and probable environmental conditions. Modified after Chatterton (1976).

palaeotectonic facies. For all biofacies the epony-mous platform genera constituted at least 65% of the total population of platform elements. The five biofacies were as follows.

1. Palmatolepid—bispathodid biofacies deposited on the continental rise and slope. This bio-facies was reported within dolomotized cherty phosphatic radiolarian-rich limestones and nodular argillaceous limestones and from large concretions of micritic limestone, all interbedded within an argillite sequence.
2. Palmatolepid—polygnathid biofacies, deposi-ted in shallow to moderately deep water on the continental shelf. The lithofacies on the continental shelf comprises basal sandy transgressive lag beds overlain by carbon-aceous shale, mudstone and siltstone.
3. Polygnathid—icriodid biofacies, deposited in moderately shallow water on the outer cratonic platform. The lithofacies consists mainly of encrinite and fossil-fragmental lime-stone interbedded with grey and green clay—shale.
4. Polygnathid—pelekysgnathid biofacies, deposi-ted in shallow water of normal salinity in the 'inner craton'. The lithofacies consists mainly of light-to medium-grey fine-grained bio-clastic or encrinitic limestone with very little interbedded shale.
5. Clydagnathid biofacies, deposited in very shallow brackish to normally saline water on off-shore banks and in associated lagoons. The lithofacies is probably lagoonal limestones, containing ostracodes and scattered ooliths which are interbedded in a sequence of dark-grey shale.

Sandberg and Ziegler (1979) noted that certain shallow-water forms have their own evolution within their own habitat. They also introduced three further shallow-water biofacies; the pandor-inellinid, the scaphignathid and the patrognathid biofacies which occupied comparable settings within the clydagnathid biofacies. The common stock that gave rise to these specialized asymmetri-cal forms was *Pandorinellina insita* (Stauffer). This species, with its distinctive anterior blade denti-

culation, first appeared in a shallow-water en-vironment of the Lower Frasnian Stage. Suc-ceeding forms gave rise to *Scaphignathus,* to *Patrognathus* and to *Clydagnathus.* In the early Famennian Stage of Belgium, where a variety of facies can be recognized, the palmatolepid—poly-gnathid and the polygnathid—icriodid biofacies are well developed (Bouckaert and Ziegler, 1965; Dreesen and Dusar, 1974; Dreesen, 1977; Dusar and Dreesen, 1977; Dusar, 1977). However, the dominance of icriodids, particularly in the near-shore environments of the younger Famennian Stage has necessitated the introduction of an ancillary zonation scheme (Sandberg and Dreesen, 1984). The *Protognathodus* fauna of Ziegler (1969) and the *S. praesulcata* fauna (Sandberg *et al.,* 1978) are also considered to be characteristic of special biofacies (Sandberg *et al.,* 1983).

According to Sandberg and Dreesen (1983), in the Upper Devonian, *Icriodus* (a euryhaline icriodontid) ranges from the near-shore to pelagic biofacies and is later replaced by *Pelekysgnathus,* a mesohaline (possibly nectobenthic) icriodontid. Advanced forms ('*Icriodus*', icriodontids with three rows of denticles) invaded deeper subtidal, more seaward niches than those occupied by *Peleks-gnathus.* The genus *Antognathus* is confined to hypersaline environments. Their model is illustrated (Fig. 4.16).

Sandberg (1979) and his co-workers (Sand-berg and Gutschick, 1979; Sandberg *et al.,* 1983; Sandberg and Poole, 1977; Sandberg *et al.,* 1978) provide additional details concerning the ecological restriction of Devonian conodonts and their relationship to facies. In recent publications it is to be noted that standard subdivisions within the Upper Devonian Series are now referred to as conodont zones or biofacies (Sandberg *et al.,* 1983).

Within the British Devonian rocks, ecological restriction of conodonts has been referred to by Orchard (1978a). Unfortunately, most publica-tions have not given information concerning the numerical abundances of the conodont genera. Nevertheless it is possible to recognize the presence of the *Icriodus* biofacies in rocks of Lower, Middle and Upper Devonian age. The non-ramiform

PALAEO-TECTONIC SETTING	OFFSHORE	NEARSHORE	'BACKSHORE'						
	MUDDY OUTER SHELF	SANDY INNER SHELF	SHOAL	BACK-MOUND	TIDAL FLAT	BARRIER	TIDAL LAGOON	SABKHA	COASTAL PLAIN
CONODONT BIOFACIES	I Palmatolepid	II Palmatolepid-polygnathid	III Polygn.-'icriodid'	IV Polygnathid-pelekysgnathid		VI, VIII, ? Scaphignathid, pandorinellinid, +?			
ICRIODONTID FAUNA	Rare Icriodus	Both types of Pelekysgnathus (transported)	Triple-row Pelekys-gnathus	Both types of Pelekysgnathus (indigenous)		Single-row Pelekys-gnathus	UNKNOWN		

Fig. 4.16 – Icriodontid biofacies model for Famennian Stage. Modified after Sandberg and Dreesen (1984).

Lower Devonian faunas of Cornwall reported by Sadler (1973a) are dominated by *Icriodus*, which represents over 98% of the total collection, *Spathognathodus* and *Polygnathus* constituting less than 2%. Orchard (1978a) provided figures which enable the relative abundance of simple cones, icriodids, linguiform polygnathids, lanceolate polygnathids, ancyrognathids, the *P. asymmetricus* group, palmatolepids and spathognathodids within the Plymouth Limestones to be determined. In the late Eifelian, fauna 5, the collections are dominated by simple cones (principally *Belodella*) which constitute 50–80% of the faunas with icriodids and polygnathids occurring in approximately equal amounts. Icriodids are absent from virtually all known Givetian Limestones throughout the western area of the Plymouth Limestone outcrop. Orchard (1978a) noted that in a late Givetian fauna from Mount Wise, with a total of 1000 elements, *Icriodus* was absent but simple cones, lanceolate and linguiform polygnathids were equally represented. *Icriodus* is extremely sparse in the Marble Cliff Limestones, and Kirchgasser (1970) commented on the effect of sorting and current reworking when interpreting the faunal content of his samples. *Icriodus* and *Polygnathus* were reported from limestones of Frasnian–Famennian age in the Steeple Aston Borehole (Poole, 1977). Representatives of the genus *Polygnathus* dominated the faunas and made up between 45% and 62% of the total assemblages. The relative of genera in the Torquay Limestone at Barton Quarry is shown in Fig. 4.17.

The application of biofacies studies to the Famennian of Southwest England has been initiated by Stewart (1981a) at levels where stratigraphic admixture of faunas is low. Considerable refinement in the lithostratigraphical interpretation is clearly possible. Thus the nodular and flaser limestones of the Petherwin Formation (columns 1–9 in Fig. 4.13) yield Lower *velifer* Zone (now Upper *marginifera* Zone) faunas that compare with the shallow-water scaphignathid biofacies of Sandberg and Ziegler (1979), being dominated (40–80% of total platform population) by *Scaphignathus pseudostrigosus* (Dreesen and Dusar, 1974), *Sc. velifer* and pandorinellinids. This occurrence not only supports the sedimentary evidence of Orchard (1974) that Givetian–Frasnian reefs stood exposed in late Devonian times but suggests extension of the period of exposure. The unusual abundance in this assemblage of *P. diversus,* a member of the *P. nodocostatus* group is noteworthy, for the group is otherwise ascribed to more seaward facies (Sandberg, 1976). However, the species shows ontogenetic developments characteristic of the shallow-water *Pandorinella–Scaphignathus* groups and is more likely to be displaced taxonomically than environmentally.

At another structural level, the ubiquitous abundance of members of the *P. nodocostatus* group which is commonest in the palmatolepid–polygnathid biofacies is consistent with the view that the Luxton Nodular Limestone accumulated on a rise-slope adjoining such submerged reefs. At the highest structural level the occurrence within

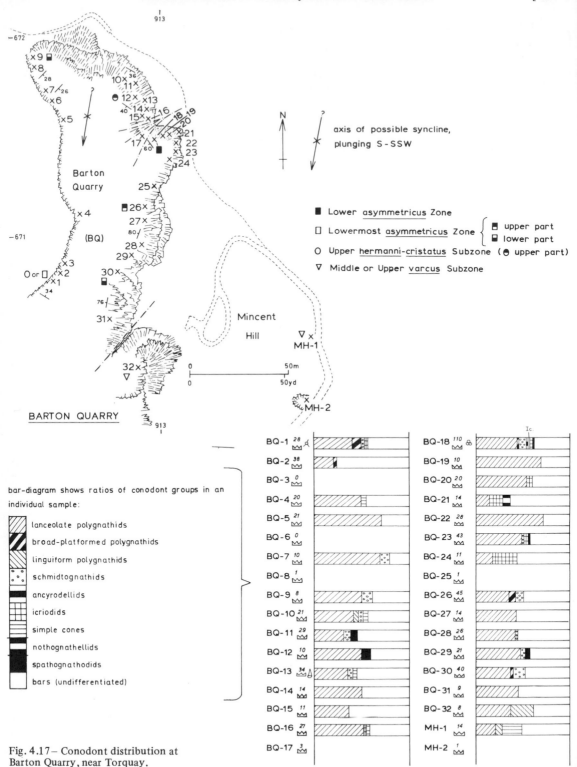

Fig. 4.17– Conodont distribution at Barton Quarry, near Torquay.

the Boscastle Nappe of an intertidal conodont assemblage (dominated by *'Icriodus'* *pectinatus* Dreesen and Houlleberghs, of *velifer* Zone age, probably topmost *cornutus* Zone) in the Buckator Formation supports the shallow-water interpretation of all the lithofacies in the nappe.

By Lower to Middle *costatus* Zone times, the influence of the local reef structures on Petherwin Formation deposition was minimal; virtually all localities yield rich faunas of the palmatolepid–bispathodid biofacies, the deepest-water continental shelf assemblage recognized by Sandberg (1976). Certain faunas show a reduction in abundance and diversity of palmatolepids which may reflect nearer-shore environments, although any polarity in faunal constituents is lost by Upper *costatus* Zone times with all lithofacies yielding comparable assemblages.

The depositional environment of the thick but generally featureless Tredorn Slate, Delabole Slate and Kate Brook Slate has long been obscure. *S. velifer* Zone faunas are typically composed of palmatolepids and nodocostate polygnathids suggestive of an outer-shelf environment in which some faunal mixing of shallow-water species is indicated in lithologies including distal turbiditic sandstones. In certain carbonate turbidites in the Delabole Slates a more proximal position is implied, with faunas concurring with the polygnathid–icriodid biofacies of Dreesen and Thorez (1980). However, the original spatial relationships of these slate formations remains unclear.

4.8 APPENDIX

(a) Previously recorded Lower Devonian localities in Great Britain

1. Great Perhaver Beach, South Cornwall (SX 01614229). Lower Devonian (Gedinnian) (Sadler, 1973a).
2. Cliff section, Pardoe Cove, South Cornwall (SW 91463765). Lower Devonian (Gedinnian); *I. woschmidti postwoschmidti* Zone (Sadler, 1973a).
3. Cliff section, south side of Mallets Cove 3, South Cornwall (SW 91513748). Lower Devonian (Gedinnian–Siegennian) *I. huddlei curvicauda–rectangularis* s.1., *angustoides* Zone (Sadler, 1973a).
4. Catasuent Cove, South Cornwall (SW 9765-4083). Lower Devonian (Siegennian) (Sadler, 1973a).
5. Cliff section, Malmanare Cove, South Cornwall, south side (SW 91503744) and north side (SW 91493745). Lower Devonian (Siegennian); *I. h. curvicauda–rectangularis* s.1. *angustoides* Zone (Sadler, 1973a).
6. Manare Head, South Cornwall (SW 93613895). Lower Devonian (Siegennian–Emsian) (Sadler, 1973a).
7. Kiberick Cove, South Cornwall (SW 92613800). Lower Devonian (Siegennian–Emsian) (Sadler, 1973a); Hendriks *et al.* (1971).
8. E of Catasuent Cove, South Cornwall (SW 97664080). Lower Devonian (Emsian) (Sadler 1973a).
9. Mallets Cove 1, South Cornwall, south side (SW 91503759). Lower Devonian (Emsian), *I. bilatericrescens–steinhornensis–Polygnathus* Zone (Sadler 1973a).
10. Mallets Cove 2, South Cornwall, north side (SW 91503756). Lower Devonian (Emsian); *I. b. bilatericrescens–steinhornensis–Polygnathus* Zone (Sadler, 1973a).
11. Mallets Cove 3, South Cornwall, north side (SW 91513751). Lower Devonian (Emsian); *I. b. bilatericrescens–steinhornensis–Polygnathus* Zone (Sadler, 1973a).
12. Mallets Cove 2, South Cornwall, south side (SW 91513751). Lower Devonian (Emsian); *I. b. bilatericrescens–steinhornensis–Polygnathus* Zone (Sadler, 1973a).
13. South end of the Jacka, South Cornwall (SW 93653914). Lower Devonian (Lower Emsian) (Sadler, 1973a).
14. Cliff section, Malmanare Cove, South Cornwall (SW 91493745). Lower Devonian (Mid-Emsian). *I. bilatericrescens–steinhornensis–Polygnathus* Zone (Sadler, 1973a).
15. Battery Point, South Cornwall (SW 97174108). Lower Devonian (Mid-Emsian) (Sadler, 1973a).
16. Porthluney Cove, South Cornwall (SW 9757-4104). Lower Devonian (Emsian) (Sadler, 1973a).

17. Parc Caragloose Cove, South Cornwall (SW 92903838). Lower Devonian (Mid-Emsian); *I. bilatericrescens* Zone (Sadler, 1973a).

(b) Previously recorded Middle Devonian conodont localities in Great Britain

1. Veryan Bay, South Cornwall (SW 98844061). Middle Devonian (Eifelian) (Sadler, 1973a).
2. North east side of Portloe Cove, Veryan Bay, South Cornwall. Middle Devonian (Eifelian) (Hendriks *et al.,* 1971).
3. Veryan Green (SW 92174031), Polgrain (SW 958424) and Pabyer Point (SW 02154264), South Cornwall. Middle Devonian (Eifelian) (Sadler, 1973a).
4. Kiberick Cove, Veryan Bay, South Cornwall. Middle Devonian (Emsian) (Hendriks *et al.,* 1971).
5. Foreshore of Gerrans Bay between Pendower Beach (SW 89843814) and Gidley Well (SW 90893814), South Cornwall. Middle Devonian (Eifelian); *'Sp.' bidentatus* and *kockelianus* zones (Sadler, 1973a); Hendriks *et al.,* 1971).
6. Dunstone Point, Plymouth, Devon (SX 48855261). Middle Devonian (Eifelian); *corniger* Zone (fauna 1, Orchard, 1978a).
7. Richmond Walk, Plymouth, Devon (SX 45915408). Middle Devonian (Eifelian); *bidentatus* Zone (fauna 2, Orchard 1978a).
8. Faraday Road, N of Cattedown, Plymouth, Devon (SX 49775422). Middle Devonian, mid-late Eifelian (fauna 3, Orchard, 1978a).
9. Faraday Road (SX 49775422), Laira Bridge (SX 50015430) and Drakes's Island (SX 46705296; SX 46735291), Plymouth, Devon. Middle Devonian, mid-late Eifelian (fauna 4, Orchard, 1978a).
10. Faraday Road (SX 49775422), Princerock Quarry (SX 49845417), Teats Hill Quarry (SX 48635406) and Cattewater Road (SX 4995425), Plymouth, Devon. Middle Devonian, mid-late Eifelian (fauna 4, Orchard, 1978a).
11. Paradoe Cove (SW 91573779), South Cornwall. Middle Devonian (Eifelian, or Lower Givetian) (Barnes, 1983). Now Lower Devonian.
12. Porthluney Cove (SW 97594106), South Cornwall. Middle Devonian (Eifelian, or Lower Givetian) (Barnes, 1983). Now Lower Devonian.
13. Princerock Quarry (SX 49845417), Cattedown Quarry (SX 4995425), Gasworks Quarry (SX 49295389). Teats Hill Quarry (SX 48585402) and foreshore of Drake's Island (SX 46855292) and Neal Point (SX 43556122), Plymouth, Devon. Middle Devonian (Givetian); *obliquimarginatus* Zone (fauna 6, Orchard, 1978a).
14. Approximately 50 yards N of Neal (Nail) Point, on the Cornwall bank of the River Tamar (SX 437614). Middle Devonian (probably middle Givetian);? *I. obliquimarginatus* Zone (Matthews, 1962).
15. Richmond Walk Plymouth, Devon (SX 46085441). Middle Devonian (Givetian); Lower *varcus* Subzone (fauna 7, Orchard, 1978a).
16. Richmond Walk (SX 46085441), Mutton Cove (SX 45305401), Deadman's Bay, Coxside (SX 48785383), West Hoe (SX 47675380) and Botus Fleming (SX 40966115), Plymouth, Devon. Middle Devonian (Givetian); Middle *varcus* Subzone (fauna 8, Orchard, 1978a).
17. Cliff section at Trevone Bay, North Cornwall (SW 890760). Middle Devonian (Givetian); *varcus* Zone (Kirchgasser, 1970; Mouravieff, 1977).
18. Foreshore section at Rock, North Cornwall (SW 935755). Middle Devonian (Givetian); *varcus* Zone (Kirchgasser, 1970).
19. Lummaton Quarry, Torquay, Devon (SX 914665). Middle Devonian (Givetian); *varcus* Zone (Matthews, 1970).
20. Old Woods Pit, Torquay, Devon (SX 904658). Middle Devonian (? Upper Givetian) (Dineley and Rhodes, 1956).
21. Broad Strand, Berrynarbor, North Devon (SS 56264786). Middle Devonian (Givetian); (Orchard, 1979).
22. Between Small Mouth and Desolation Cove, Berrynarbor, North Devon (SS 56084803).

Middle Devonian (Givetian) (Orchard, 1979).

23. N. of Shale Mouth, Berrynarbor, Devon (SS 55984811). Middle Devonian (Givetian) (Orchard, 1979).

24. Mount Wise, Plymouth, Devon (SX 45555404). Middle Devonian (Givetian) Middle *varcus* Subzone (fauna 9, Orchard, 1978a).

25. West Hoe, Plymouth, Devon (SX 47445387). Middle Devonian (Frasnian); ?Lowermost *asymmetricus* Zone (fauna 10, Orchard 1978a).

26. Cliff section at Marble Cliff, North Cornwall (SW 891765). Upper Devonian (Frasnian); Upper *hermanni–cristatus* Zone, Lower *asymmetricus* Zone (Kirchgasser, 1970; Mouravieff, 1977; House *et al.*, 1978; House and Dineley, in press).

27. Barton Quarry, Torquay Holiday Village (SX 91256710). Middle–Upper Devonian (Upper Givetian–Frasnian); *varcus, hermanni–cristatus* and *asymmetricus* Zones (Castle, 1977).

28. North of Briery Cove, Berrynarbor, North Devon (SS 55894820). Middle Devonian (Givetian) (Orchard, 1979).

29. Base of cliff, White Pebble Bay, Ilfracombe, North Devon (SS 50884573). Middle Devonian (Givetian), *varcus* Zone (Orchard, 1979).

30. Mullion Island, west side. Middle Devonian (Lower 'Frasnian') (Hendriks *et al.*, 1971).

31. Devon Borehole (52 m of strata), near Newton Abbot, South Devon. Upper Devonian (? Frasnian–?Famennian) suggested by Rhodes and Dineley (1957a, 1959b) but assigned to the Middle Devonian, probably Givetian (House *et al.*, 1977).

(c) Previously recorded Upper Devonian conodont localities in Great Britain

1. Western King (SX 46065331), Eastern King Point (SX 46665347) and Radford Quarry (SX 50525300), Plymouth, Devon. Upper Devonian (Frasnian); Lower *asymmetricus* Zone (fauna 11, Orchard, 1978a).

2. Durnford Street (SX 46395369), Barn Pool (SX 45645317) and Hooelake Quarry (SX 49575306), Plymouth, Devon. Upper Devonian (Frasnian); ?Middle *asymmetricus* Zone (fauna 12, Orchard, 1978a).

3. Western King, Plymouth, Devon (SX 4608-5329). Upper Devonian (Frasnian); *Polygnathus asymmetricus–An. triangularis* Zone; (fauna 13, Orchard 1978a).

4. Radford Quarry (SX 50485315), Durnford Street (SX 46385362) and Fisons Quarry, Cattedown (SX 49315377), Plymouth, Devon. Upper Devonian (Frasnian); *An. triangularis* Zone (fauna 14, Orchard, 1978a).

5. Ransleigh (Ransley) Quarry, East Ogwell, Devon (SX 844702). Upper Devonian (Lower Frasnian) (Dineley and Rhodes, 1956).

6. Holmans Wood near Chudleigh, Devon (SX 879809). Upper Devonian (Lower Frasnian) (Dineley and Rhodes, 1956).

7. Old Quarry, Lower Dunscombe Farm (SX 886791). Upper Devonian (Frasnian); Middle *asymmetricus* to Lowermost *gigas* Zone (Tucker and Straaten, 1970a; Rhodes *et al.*, 1973. Dineley and Rhodes, 1956).

8. Kiln Wood Quarry, Chudleigh, Devon (SX 861779). Upper Devonian (Frasnian– Famennian); Upper *asymmetricus* Zone– *crepida* Zone (Tucker and Straaten, 1970a).

9. Outcrops above Palace Quarry in the Riding Parks, Chudleigh, Devon (SX 869787). Upper Devonian (Famennian); *crepida* Zone (Tucker and Straaten, 1970a).

10. Western King, Plymouth, Devon (SX 4614-5326). Upper Devonian (Famennian); *Pa. triangularis* Zone (fauna 15, Orchard, 1978a).

11. Kiln Wood, road section, Chudleigh, Devon. Upper Devonian (Famennian); *crepida–* Lower *marginifera* Zones (Tucker and Straaten, 1970a). 12.

12. Radford Quarry, Plymouth, Devon (SX 50405314). Upper Devonian (Famennian); *?crepida* Zone (Orchard, 1978a).

13. Winston Cottages section, Chudleigh, Devon. Upper Devonian (Famennian), *styriacus* Zone (Tucker and Straaten, 1970a).

14. Institute of Geological Sciences Borehole at Rydon Ball Farm, Newton Abbot. Upper Devonian (Famennian); *marginifera* and *velifer* Zones (Riddolls, 1970a).

15. Foreshore, Saunton, North Devon (SS 445388). Upper Devonian (Famennian) (Dineley and Rhodes, 1956).

16. Fremington Pill, Croyde Bay, North Devon. Upper Devonian; *costatus* Zone (Rhodes *et. al.*, 1973; Austin *et al.*, 1970).

17. Landlake Quarry, North Cornwall (SX 3285-8234). Upper Devonian; Lower *velifer* Zone (Stewart, 1981a).

18. Landlake Mill Quarry, North Cornwall (SX 32838235). Upper Devonian; Upper *marginifera* Zone to Lower *velifer* Zone (Stewart, 1981a).

19. Trenault Limestone Mines, North Cornwall (SX 26258292). Upper Devonian; Lower *velifer*—Upper *costatus* Zones (Stewart, 1981a).

20. Petherwin Water Quarry, North Cornwall (SX 31468251). Upper Devonian; *velifer* Zone (Stewart, 1981a).

21. Landerslake Quarry, North Cornwall (SX 26658110). Upper Devonian; Upper *velifer*—Lower *styriacus* Zones; Stewart (1981a).

22. North face, West Petherwin Quarry North Cornwall (SX 30578231). Upper Devonian *marginifera*—*velifer* Zones. South face reworked *marginifera*—*costatus* Zones (Stewart, 1981a).

23. Strayerpark Plantation, North Cornwall (SX 26518121) and a nearby roadside cutting (SX 26688130). Upper Devonian; Lower—Middle *costatus* Zone (Stewart, 1981a).

24. Overwood Farm, North Cornwall (SX 3025-8722). Upper Devonian; Middle—Upper *costatus* Zone (Stewart, 1981a).

25. Penfoot, North Cornwall (SX 30168324).

Upper Devonian; Upper *costatus* Zone (Stewart, 1981a).

26. Treguddick Mill Quarry, North Cornwall (SX 27578142). Upper Devonian; Upper *costatus* Zone (Stewart, 1981a).

27. Strayerpark main Quarry, North Cornwall (SX 26548103), Tredorn Slates. Upper Devonian; Upper *marginifera* Zone (Stewart, 1981a).

28. Blackhill Quarry, North Cornwall (SX 2963-8180). Upper Devonian; *costatus* Zone (Stewart, 1981a).

29. Outcrop, W of Callington, Cornwall (SX 32416785) Upper Devonian; *costatus* Zone (Stewart, 1981a).

30. Tavistock Railway Cutting, Tavistock, Devon (SX 47407432). Upper Devonian, *costatus* Zone (Stewart, 1981a).

31. Trebarwith Strand, S of Tintagel, Cornwall, (SX 05088729 and SX 05098730). Upper Devonian; *Sc. velifer* Zone (Stewart, 1981a).

32. Infilled type locality Cephalopod Limestone, North Cornwall (SX 32868229). Upper Devonian *styriacus* or Lower *costatus* Zones (Stewart, 1981a).

33. Two boreholes near Chillaton (SX 44148190 and SX 44148193). Upper Devonian (*costatus* Zone)—Lower Carboniferous (Selwood *et al.*, 1982).

34. Viverdon Down Quarry, Cornwall (37646754). Upper Devonian; Upper *styriacus*—Lower *costatus* Zone (Whiteley, 1981).

35. Borehole, Steeple Aston (SP 46872586), S of Banbury, Oxfordshire. Upper Devonian (Frasnian—Famennian) (Poole, 1977).

Pl. 4.1]   **Conodonts of the Devonian System from Great Britain**   135

On this and following plates, except where indicated, all illustrated material represents the pectiniform element of the conodont apparatus.

PLATE 4.1

Icriodus woschmidti postwoschmidti Mashkova 1968
Plate 4.1, Fig. 1. Table 3. Diagnosis: a species of *Icriodus* with a short platform. The nodes coalesce into strong ridges that are separated by deep troughs. The three nodes which comprise each ridge remain more clearly distinguishable than in *I. woschmidti woschmidti* Ziegler but never quite fail to coalesce. A lateral process diverges from the main platform at a high angle. In the similar *I. rectangularis* group the denticles of the lateral row are distinctly larger and are separated from the median row by ridges.
Upper view, SAQ 57 K1/1, ×48. Meneage Formation, Paradoe Cove, Cornwall. *I. woschmidti* fauna (Sadler, 1973b).

Pelekysgnathus serratus elongatus Carls and Gandl 1969
Plate 4.1, Figs. 2 and 3. Table 3. Diagnosis: the element is relatively long with short rounded free denticles forming a single row of denticles. The conspicuous main cusp in the Cornish example carries a fine ridge transversely on the upper surface of the outer side.
Fig. 2, upper view; Fig. 3, lateral view, SAQ 117 K1/7, ×48. Meneage Formation, Great Perhaver Beach, Cornwall. *I. woschmidti* fauna (Sadler 1973b).

Pelekysgnathus serratus subsp. A, Carls 1969
Plate 4.1, Fig. 4. Table 3. Diagnosis: an element with five to eight spike-like, laterally compressed denticles. The main cusp is separated from the longitudinal row by a distinct notch.
Lateral view, SAQ 117 K1/7, ×48. Meneage Formation, Great Perhaver Beach, Cornwall. *I. woschmidti* fauna (Sadler, 1973b).

Icriodus huddlei curvicauda Carls and Gandl 1969
Plate 4.1, Fig. 5. Table 3. Diagnosis: a subspecies of *Icriodus* with a lateral process arising from the posterior end of the main denticle row. The process is produced as a gradual outward curvature. The platform is narrow and parallel sided. The outer denticles are slightly larger than those of the central row. Individual denticles are linked by a longitudinal ridge. Successive transverse triplets of denticles tend to be distinctly spaced.
Upper view, SAQ 105 K1/1, ×48. Meneage Formation, Catasuent Cove, Cornwall. *I. huddlei* fauna (Sadler, 1973b).

Icriodus huddlei huddlei Klapper and Ziegler 1967
Plate 4.1, Fig. 6. Table 3. Diagnosis: a subspecies of *Icriodus* similar to *I. huddlei curvicauda* but with a lateral process, which is produced as a sharp deflection of the posterior part of the median row of denticles.
Upper view, SAQ 61 K2/1, ×48. Meneage Formation, Mallet's Cove, Cornwall. *I. bilatericrescens* fauna (Sadler 1973b).

Caudicriodus huddlei? celtibericus (Carls and Gandl 1969)
Plate 4.1, Fig. 7. Table 3. Diagnosis: a subspecies of *Icriodus* with two strong cusps at the posterior end of the median denticle row. A simple almost straight deflected denticulate lateral process and a spur on the inner side of the basal cavity. The spur is the diagnostic feature for Cornish specimens.
Upper view, SAQ 61 K2/2, ×48. Meneage Formation, Mallet's Cove, Cornwall. *I. bilatericrescens* fauna (Sadler, 1973b).

Icriodus bilatericrescens bilatericrescens Ziegler 1956
Plate 4.1, Fig. 8. Table 3. Diagnosis: a subspecies of *Icriodus* with two lateral processes, an outer one directed posteriorly and an inner one directed anteriorly from a point slightly forward. The processes, so directed lie at 180° to one another and at 45° to the main axis. The inner process may be a simple spur which usually carries a thin rib. Some elements have a line of nodes on the inner process. The outer process always has at least one row of nodes. In many elements the outer process bears two and three rows of nodes, more or less coalesced into transverse ridges. The wall of the basal cavity (the skirt) between the outer process and the main platform may be extensive. The main platform is widest at midlength or posterior to midlength. The denticles are almost exactly alinged in parallel transverse rows. The outer and inner denticles are linked by short ridges. Little space is available between the transverse rows.
Upper view, SAQ 82 K3/5, ×48. Meneage Formation, Parc Caragloose Cove, Cornwall. *I. bilatericrescens* fauna (Sadler, 1973b).

Icriodus aff. *I. angustus* Stewart and Sweet 1956
Plate 4.1, Fig. 9. Table 3. Diagnosis: an *Icriodus* with a short weakly curved spindle-shaped platform. The denticles are small, of uniform height and arranged in 3 relatively widely spaced longitudinal rows. There is a retreat of the lateral denticles away from the anterior end
Upper view, SAQ 46 K2/2, ×48. Meneage Formation. Veryan Green, Cornwall (Sadler 1973b).
Remarks: The illustrated specimen is of Middle Devonian age.

Icriodus bilatericrescens multicostatus Carls and Gandl 1969
Plate 4.1, Fig. 10. Table 3. Diagnosis: a subspecies similar to *I. b. bilatericrescens* in that it has an outer and an inner process. The ornamentation differs since the outer nodes of the main process fuse with the transverse ridges to produce tear-shaped ribs.
Upper view, SAQ 82 K3/3, ×48. Meneage Formation, Parc Caragloose Cove, Cornwall. *I. bilatericrescens* fauna (Sadler, 1973b).

Icriodus bilatericrescens aff. *multicostatus* Carls and Gandl 1969
Plate 4.1, Fig. 11. Table 3. Diagnosis: this subspecies is identical with *I. b. multicostatus* but with a third lateral process.
Upper view, SAQ 82 K3/6, ×48. Meneage Formation, Parc Caragloose Cove, Cornwall. *I. bilatericrescens* fauna (Sadler, 1973b).

Icriodus bilatericrescens? beckmanni Ziegler 1965
Plate 4.1, Fig. 12. Table 3. Diagnosis: a subspecies with the same denticulation of the main process as *I. b. bilatericrescens*, but with a third lateral process. This additional process may be a smooth spur or may bear nodes and transverse ridges.
Upper view, SAQ 82 K3/4, ×48. Meneage Formation, Parc Caragloose Cove, Cornwall. *I. bilatericrescens* fauna (Sadler, 1973b). Specimen is broken.

Icriodus sigmoidalis Carls and Gandl 1969
Plate 4.1, Fig. 13. Table 3. Diagnosis: a distinctive subspecies. The lateral denticle rows comprise transverse ribs and the median row shows a sigmoidal curvature, which is pronounced towards the posterior and has the appearance of an outer lateral process.
Upper view, SAQ 75 K1/1, ×48. Meneage Formation, Kiberick Cove, Cornwall. *I. bilatericrescens* fauna (Sadler, 1973b).

Polygnathus dehiscens Philip and Jackson 1967
Plate 4.1, Fig. 14. Table 3. Diagnosis: an element with a long, almost parallel-sided platform which is curved posterior of midlength. The carina continues to the posterior end as a line of small nodes. There is a characteristic long large basal cavity that occupies most of the underside of the platform. This latter feature distinguishes this species from the *P. costatus* group.
Upper view, SAQ 92 K1/2, ×48. Meneage Formation, near Portloe, Cornwall. *I. bilatericrescens* fauna (Sadler, 1973b).

Pandorinellina steinhornensis steinhornensis (Ziegler 1956)
Plate 4.1, Fig. 15. Table 3. Diagnosis: a straight element with a characteristic large asymmetrical basal cavity situated posterior of midlength.
Upper view, SAQ 99 K1/3, ×48. Meneage Formation, Battery Point, Cornwall. *Spathognathodus* fauna (Sadler, 1973b).

Pandorinellina optimus (Moskalenko 1966)
Plate 4.1, Fig. 16. Table 3. Diagnosis: the basal cavity is symmetrically rounded and centrally, or somewhat anteriorly situated. The characteristic feature is the offset of the blade to the right in the anterior third, as seen in upper view.
Upper view, SAQ 98 K1/2, ×48. Meneage Formation, Battery Point, Cornwall. *Spathognathodus* fauna (Sadler, 1973b).

Pandorinellina steinhornensis aff. *repetitor* Carls and Gandl 1969
Plate 4.1, Fig. 17. Table 3. Diagnosis: a subspecies with a high blade, with fused laterally compressed denticles. The basal cavity is small and asymmetrical.
Upper view, SAQ 86 K1/1, ×48. Meneage Formation, Portloe, Cornwall. *Spathognathodus* fauna (Sadler, 1973b).

Pl. 4.1]   Conodonts of the Devonian System from Great Britain   137

Plate 4.1

PLATE 4.2

Icriodus retrodepressus Bultynck 1970
Plate 4.2, Fig. 1. Table 4. Diagnosis: a lachrymiform to triangular species with the outer posterio-lateral denticles strongly developed on one side of a median depression. The cusp is large and prominent, and there is a spur on the lower inner margin.
Upper view, TP.28/I2, ×65. C. Castle collection. Daddyhole Limestone, Torquay Limestone Group, Triangle Point, Torquay.

Polygnathus costatus costatus Klapper 1971
Plate 4.2, Figs. 2 and 3. Table 4. Diagnosis: the anterior third of the platform is constricted, and the medial third expands gradually, particularly on the outer side, up to the point of maximum width, which is just in front of the posterior third. The upper surface of the platform is ornamented by closely spaced transverse ridges.
Lower and upper views, SAQ 21 K2/1, ×50. P. M. Sadler collection. Veryan Limestone Unit, Gramscatho Grits, Carne Beach, Gerrans Bay (SW 90733822).

Polygnathus trigonicus Bischoff and Ziegler 1957
Plate 4.2, Figs. 4 and 5. Table 4. Diagnosis: the platform is flat, triangular in outline and bears discrete nodes that are anteriorly aligned into two diagonal rows that converge toward the carina. The pit lies at, or near the anterior end of the platform.
Upper and lower views, SAQ 40 K2/1, ×50 P. M. Sadler collection. Veryan Limestone Unit, Gramscatho Grits, Gidley Well, Gerrans Bay (SW 9085038151).

Polygnathus eiflius Bischoff and Ziegler 1957
Plate 4.2, Fig. 6. Table 4. Diagnosis: a species characterized by a strongly expanded, finely nodose, flat posterior platform. The anterio platform is constricted and bears two diagonal rostral ridges.
Upper view, SAQ 39 Ks/2, ×60. P. M. Sadler collection. Veryan Limestone Unit, Gramscatho Grits, Gidley Well, Gerrans Bay (SW 9088038150).
Remarks: the free blade is missing in this specimen.

Icriodus corniger corniger Wittekindt 1966
Plate 4.2, Fig. 7. Table 4. Diagnosis: a distinctive inner spur and a posterior antispur is characteristic of the lower surface. The upper surface has five to seven rows of denticles that in the posterior part are connected by transverse ridges. Median row denticles are lacking in the anterior part.
Upper view, SM H10083, ×47. M. J. Orchard collection. Jennycliff Slates–Plymouth Limestone transition beds, sample MB23, Dunstone Point, Plymouth.
Remarks: this is a relatively early growth stage. The anterior tip is missing. Copy of Orchard (1978a, plate 107, Fig. 6).

Polygnathus linguiformis bultyncki Weddige 1977
Plate 4.2, Figs. 8 and 9. Table 4. Diagnosis: the anterior platform margins are parallel, upturned and of equal height. Posteriorly, the platform flattens out and is deflected inwards and downwards with neither a sharp deflection nor a lateral expansion on the outer side. The tongue is ornamented with continuous transverse ridges. The pit is small and symmetrical and lies beneath the anterior third of the platform.
Oblique-lateral and upper views, SAQ 21 K2/9, ×55. P. M. Sadler collection. Veryan Limestone Unit, Gramscatho Grits, Carne Beach, Gerrans Bay (SW 90733822).
Remarks: the anterior blade is broken in this specimen.

Polygnathus angustipennatus Bischoff and Ziegler 1957
Plate 4.2, Fig. 10. Table 4. Diagnosis: a species with a high carina that extends three to five denticles posteriorly beyond the small platform, the margins of which are parallel, upturned and denticulate and enclose deep adcarinal grooves.
Upper view, SAQ 40 K2/4, ×50. P. M. Sadler collection. Veryan Limestone Unit, Gramscatho Grits, Gidley Well, Gerrans Bay (SW 9085038151).

Ozarkodina bidentata (Bischoff and Ziegler 1957)
Plate 4.2, Fig. 11. Table 4. Diagnosis: the subquadrate carminate element has a medial, broadly expanded, subsymmetrical basal cup that typically narrows markedly posteriorwards. The posterior denticles are few and broad, and those anterior to the cavity are more numerous and narrow.
Upper view, SM H10116, ×95. M. J. Orchard collection. Plymouth Limestone, sample TH44/3, Teats Hill Quarry, Plymouth.
Remarks: this specimen is sinuous because of deformation. Copy of Orchard (1978a, Plate 108, Fig. 31).

Pl. 4.2]
Conodonts of the Devonian System from Great Britain
139

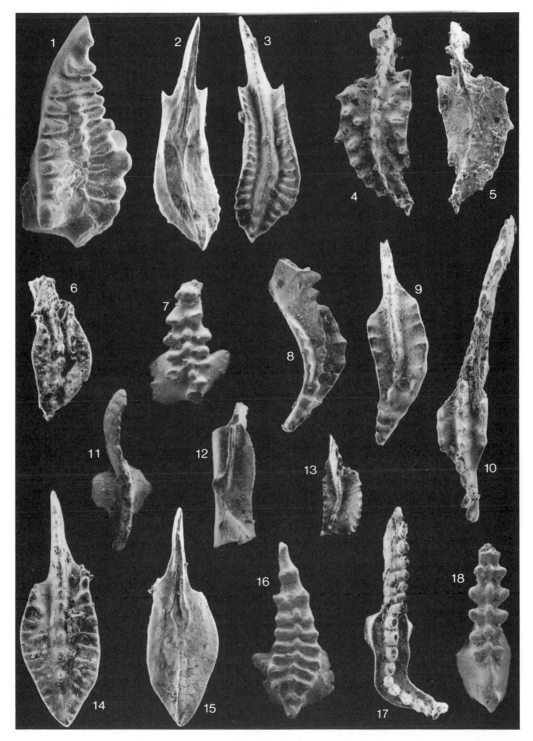

Plate 4.2

Polygnathus serotinus Telford 1975
Plate 4.2, Figs. 12 and 13. Table 4. Diagnosis: a linguiform polygnathid with a distinctive asymmetric pit with a semi-circular shelf-like protuberance on its outer side immediately anterior of the inward bend of the keel. The outer anterior platform margin is higher than both the carina and the inner margin, and posteriorly it turns inwards at right angles.
Fig. 12, lower views, SAQ 21 K2/8, ×60; SAQ 21 K2/2, ×65. P. M. Sadler collection. Veryan Limestone Unit, Gramscatho Grits, Carne Beach, Gerrans Bay (SW 90733822).
Remarks: the larger specimen is broken posteriorly; the smaller is an early growth stage.

Polygnathus robusticostatus Bischoff and Ziegler 1957
Plate 4.2, Figs. 14. and 15. Table 4. Diagnosis: the heart-shaped platform is widest at midlength and has a straight axis. The upper surface bears transverse ridges that may be continuous or broken. The lower surface has an anteriorly situated pit with prominent rims. The free blade is about one-third unit length.
Upper and lower views, SAQ 46 K2/3, ×50. P. M. Sadler collection. Veryan Limestone Unit, Gramscatho Grits, Veryan Green (SW 92174036).
Remarks: this specimen is atypical in having a poorly developed posterior carina.

Icriodus struvei Weddige 1977
Plate 4.2, Fig. 16. Table 4. Diagnosis: a lachrymiform species with five to seven rows of subalternating discrete denticles, a prominent cusp and a posteriorly rounded basal margin with a distinct inner spur. The lateral denticles are elongate and vary in orientation from transverse in the anterior to oblique at the posterior. The median denticles pass from round to longitudinally elongate toward the anterior.
Upper view, SM H10440, ×50. M. J. Orchard collection. Plymouth Limestone, sample 47, Teats Hill Quarry, Coxside, Plymouth.

Tortodus kockelianus kockelianus (Bischoff and Ziegler 1957)
Plate 4.2, Fig. 17. Table 4. Diagnosis: the unit is twisted inwards posteriorly so as to turn the carina outwards. A narrow platform is developed above the large asymmetric basal cavity and posterior of it. Platform margins are raised and smooth and enclose relatively low and discrete carina denticles, which contrast with the larger closer-set blade denticles.
Upper view, SAQ 39 K3/6, ×60. P. M. Sadler collection. Veryan Limestone Unit, Gramscatho Grits, Gidley Well, Gerrans Bay (SW 9088038150).

Icriodus regularicrescens Bultynck 1970
Plate 4.2, Fig. 18. Table 4. Diagnosis: a slender species in which the lateral denticles in the posterior half of the unit increase in size in an anterior direction. Two or three median denticles extend posteriorly beyond those of the lateral rows, becoming higher and terminating in an erect posterior border.
Upper view, SM H10441, ×70. M. J. Orchard collection. Rodhuish Limestone, Ilfracombe Beds, NNE of Hill Farm, S of Withycombe (ST 015408).

PLATE 4.3

Polygnathus linguiformis ssp. b, Weddige 1977
Plate 4.3, Fig. 1. Table 4. Diagnosis: a small linguiform polygnathid with strongly serrated platform margins separated from the carina by relatively wide and deep adcarinal troughs. The small tongue bears strong transverse ridges. The basal pit is relatively large.
Oblique-posterior, upper view, SM H10244, ×57. M. J. Orchard collection. Plymouth Limestone, sample GW20, Gasworks Quarry, Cattedown, Plymouth.
Remarks: Copy of Orchard (1978a, Plate 113, Fig. 29).

Pl. 4.3]   Conodonts of the Devonian System from Great Britain   141

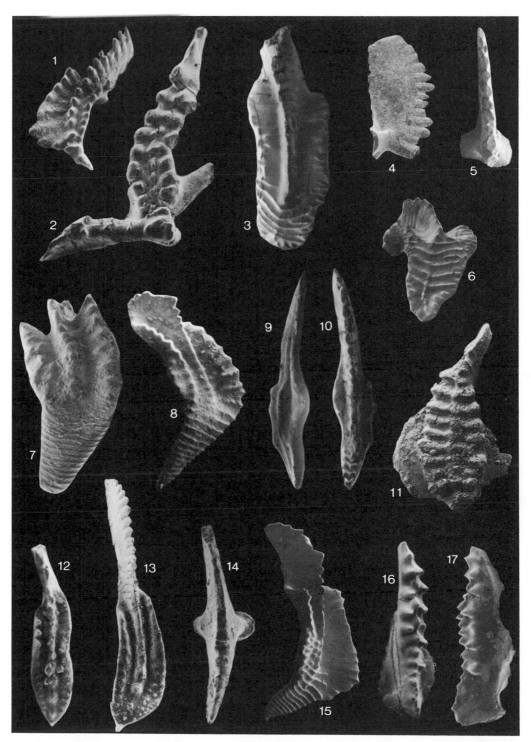

Plate 4.3

Icriodus latericrescens latericrescens Branson and Mehl 1938
Plate 4.3, Fig. 2. Table 4. Diagnosis: an outer lateral process is developed anterior of the posterior tip. The median denticles in the posterior platform are suppressed and lie in an elongate trough. Lateral denticles are discrete and rounded.
Upper view, SM H10442, ×50. M. J. Orchard collection. Plymouth Limestone, sample RW11, Richmond Walk, Plymouth.

Tortodus? n. sp. A
Plate 4.3, Figs. 3, 6, 9 and 10. Table 4. Diagnosis: the platform element has a high carina and an elongate flat platform, the posterior part of which is linguiform and bears transverse ridges. The high carina terminates abruptly in front of the tongue although it may continue as a faint ridge. The anterior platform is very narrow in early growth stages but broadens and develops nodes and ridges later. There is a relatively large thick-lipped basal cavity, which occupies much of the lower surface in small growth stages.
Figs. 3 and 6, upper and posterior views, SM H10159, ×26; Figs. 9 and 10, lower and upper views, SM H10160, ×27. M. J. Orchard collection. Plymouth Limestone. Figs. 3 and 6, sample GW20. Gasworks Quarry, Cattedown; Figs. 9 and 10, Princerock Quarry, Plymouth.
Remarks: the blade is broken anteriorly in the larger specimen. This species has formerly been confused with *T. variabilis* but differs in possessing a tongue. It differs from *Polygnathus linguiformis* in its lower surface morphology. Copy of Orchard (1978a, Plate 110, Figs. 5, 6, 15 and 16).

Ozarkodina brevis (Bischoff and Ziegler 1957)
Plate 4.3, Figs. 4 and 5. Table 4. Diagnosis: a very short subquadrate carminate element with a prominent posteriormost denticle, beneath which lies a subrectangular basal cavity.
Fig. 4, upper view, SM H10443, ×60; Fig. 5, oblique-lateral view, SM H10111, ×70,; Fig. 4, Lummaton Shell Bed, Barton Limestone, Lummaton Quarry, Torquay; Fig. 5, unnamed limestone—argillite, Botus Fleming, East Cornwall. Both M. J. Orchard collection.
Remarks: Fig. 5 is copy of Orchard (1978a, Plate 108, Fig. 27).

Polygnathus linguiformis klapperi Clausen, Leuteritz and Ziegler 1979
Plate 4.3, Figs. 7 and 8. Table 4. Diagnosis: a subspecies in which strong transverse ridges are developed both on the relatively low anterior platform margins and on the well-differentiated tongue, the two parts of which are united in a sharply rounded curve. Rostral ridges may be developed parallel to the carina on the anterior platform. The basal pit is small and symmetrical.
Fig. 7, upper view, SM H10164, ×27; Fig. 8, oblique-lateral view, SM H10165, ×31. Both M. J. Orchard collection. Fig. 7, sample RW28. Richmond Walk, Plymouth; Fig. 8, sample MC32, Mutton Cove, Plymouth. Plymouth Limestone.
Remarks: the free blade is missing in Fig. 7. Copy of Orchard (1978a, Plate 110, Figs. 14 and 30).

Icriodus arkonensis Stauffer 1938
Plate 4.3, Fig. 11. Table 4. Diagnosis: the platform is biconvex to lachrymiform and bears transversely expanded lateral denticles that are usually joined to the small median denticles, which are themselves connected by a longitudinal ridge.
Upper view, PF 9/I1, ×62. C. Castle collection, Daddyhole Limestone, Torquay Limestone Group, Parkfield Road, Torquay.
Remarks: the anterior part of this specimen is deformed.

Polygnathus xylus ensensis Ziegler, Klapper and Johnson, 1976
Plate 4.3, Fig. 12. Table 4. Diagnosis: a lanceolate, posteriorly down-arched species in which the relatively narrow anterior platform is characterized by serrated rostral ridges. The posterior platform is broader and bears fine nodes.
Upper view, SM H10103, ×53. M. J. Orchard collection. Plymouth Limestone, sample TH44/1, Teats Hill Quarry, Coxside, Plymouth.
Remarks: the free blade is missing in this specimen. Copy of Orchard (1978a, Plate 108, Fig. 2).

Polygnathus pseudofoliatus Wittekindt 1966
Plate 4.3, Fig. 13. Table 4. Diagnosis: the platform margins are anteriorly constricted and enclose narrow deep adcarinal grooves which shallow posteriorly where the platform is broader, flatter and commonly ornamented with nodes.
Upper view, SM H10444, ×53. M. J. Orchard collection. Plymouth Limestone, sample PS02, Princerock Quarry, Plymouth.

Eognathodus bipennatus (Bischoff and Ziegler 1957)
Plate 4.3, Fig. 14. Table 4. Diagnosis: the carminate element has a narrow basal expansion restricted to the approximate midlength of the unit, above which the broad carina has a medial groove. The posterior carina nodes are laterally enlarged. The variable character of the anterior blade leads to subspecies differentiation.
Upper view, TP 12/E1, ×66. C. Castle collection. Daddyhole Limestone, Torquay Limestone Group, Triangle Point, Torquay.
Remarks: the anterior blade is broken in this specimen.

Pl. 4.3]   **Conodonts of the Devonian System from Great Britain**   143

Polygnathus linguiformis linguiformis Hinde 1879
Plate 4.3, Fig. 15. Table 4. Diagnosis: a linguiform polygnathid with the anterior platform margins strongly upturned, particularly on the outer side, which is posteriorly deflected downwards and inwards, often with a lateral expansion. The posterior tongue is covered with continuous transverse ridges, and the anteriorly situated pit is small and symmetrical. Oblique-lateral view, SM H10263, ×23. M. J. Orchard collection. Plymouth Limestone, Mount Wise, Plymouth.
Remarks: Copy of Orchard (1978a, Plate 114, Fig. 24).

Icriodus obliquimarginatus Bischoff and Ziegler 1957
Plate 4.3, Figs. 16 and 17. Table 4. Diagnosis: a spender species in which the denticulation is characteristically irregular: lateral denticles are often unpaired and additional nodes may be present in the median row. The posterior blade is composed of at least four denticles that typically have an arcuate profile and a reclined posterior border.
Upper and lateral views, SM H10087, ×42, M. J. Orchard collection. Plymouth Limestone, sample PS4, Princerock Quarry, Plymouth.
Remarks: Copy of Orchard (1978a, Plate 107, Figs. 13 and 14).

PLATE 4.4

Polygnathus tuberculatus Hinde 1879
Plate 4.4, Fig. 1. Table 4. Diagnosis: a large species with a massive, coarsely ornamented, oval platform, the posterior part of which is deflected inward. Rostral ridges, transverse ridges and large nodes cover the upper surface. A thick-lipped pit passes anteriorly under the blade as an equally broad furrow.
Upper view, SM H10230, ×22. M. J. Orchard collection. Plymouth Limestone, Mount Wise, Plymouth.
Remarks: Copy of Orchard (1978a, Plate 113, Fig. 1).

Polygnathus ansatus Ziegler, Klapper and Johnson, 1976
Plate 4.4, Fig. 2. Table 4. Diagnosis: a lanceolate polygnathid with a long free blade and a variably ornamented platform that has a pronounced constriction at the geniculation point on the outer side and bowed anterior trough margins. The geniculation points and anterior platform margins are generally opposite.
Upper view, SM H10445, ×52. M. J. Orchard collection. Plymouth Limestone, Mount Wise, Plymouth.

Polygnathus timorensis Klapper, Philip and Jackson, 1970
Plate 4.4, Fig. 3. Table 4. Diagnosis: a lanceolate polygnathid with a long free blade and an elongate, relatively narrow platform in which the outer trough margin meets the blade further anteriorward than the inner margin. The genicula-tion points are generally not opposite.
Upper view, SM H10446, ×50. M. J. Orchard collection. Plymouth Limestone, sample RW12, Richmond Walk, Plymouth.
Remarks: This species is narrower than *P. ansatus* but is connected to it by transitional specimens.

Polygnathus varcus Stauffer 1940
Plate 4.4, Fig. 4. Table 4. Diagnosis: a lanceolate polygnathid with a short symmetrical platform and a long free blade equal to about two-thirds of the unit length. The anterior platform margins and the geniculation points are opposite and the posterior platform is unornamented.
Upper view, SM H10154, ×32. M. J. Orchard collection. Plymouth Limestone, Mount Wise, Plymouth.
Remarks: Copy of Orchard (1978a, Plate 109, Fig. 29).

Polygnathus linguiformis weddigei Clausen, Leuteritz and Ziegler 1979
Plate 4.4, Figs. 5 and 6. Table 4. a subspecies in which the anterior platform is relatively flat and the outer margin curves inwards and downwards in a regular convex curve. Transverse ridges are radially arranged on the outer platform and weakly developed on the posterior platform, where they may be interrupted by the carina. The pit is small and symmetrical.
Fig. 5, upper view, SM H10171, ×55; Fig. 6, oblique-lateral view, SM H10447, ×42. sample BF3, unnamed limestone–argillite, Botus Fleming, East Cornwall. Both M. J. Orchard collection. Fig. 7, Plymouth Limestone, sample RW11, Richmond Walk, Plymouth.
Remarks: Copy of Orchard (1978a, Plate 110, Fig. 23).

Ozarkodina semialternans (Wirth 1967)
Plate 4.4, Fig. 7. Table 4. Diagnosis: an elongate carminate element, the posterior one-third of which has broad denti-cles beneath which the lower margin of the narrowly expanded basal cavity is arched first upwards and, at the posterior end of the unit, downwards. The upper profile is of uniform height anteriorly and a convex arch posteriorly.
Lateral view, (BGS) 725 K1/11, × 65. British Geological Survey collection. Kentisbury Slates, sample K2, White Pebble Bay, Ilfracombe.
Remarks: the specimen is broken at both ends. Copy of Orchard 1979 (Plate 1, Fig. 25).

Polygnathus ovatinodosus Ziegler and Klapper 1976
Plate 4.4, Fig. 8. Table 4. Diagnosis: a polygnathis with a relatively broad flat oval-shaped platform covered in nodes and a very short anterior rostrum which encloses narrow adcarinal grooves. The platform is about equal in length to the uniformly denticulated free blade.
Upper view, SM H10448, ×45. M. J. Orchard collection. Barton Limestone, Torquay Limestone Group, Barton Quarry, Torquay.
Remarks: the free blade is broken in this specimen.

Icriodus brevis Stauffer 1940
Plate 4.4, Figs. 9 and 10. Table 4. Diagnosis: a slender species with a relatively long blade composed of three to four denticles, the posteriormost of which is large and slightly inclined. The median row denticles tend to alternate with those of the lateral rows.
Lateral and upper views, (BGS) 725 K1/5, ×80. British Geological Survey collection. Kentisbury Slates, sample K2, White Pebble Bay, Ilfracombe.
Remarks: the figured specimen is a small growth stage. Copy of Orchard (1979, Plate 1, Figs. 14 and 20).

Pl. 4.4]   Conodonts of the Devonian System from Great Britain   145

Plate 4.4

Icriodus difficilis Ziegler and Klapper 1976
Plate 4.4, Figs. 11 and 12. Table 4. Diagnosis: this species is characterized by round, closely spaced, subequal and aligned nodes, a blade composed of two to three denticles and a prominent anteriorly directed spur on the inner margin of the basal cup. The posterior median denticles tend to be higher than those of the lateral rows.
Upper and lateral views, SM H10136, ×57. M. J. Orchard collection. Unnamed limestone−argillite, sample NP15, Neal Point, East Cornwall.
Remarks: the lower margin is broken in this specimen. Copy of Orchard (1978a, Plate 109, Figs. 9 and 16).

Schmidtognathus hermanni Ziegler 1966
Plate 4.4, Figs. 13 and 14. Table 4. Diagnosis: this species has a very short free blade and a slightly asymmetric platform that is broadest at midlength. The margins are slightly elevated, are downturned at the anterior end are covered by fine irregular nodes. On the lower side there is a large, strongly asymmetric pit.
Fig. 13, upper view, SM H10449, ×33; Fig. 14, lower view, BQ 18/31, ×44. Fig. 13, M. J. Orchard collection; Fig. 14, C. Castle collection. Fig. 13, Marble Cliff Beds, sample MC10B, Marble Cliff, Trevone; Fig. 14, Barton Limestone, Torquay Limestone Group, Barton Quarry, Torquay.
Remarks: the anterior part of Fig. 14 is broken.

Schmidtognathus peracutus (Bryant 1921)
Plate 4.4, Figs. 15 and 16. Table 4. Diagnosis: a species with an elongate, arched, subtriangular platform developed unequally on the two sides of nodose carina. Rows of round nodes parallel the carina. A relatively large pit occurs near the anterior end of the platform.
Upper and lower views, BQ 11/31, ×51. C. Castle collection. Barton Limestone, Torquay Limestone Group, Barton Quarry, Torquay.

Polygnathus linguiformis mucronata Wittekindt 1966
Plate 4.4, Fig. 17. Table 4. Diagnosis: a linguiform polygnathid in which the carina is continuous to the posterior tip of the very narrow tongue, anterior of which the platform is strongly constricted. Both anterior platform margins are strongly upturned and coarsely serrate.
Oblique-lateral view, LM 11/Pol, ×50. C. Castle collection, Lummaton Shell Bed, Barton Limestone, Torquay Limestone Group, Lummaton Quarry, Torquay.

PLATE 4.5

Palmatolepis disparalvea Orr and Klapper 1968
Plate 4.5, Figs. 1 and 2. Table 4. Diagnosis: this triangular species has a large L-shaped basal cavity that extends from the posterior end of the unit anteriorly and laterally beneath the outer lobe up to about platform midlength. The carina is straight and lacks a strongly differentiated azygous node.
Upper and lower views, SM H9335, ×64. W. T. Kirchgasser collection. Marble Cliff Beds, sample 8, Marble Cliff, Trevone.
Remarks: copy of Kirchgasser (1970, Plate 63, Fig. 1).

Palmatolepis disparilis Ziegler, Klapper and Johnson, 1976
Plate 4.5, Figs. 3 and 4. Table 4. Diagnosis: the oval to triangular shaped platform has an asymmetric pit, lacks a clearly differentiated outer platform lobe and has a straight carina that generally does not extend onto the posterior platform, where a longitudinal trough may be developed.
Upper and lower views, SM H9336, ×50. W. T. Kirchgasser collection. Marble Cliff Beds, sample 8, Marble Cliff, Trevone.
Remarks: Copy of Kirchgasser (1970, Plate 63, Fig. 8).

Polygnathus cristatus Hinde 1879
Plate 4.5, Figs. 5 and 9. Table 4. Diagnosis: a species with a broad flat, slightly asymmetric platform with rows of discrete nodes arranged parallel to the carina. As conceived at present, the species has a small pit of variable symmetry.
Fig. 5, upper view, (BGS) AD802/4, ×30; Fig. 5, British Geological Survey collection; Fig. 9, W. T. Kirchgasser collection. fig. 5, Norden Slate, quarry near Broadhempston. Fig. 9, upper view, SM H9339, ×59. Marble Cliff Beds, sample 8, Marble Cliff, Trevone.
Remarks: Part copy of Kirchgasser (1970, Plate 63, Fig. 3).

Polygnathus dengleri Bischoff and Ziegler 1957
Plate 4.5, Figs. 6 and 8. Table 4. Diagnosis: this species is similar to *P. asymmetricus* but is narrower and has upturned, symmetrical and thicker platform margins, a higher carina and an elongate, more anteriorly situated pit.
Upper and lower views, SM H10455, ×50. M. J. Orchard collection. Marble Cliff Beds, bed 132 of House *et al.* (1978), Marble Cliff, Trevone.

Pl. 4.5] Conodonts of the Devonian System from Great Britain 147

Plate 4.5

Polygnathus asymmetricus asymmetricus Bischoff and Ziegler 1957
Plate 4.5, Fig. 7. Table 4. Diagnosis: the pectiniform element has a thin, arched and asymmetric oval platform with a straight inner margin and a rounded outer margin. A small subcentral pit occurs on the lower surface, eccentric with respect to the growth centre.
Upper view, SM H10450, ×49. M. J. Orchard collection. Plymouth Limestone, sample WK08, Western King, Plymouth.

Polygnathus asymmetricus ovalis Ziegler and Klapper 1964
Plate 4.5, Fig. 10. Table 4. Diagnosis: this subspecies has rounded margins on both the inner and the outer side of the platform, the surface of which bears fine to coarse nodes. The rounded pit is slightly larger than the nominate subspecies. Upper view, SM H10451, ×80. M. J. Orchard collection. Marble Cliff Beds, sample MC40B, approximates bed no. 61 of House *et al.* (1978), Marble Cliff, Trevone.

Polygnathus alatus Huddle 1934
Plate 4.5, Fig. 11. Table 4. Diagnosis: a species with an asymmetric, anteriorly constricted and smooth platform, the margins of which are upturned, particularly anteriorly on the outer side, and border deep and narrow acardinal troughs. Upper view, SM H10452, ×50. M. J. Orchard collection. Marble Cliff Beds, bed no. 132 of House *et al.* (1978), Marble Cliff, Trevone.

Schmidtognathus wittekindti Ziegler 1966
Plate 4.5, Figs. 12, 13, 15. Table 4. Diagnosis: this species has a narrow, strongly arched and pointed platform covered with coarse discrete nodes, and a high free blade with a distinctive arcuate profile.
Lower, lateral and upper views, SM H9369, ×57. W. T. Kirchgasser collection. Marble Cliff Beds, sample 12, Marble Cliff, Trevone.
Remarks: Copy of Kirchgasser (1970, Plate 65, Fig. 3).

Polygnathus pennatus Hinde 1879
Plate 4.5, Fig. 14. Table 4. Diagnosis: a polygnathid in which the upper surface of the flat platform is covered by strong sharp-edged transverse ridges. Anteriorly, the platform ends relatively abruptly. The lower surface bears a slit-like pit and a grooved keel.
Upper view, SM H10453, ×32. M. J. Orchard collection. Marble Cliff Beds, bed 132 of House *et al.* (1978), Marble Cliff, Trevone.

Polygnathus norrisi Uyeno 1967
Plate 4.5, Fig. 16. Table 4. Diagnosis: an unusual species with subparallel fluted margins and a platform that is ornamented with numerous, vertically oriented needle-like projections that may coalesce into plates arranged in a chevron pattern.
Upper view, SM H10454, ×60. M. J. Orchard collection. Marble Cliff Beds, bed 131 of House *et al.* (1978), Marble Cliff, Trevone.

PLATE 4.6

Palmatolepis subrecta Miller and Youngquist 1947
Plate 4.6, Fig. 1. Table 5. Diagnosis: a species of *Palmatolepis* with a pronounced round ended outer lobe, subcircular inner platform margin, straight anterior carina and anterior free blade bearing uniform denticles.
Upper view, AD822/2, ×30. British Geological Survey, Newton Abbot, collection. East Ogwell Limestone, Ransley Quarry (SX 84487036). Illustrated by Selwood *et al.* (1984, Plate 6, Fig. 11).

Ancryodella curvata (Branson and Mehl 1934)
Plate 4.6, Figs. 2, 3 and 7. Table 5. Diagnosis: a species of *Ancryodella* having a bilaterally asymmetric platform with a lobelike protusion on one of the posterior lobes. Secondary carinas are well developed.
Figs. 2 and 3, upper and lower views, AD 822/13, ×30; Fig. 7. upper view, large specimen, AD 822/4, ×30. B. W. Ridolls collection, East Ogwell Limestone, NE of Ransley Quarry (SX 84487036). Illustrated by Selwood *et al.* (1984, Plate 6, Fig. 1).

Pl. 4.6]   Conodonts of the Devonian System from Great Britain   149

Plate 4.6

Ancyrognathus triangularis Youngquist 1945
Plate 4.6, Figs. 4, 5 and 6. Table 5. Diagnosis: this species of *Ancyrognathus* has a broad asymmetric platform ornamented by transverse ridges normal to the carina. A pronounced lobe on the outer posterior bears a well developed
secondary carina.
Figs. 4, 5, upper and lower views, AD 822/7, ×30; Fig. 6, upper view, AD 822/15, ×30. B. W. Riddolls collection.
East Ogwell Limestone, NE of Ransley Quarry (SX 84487036). Illustrated by Selwood *et al.*, (1984, Plate 6, Figs.
6, 5 and 3).

Palmatolepis gigas Miller and Youngquist 1947
Plate 4.6, Figs. 8, 9 and 10. Table 5. Diagnosis: *Palmatolepis gigas* is distinguished by its markedly elongate outer lobe.
Figs. 8 and 9, upper and lower views, AD 822/3, ×30; Fig. 10, upper surface view of specimen transitional from *Pa.*
hassi RQ01, ×45. Figs. 8 and 9, B. W. Ridolls collection. Figs. 8 and 9, East Ogwell Limestone, NE of Ransley Quarry
(SX 84487036); Fig. 10, Ransley Quarry, Newton Abbot (SX 84487036). Figs. 8 and 9, illustrated by Selwood *et al.*
(1984, Plate 6, Figs. 13 and 15 as *Pa. subrecta*).

Ancryognathus asymmetricus (Ulrich and Bassler 1926)
Plate 4.6, Figs. 11 and 12. Table 5. Diagnosis: asymmetric platform element with a sharply terminating lobe on the
outer posterior platform deflected posteriorly. Angle between secondary and primary carina is acute.
Upper and lower views, AD 3775/8, ×30. British Geological Survey, Newton Abbot, collection. Luxton Nodular
Limestone (Kiln Wood Beds), field exposure (SX 87677468) near Whiteway Barton. Illustrated by Selwood *et al.*
(1984, Plate 6, Figs. 9 and 8).

Palmatolepis triangularis Sannemann 1955
Plate 4.6, Fig. 13. Table 5. Diagnosis: a species of *Palmatolepis* with a sigmoidal carina, wide raised inner platform and
sharp triangular lobe on outer platform.
Upper view, SM H0456, ×30. M. J. Orchard collection. Plymouth Limestine, Western King (SX 46085329), Plymouth.

Palmatolepis subperlobata Branson and Mehl 1934
Plate 4.6, Fig. 14. Table 5. Diagnosis: a species of *Palmatolepis* with a prominent outer lobe, rounded platform outline
and shagreen upper platform surface.
Upper view, AD 3780/2, ×30. British Geological Survey, Newton Abbot, collection. Luxton Nodular Limestone, field
exposure (SX 87667470) N of Lindridge Hill Cottages. Illustrated by Selwood *et al.* (1984, Plate 6, Fig. 24).

Palmatolepis quadrantinodosalobata Sannemann 1955
Plate 4.6, Fig. 15. Table 5. Diagnosis: this species is characterized by a long outer lobe, relatively straight carina and
blade and a cluster of small nodes on the anterior inner platform surface.
Upper view, AD 3776/2, ×30. British Geological Survey, Newton Abbot, collection. Luxton Nodular Limestone,
field exposure (SX 88217502) SW of Whiteway Barton. Illustrated by Selwood *et al.* (1984, Plate 6, Fig. 23).

Palmatolepis circularis Szulczewski 1971
Plate 4.6, Fig. 16. Table 5. Diagnosis: a species of *Palmatolepis* with an extensive platform, subcircular in outline, and
a small outer lobe. Posterior carina is absent.
Upper view, AD 3776/1, ×30. British Geological Survey, Newton Abbot, collection. Luxton Nodular Limestone,
field exposure (SX 88217502) SW of Whiteway Barton. Illustrated by Selwood *et al.*, (1984, Plate 6, Fig. 25).

Palmatolepis glabra prima Ziegler and Huddle 1968
Plate 4.6, Figs 17 and 18. Table 5. Diagnosis: this subspecies of *Palmatolepis glabra* has relatively wide shagreen platform showing a rounded anterior outer margin and slightly raised elongated parapet.
Upper views: Fig. 17, AD 3776/4, ×30; Fig. 18, AD 3780/10, ×30. Both British Geological Survey, Newton Abbot,
collection. Fig. 17, Luxton Nodular Limestone, most southerly field exposure (SX 88217502), SW of Whiteway Barton; Fig. 18, Luxton Nodular Limestone, field exposure (SX 87667470), N of Lindridge Hill Cottages. Illustrated by
Selwood *et al.* (1984, Plate 6, Figs. 17 and 14).

Palmatolepis glabra distorta Branson and Mehl 1934
Plate 4.6, Figs. 19 and 20. Table 5. Diagnosis: this subspecies has a narrow elongate shagreen platform, pronounced
sigmoidal carina and a sharp raised parapet on the inner platform which diverges slightly anteriorly.
Fig. 19, upper view, AD 3786/12, × 30; Fig. 20, upper view of specimen transitional from *Pa. g. acuta*, AD 3786/14,
×30. Both British Geological Survey, Newton Abbot, collection. Luxton Nodular Limestone, track (SX 88037697)
near Well. Illustrated by Selwood *et al.* (1984, Plate 6, Figs. 15 and 16).

Palmatolepis marginifera marginifera Helms 1959
Plate 4.6, Figs. 21 and 22. Table 5. Diagnosis: the platform is round, almost oval, commonly with a shagreen upper
surface. The parapet extends posterior to the central node.

Pl. 4.6]   Conodonts of the Devonian System from Great Britain   151

Fig. 21, upper view, AD 3789/2, ×30; Fig. 22, upper view, juvenile specimen, AD 3777/14, ×30. Fig. 21, Luxton Nodular Limestone, trench (SX 87637710, SX 87077708) near Well; Fig. 22. Luxton Nodular Limestone, quarry (SX 88207500), SW of Whiteway Barton. Both British Geological Survey, Newton Abbot, collection. Illustrated by Selwood *et al.* (1984, Plate 6, Figs. 21 (unnumbered) and 22).

Palmatolepis rugosa cf. *ampla* Müller 1956
Plate 4.6, Figs. 23 and 24. Table 5. Diagnosis: (*Palmatolepis rugosa ampla*): this subspecies has a wide platform ornamented by many small random nodes on the upper surface which may coalesce to form ridges on the outer platform surface. cf. *ampla* is a *marginifera—velifer* Zone homeomorph of *ampla*.
Upper and lower views, AD 3778/2, ×30. Luxton Nodular Limestone, quarry (SX 88207500), SW of Whiteway Barton. Illustrated by Selwood *et al.* (1984, Plate 6, Figs. 29 and 30) as *Pa. rugosa ampla*.

Polygnathus hassi Helms 1961
Plate 4.6, Fig. 25. Table 5. Diagnosis: a nodocostate polygnathid with an elongate rhomboidal platform which bears adcarinal ridges that are subparallel to the carina. The species first appears in the *velifer* Zone in South-west England.
Upper view, AD 3778/23, ×30. British Geological Survey, Newton Abbot, collection. Luxton Nodular Limestone, quarry (SX 88207500), SW of Whiteway Barton. Illustrated by Selwood *et al.* (1984, Plate 6, Fig. 10).

PLATE 4.7

Pandorinellina cf. *insita* (Stauffer 1940)
Plate 4.7, Figs. 1 and 6. Table 5. Diagnosis: a single-rowed element with a wide deep basal cavity and elevated anterior denticles which form a 'fin'. The species is regarded as a member of a stock which gave rise to *Scaphignathus* and related genera in the late Devonian.
Fig. 1, lateral view, TMT201, ×45; I. J. Stewart collection (Stewart, 1981a). Fig. 6, upper view of specimen transitional to *Scaphignathus pseudostrigosus* (Dreesen and Dusar, 1974), ×45, Fig. 1, Buckator Formation, Trenault Main Quarry (SX 26258292): Fig. 6, Landlake Limestone, Trenault B Quarry (SX 26548260).

Scaphignathus velifer Helms 1959
Plate 4.7, Figs. 2, 3 and 4. Table 5. Diagnosis: a species of *Scaphignathus* with an offset high blade attached to right side of platform. In mature specimens (e.g. Fig. 2) a carina is developed posteriorly, with the central trough of less mature specimens (Figs 3 and 4) only preserved in the anterior portion.
Fig. 2, upper view of mature specimen, W5011, ×45; I. J. Stewart collection (Stewart, 1981a). Fig. 3 and 4, upper and lateral views of typical form, LLB102, ×45. Fig. 2, reworked Landlake Limestone in early Carboniferous, West Petherwin Quarry, Launceston (SX 30578231); Figs 3 and 4, Landlake Limestone (Petherwin Formation), Landlake Quarry, Launceston (SX 42718228).

Scaphignathus subserratus (Branson and Mehl, 1934)
Plate 4.7, Fig. 5. Table 5. Diagnosis: the free blade, here broken, is attached medially and is generally continuous with the carina. The carina typically extends the length of the platform.
Upper view of adult specimen, LM202, ×45. I. J. Stewart collection (Stewart, 1981a). Landlake Limestone, Landlake Mill Quarry, Launceston (SX 32838235).

Polygnathus? diversus Helms 1959
Plate 4.7, Figs. 7 and 8. Table 5. Diagnosis: an asymmetric platform element, with an offset straight free blade. Two morphotypes are known; 'juvenile' specimens (Fig. 8) display a microdentate upper surface ornamentation and a flared basal cavity. 'Adult' morphotypes are typically triple rowed with a pronounced offset between the carina and free blade (Fig. 7). Two species are probably represented.
Fig. 7, upper views, 'adult morphotype', LMB011, ×45. Fig. 8, upper view of microdentate morphotype, TBP301, ×45. I. J. Stewart collection (Stewart, 1981a). Fig. 7, Landlake Limestone, Landlake Mill Quarry, Launceston (SX 32878238).

Scaphignathus pseudostrigosus (Dreesen and Dusar 1974)
Plate 4.7, Figs. 9, 10 and 11. Table 5. Diagnosis: a species of *Scaphignathus* with medially attached free blade bearing enlarge anterior denticles. The platform is asymmetric, triangular in section, with an inverted basal cavity located anteriorly. A posterior keel is present in mature specimens.
Upper, lateral and lower surface views of mature specimen, TBP 806, ×45. I. J. Stewart collection (Stewart, 1981a). Landlake Limestone, Trenault B Quarry (SX 26548260).

Palmatolepis perlobata maxima Müller 1956
Plate 4.7, Fig. 12. Table 5. Diagnosis: an elongate palmatolepid with a sharp outer lobe, sigmoidal carina, raised parapet and upward flexed, pointed posterior platform. Adult specimens develop fused nodose ornamentation on the lobe and parapet areas.
Upper view, W12022. ×22. I. J. Stewart collection (Stewart, 1981a). West Petherwin Quarry, Launceston (SX 30578231).

'Icriodus' pectinatus Dreesen and Houlleberghs 1980
Plate 4.7, Fig. 13. Table 5. Diagnosis: a narrow icriodontiform (I) element with transverse crest-like ridges of fused denticles.
Upper view of typical form but with broken posterior cusp, TMTO5, ×45. I. J. Stewart collection (Stewart, 1981a). Buckator Formation, Trenault Main Quarry (SX 26258292).

Palmatolepis glabra lepta Ziegler and Huddle 1968
Plate 4.7, Fig. 14. Table 5. Diagnosis: narrow elongate subspecies of *Palmatolepis glabra* with a pronounced parapet area, triangular in outline, on the inner platform.
Upper view of extremely narrow morphotype, TBP 401, ×45. I. J. Stewart collection (Stewart, 1981a). Landlake Limestone, Trenault B. Quarry (SX 26548260).

Pl. 4.7]   Conodonts of the Devonian System from Great Britain   153

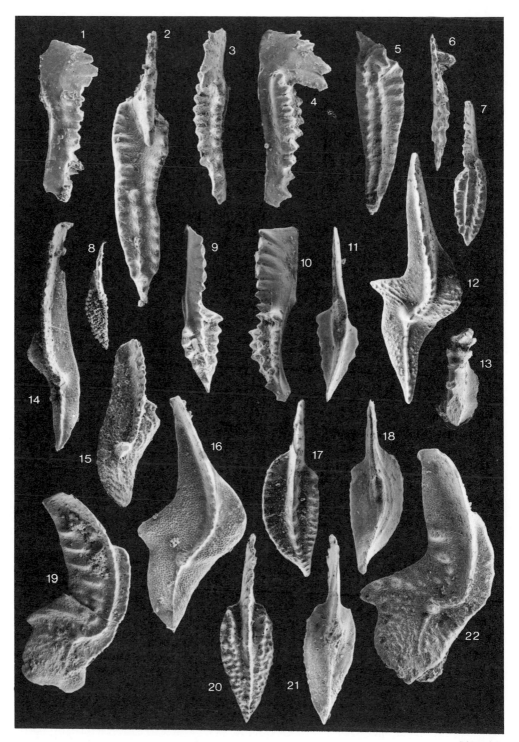

Plate 4.7

Palmatolepis perlobata helmsi Ziegler 1962
Plate 4.7, Fig. 15. Table 5. Diagnosis: palmatolepid element with a narrow elongate shagreen platform that is flexed upwards posterior to the central node. Outer lobe is poorly developed or lacking.
Upper view of silt encrusted specimen, TMEb401, ×70. I. J. Stewart collection (Stewart, 1981a). Landlake Limestone, Trenault Main Quarry (SX 26258292).

Palmatolepis perlobata schindewolfi Müller 1956
Plate 4.7, Fig. 16. Table 5. Diagnosis: the subspecies is characterized by a shagreen unornamented platform surface, a rounded raised parapet, sigmoidal carina and slight lateral lobe. A wide range of morphotypes is known.
Upper view of typical morphotype, W12422, ×45. I. J. Stewart collection (Stewart, 1981a). Landlake Limestone, West Petherwin Quarry (SX 30578231).

Polygnathus semicostatus Branson and Mehl 1934
Plate 4.7, Figs. 17 and 18. Table 5. Diagnosis: a species of *Polygnathus* with a rounded, slightly asymmetric gently arched platform with a tapered posterior ornamented by transverse ridges. A wide range of morphological variation is recognized.
Upper and lower views of typical form, LLB1601, ×45. I. J. Stewart collection (Stewart, 1981a). Landlake Limestone, Landlake Quarry (SX 32718226).

Palmatolepis rugosa trachytera Ziegler 1962
Plate 4.7, Fig. 19. Table 5. Diagnosis: a subspeices of *Palmatolepis rugosa* with a wide posterior platform, a weak outer lobe and an anterior outer platform ornamented by nodes fused to form elongate transverse ridges.
Upper view, TMEb401, ×45. I. J. Stewart collection (Stewart, 1981a). Landlake Limestone, Trenault Main Quarry (SX 26258292).

Polygnathus nodocostatus Branson and Mehl 1934
Plate 4.7, Figs. 20 and 21. Table 5. Diagnosis: the symmetrical platform is ornamented by numerous more or less random nodes posteriorly which become more organised and may develop as adcarinal ridges anteriorly. Pronounced keel on lower surface.
Upper and lower views, LLB1710, ×45. I. J. Stewart collection (Stewart, 1981a). Landlake Quarry, Launceston (SX 32718226).

Palmatolepis rugosa rugosa Branson and Mehl 1934
Plate 4.7, Fig. 22. Table 5. Diagnosis: the nominate subspecies is characterized by coarse ridges or nodes in the parapet area of the inner platform, a strong outer lobe with nodose ornamentation on the anterior edge which extends anteriorly on the outer platform surface.
Upper view, W12032, ×45. I. J. Stewart collection (Stewart, 1981a). Landlake Limestone reworked into the early Carboniferous, West Petherwin Quarry (SX 30578231).

PLATE 4.8

Polygnathus styriacus Ziegler 1962
Plate 4.8, Figs. 1 and 2. Table 5. Diagnosis: the former zonal index is characterized by a relatively thin, arched platform, with essentially concave lower surface, and an upper surface ornamented by numerous small nodes. The anterior upper surface shows coarse asymmetric ornamentation, and smooth downward deflected anterior margins.
Upper and lower views, W12095, ×45. I. J. Stewart collection (Stewart, 1981a). Landlake Limestone reworked into early Carboniferous, West Petherwin Quarry, Launceston (SX 30578231)

Pseudopolygnathus contraversus Sandberg and Ziegler 1979
Plate 4.8, Fig. 3. Table 5. Diagnosis: a species of *Pseudopolygnathus* with an elongate platform, the right half of which extends further anteriorly than the left half, as a row of isolated nodes or transverse ridges. The figured specimen corresponds to morphotype 2 of Sandberg and Ziegler (1979).
Upper view, LLT2101, ×45. I. J. Stewart collection (Stewart, 1981a). Cephalopod Limestone, Landlake Quarry (SX 26428111).

Clydagnathus ormistoni Beinert, Klapper, Sandberg and Ziegler 1971
Plate 4.8, Fig. 4. Table 5. Diagnosis: the form is assigned to *Clydagnathus* because of its gross morphology. The species has a high blade (here broken) attached to the right side of the platform. A medial trough characterizes the upper surface while the lower surface exhibits a large open basal cavity.
Upper surface view of silt encrusted specimen, LLT104, ×45. I. J. Stewart collection (Stewart, 1981a). Specimen from condensed fauna with mixture of *styriacus* and Lower *costatus* Zone indices, Landlake Quarry (SX 26428111).

Pl. 4.8]　　Conodonts of the Devonian System from Great Britain　　155

Plate 4.8

Pseudopolygnathus marburgensis marburgensis Bischoff and Ziegler 1957
Plate 4.8, Fig. 5. Table 5. Diagnosis: the nominate subspecies has a nodose upper surface ornamentation with bifurcate ornamentation on the inner lobe and a weak outer lobe.
Upper view, UST4401, ×45. I. J. Stewart collection (Stewart, 1981a). Strayerpark Beds (Stourscombe Formation), Strayerpark Plantation, Lewannick (SX 26588122).

Pseudopolygnathus brevipennatus Ziegler 1962
Plate 4.8, Fig. 6. Table 5. Diagnosis: a nearly symmetrical platform with wide rounded anterior section bearing node or ridge-like ornamentation, and a weakly ornamentated tapered posterior platform.
Upper view of specimen with symmetrical platform, LLT401, ×45. I. J. Stewart collection (Stewart, 1981a). Cephalopod Limestone, site of Landlake Quarry, Launceston (SX 26428111).

Bispathodus jugosus (Branson and Mehl 1934)
Plate 4.8, Fig. 7. Table 5. Diagnosis: a member of the double-rowed *Bispathodus* Group with denticles on the right-hand side starting far anterior of the basal cavity. The main blade denticles are commonly fused in adult specimens.
Upper view, W25022, ×45. I. J. Stewart collection (Stewart, 1981a). Upper *styriacus* Zone fauna reworked into early Carboniferous, West Petherwin Quarry (SX 30578231).

Palmatolepis gracilis gracilis Branson and Mehl 1934
Plate 4.8, Fig. 8. Table 5. Diagnosis: the nominate subspecies has a high carina deflected immediately anterior to the large central node, a narrow platform which generally terminates halfway along the blade and raised margins of the upper platform surface.
Upper view, W12032, ×45. I. J. Stewart collection (Stewart, 1981a). Landlake Limestone, West Petherwin (SX 30578231).

Bispathodus costatus (E. R. Branson 1934)
Plate 4.8, Figs. 9 and 10. Table 5. Diagnosis: the former zone fossil possesses lateral nodes or transverse ridges extending close to the posterior tip on the right side of the blade and an unornamented left side posterior to the basal cavity.
Upper and lower lateral views, W1702, ×45. I. J. Stewart collection (Stewart, 1981a). Landlake Limestone, West Petherwin (SX 30578231).

Bispathodus aculeatus aculeatus (Branson and Mehl 1934)
Plate 4.8, Fig. 11. Table 5. Diagnosis: a double-rowed element with one or more accessory denticles above the basal cavity on the right side of the blade. The denticles do not extend to the posterior tip.
Upper view, W12021, ×45. I. J. Stewart collection (Stewart, 1981a). Landlake Limestone, West Petherwin (SX 30578231).

Bispathodus spinulicostatus (E. R. Branson 1934)
Plate 4.8, Figs. 12 and 13. Table 5. Diagnosis: a species of *Bispathodus* with offset lateral nodes posterior to the basal cavity on the left side of the blade, and denticles on the right side that extend close to the posterior tip.
Upper and lower views, W18A403, ×45. I. J. Stewart collection (Stewart, 1981a). Landlake Limestone reworked into early Carboniferous, West Petherwin (SX 30578231).

Bispathodus aculeatus anteposicornis (Scott 1961)
Plate 4.8, Figs 14 and 15. Table 5. Diagnosis: a subspecies of *Bispathodus aculeatus* with a single side denticle on the right side of the blade anterior to the basal cavity.
Upper and lateral views of specimen with '*plumulus*'-like anterior blade, W8A701, ×45. I. J. Stewart collection (Stewart, 1981a). Landlake Limestone, reworked into early Carboniferous, West Petherwin (SX 30578831).

Palmatolepis gracilis gonioclymeniae Müller 1956
Plate 4.8, Fig. 16. Table 5. Diagnosis: a subspecies of *Palmatolepis gracilis* with a sigmoidal blade and carina that bends sharply anteriorly of the central node. The relatively wide platform has a broad rounded lobe on the outer margin.
Upper view, W15051, ×45. I. J. Stewart collection. Landlake Limestone reworked into early Carboniferous, West Petherwin Quarry (SX 30578231), Launceston.

Pseudopolygnathus marburgensis trigonicus Ziegler 1962
Plate 4.8, Fig. 17. Table 5. Diagnosis: this subspecies differs from the nominate subspecies in its markedly asymmetrical platform with characteristic bifurcate nodose ornamentation on the inner lobe of the upper surface and a prominent outer lobe.
Upper view, W2021, ×45. I. J. Stewart collection (Stewart, 1981a). Landlake Limestone, West Petherwin Quarry (SX 30578231).

Pl. 4.8]   **Conodonts of the Devonian System from Great Britain**   157

Siphonodella praesulcata Sandberg 1972
Plate 4.8, Fig. 18. Table 5. Diagnosis: the species has a narrow symmetrical platform ornamented by weak transverse ridges which do not extend to the carina. The lower surface (not illustrated) exhibits an elongate open basal cavity which becomes partly inverted in adult specimens.
Upper view of elongate specimen, W13082, ×45. I. J. Stewart collection (Stewart, 1981a). Landlake Limestone, West Petherwin Quarry (SX 30578231).

Pseudopolygnathus graulichi Bouckaert and Groessens 1976
Plate 4.8, Fig. 19. Table 5. Diagnosis: the species has a slightly asymmetric strongly ornamented platform with an upturned margin along one side of the plate. The species is an apparent homeomorph of *Siphonodella praesulcata* and has a comparable range in South-west England.
Upper view, TMK8010, ×45. I. J. Stewart collection (Stewart, 1981a). Yeolmbridge Formation, Treguddick Mill, Lewannick (SX 27578142).

Protognathodus collinsoni Ziegler 1969
Plate 4.8, Fig. 20. Table 5. Diagnosis: the genus *Protognathodus* is characterized by a rounded 'cup' and anterior free blade. This species has slightly asymmetrical cup and weakly developed nodes on the upper surface.
Upper view, TB 102, ×45. I. J. Stewart collection (Stewart, 1981a). Landlake Limestone, Trenault B Quarry (SX 26548260).

PLATE 4.9

Palmatolepis gracilis manca Helms, 1959
Plate 4.9, Figs. 1, 2. Table 5. Diagnosis: this species is distinguished by a carina that is deflected anterior of the central node, a wide shagreen platform and an outer platform that extends virtually to the anterior tip.
Fig. 1, upper view, W12011, ×70; Fig. 2, upper view, W12013, ×70. Landlake Limestone, West Petherwin (SX 3061-8238). Upper *styriacus* Zone fauna reworked into early Carboniferous.

Palmatolepis gracilis expansa Sandberg and Ziegler 1979
Plate 4.9, Fig. 3. Table 5. Diagnosis: the species is separated from *Pa. gracilis gracilis* by its expanded platform with incipient outer lobe.
Upper view, W12054, ×35. Landlake Limestone, West Petherwin (SX 30618238). Upper *styriacus* (Lower *expansa* Zone).

'Icriodus' pectinatus Dreeson and Houlleberghs 1980
Plate 4.9, Fig. 4. Table 5. Diagnosis: drepanodiform element probably from the apparatus of *'I.' pectinatus*. Simple cone-like element with longitudinal striations.
Lateral view, TMT 11, ×70. Buckator Formation Trenault (SX 26318303). Probable uppermost *marginifera* Zone (Lower *'Icriodus' costatus* Zone).

Bispathodus ultimus (Bischoff 1957)
Plate 4.9, Fig. 5. Table 5. Diagnosis: a species of *Bispathodus* with a right-lateral row ornamented by cross ridges attached to the main blade.
Upper view, LLT 801, ×35. Cephalopod Limestone, Petherwin Formation, Landlake Quarry Tip (SX 32858234). Middle *costatus* Zone.

Pelekysgnathus inclinatus Thomas 1949
Plate 4.9, Figs. 6, 7 and 8. Table 5. Diagnosis: icriosontiform element with single row of discrete denticles and a pronounced anterior denticle of 'cusp'.
Fig. 6, upper view, LM2124, ×70; Fig. 7, upper view, LM2141, ×70. Fig. 8, lateral view of a specimen transitional from *'Icriodus' pectinatus*, TMT05, ×70. Landlake Limestone, Landlake Mill Quarry (SX 32878238). (*velifer* Zone).

'Icriodus' costatus (Thomas 1949)
Plate 4.9. Fig. 9. Table 5. Diagnosis: icriodontiform element with three rows of denticles, the lateral row denticles being connected to the central row by ridges.
Upper view of specimen, LM4061, close to *'I.' costatus bultyncki*, Dreesen and Houlleberghs, 1980, ×70. Landlake Limestone, Landlake Mill Quarry (SX 32878238). Lower *velifer* Zone.

Icriodus alternatus Branson and Mehl 1934
Plate 4.9, Figs. 10 and 11. Table 5. Diagnosis: an elongate species of *Icriodus* with a narrow platform and lateral row denticles that alternate with the elongate middle row denticles.
Fig. 10, upper view, LSTR12, ×35; Fig. 11, upper view, LSTR11, ×35. Landerslake Slate, Petherwin Formation, Landerslake Quarry, Launceston (SX 26428111). (*velifer* Zone).

'Icriodus' cornutus Sanneman 1955
Plate 4.9, Fig. 12. Table 5. Diagnosis: the species has alternating lateral denticles and a pronounced cusp (broken on the illustrated specimen) on the posterior upper surface.
Lateral view, TREDA1003, ×70. Tredorn Slates, Strayerpark Main Quarry, Launceston (SX 26538102). Upper *marginifera* Zone (*'Icriodus' cornutus* Zone).

Protognathodus kockeli (Bischoff 1957)
Plate 4.9, Fig. 13. Table 5. Diagnosis: A species of *Protognathodus* with nodose ornamentation on upper surface of 'cup'. This is a Carboniferous species.
Upper view, TBS103, ×70. Landlake Limestone, Trenault 'B' Quarry, Launceston (SX 26548260).
Remarks: the ornamentation of the illustrated specimen is weakly developed.

Protognathodus meischneri Ziegler 1969
Plate 4.9, Fig. 14. Table 5. Diagnosis: a *Protognathodus* with a symmetrical unornamented cup.
Upper view specimen, TMC 41, ×35. Landlake Limestone, Trenault 'B' Quarry (SX 26548260).

Pl. 4.9]   Conodonts of the Devonian System from Great Britain   159

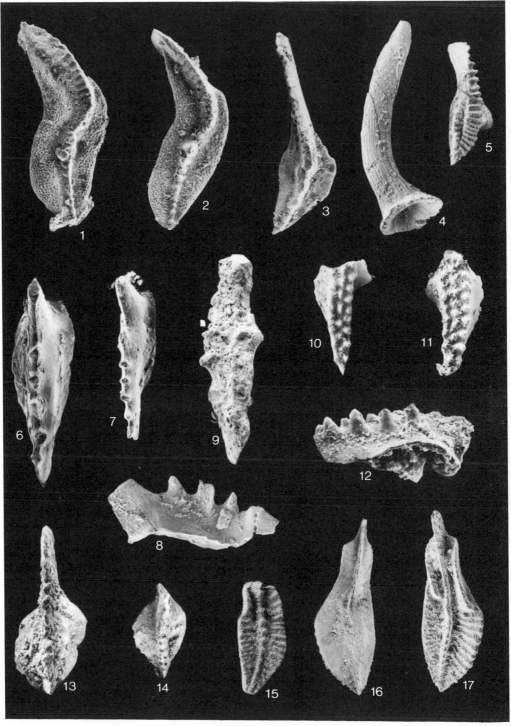

Plate 4.9

Siphonodella sulcata Huddle 1934

Plate 4.9, Fig. 15. Table 5. Diagnosis: a species of *Siphonodella* with a gently curved carina and slightly asymmetrical platform. This is a Carboniferous species.

Upper view. TBS902, ×35. Landlake Limestone, Trenault 'B' Quarry, Launceston (SX 26548260).

Siphonodella duplicata

Plate 4.9, Figs. 16 and 17. Table 5. Diagnosis: the species bears two ridges parallel to the anterior carina. The basal cavity is distinctive. This is a Carboniferous species.

Lower and upper views, W2410, ×35. Landlake Limestone reworked into early Carboniferous, West Petherwin Quarry (SX 30618238).

All illustrated material from the I. J. Stewart Collection (Stewart, 1981a).

4.9 REFERENCES

Alberti, H., Uffenorde, H. Groos-, Streel, M., Uffendorde, H. and Walliser, O. H. 1974. The stratigraphical significance of the *Protognathodus* fauna from Stockum (Devonian–Carboniferous boundary, Rhenish Schiefergebirge). *Newsl. Stratigr.*, **3**, 263–76.

Austin, R. L. 1967. New conodont horizons in S.W. England. *Proc. Ussher Soc.*, **1** (6), 140.

Austin, R. L., Druce, E. C., Rhodes, F. H. T. and Williams, J. A. 1970. The value of conodonts in the recognition of the Devonian–Carboniferous boundary, with particular reference to Great Britain. *C.R. 6éme Congr. Int. de Stratigraphie et de Géologique du Carbonifère, Sheffield, 1967*, **11**, 431–44, 1 plate.

Austin, *et al.* In press. Devonian and Dinantian conodont localities in Southwest England. University of Southampton.

Barnes, R. P. 1982. The geology of South Cornish mélanges. *Unpublished Ph.D. Thesis*, University of Southampton.

Barnes, R. P. 1983. The stratigraphy of a sedimentary mélange and associated deposits in South Cornwall, England. *Proc. Geol. Assoc.*, **94**, 217–229.

Barnes, R. P. and Bultynck, P. In prep. Lower Devonian conodonts from the Meneage Formation, South Cornwall.

Bassett, M. G. and Jenkins, T. B. H. 1977. Tournaisian conodont and spore data from the uppermost Skrinkle Sandstones of Pembrokeshire, South Wales. *Geol. Palaeontol.*, **11**, 121–34, 2 plates.

Beinert, R. J., Klapper, G. Sandberg, C. A. and Ziegler, W. 1971. Revision of *Scaphignathus* and description of *Clydagnathus? ormistoni* n. sp. (Conodonta, Upper Devonian). *Geol. Palaeontol.*, **5**, 81–91, 2 plates.

Bischoff, G. 1957. Die Conodonten-Stratigraphie des rhenoherzynischen Unter-karbons mit Berücksichtigung der *Wocklumeria*-Stufe und der Devon/Karbon-Grenze. *Abh. Hess Landesamtes Bodenforsch.*, **19**, 1–64, 6 plates.

Bischoff, G. and Ziegler, W. 1957. Die Conodontenchronologie des Mittledevons und des tiefsten Oberdevons. *Abh. Hess. Landesamtes Bodenforsch.*, **22**, 1–136, 21 plates.

Boersma, K. T. 1973. Devonian and Lower Carboniferous conodont biostratigraphy, Spanish Central Pyrenees. *Leidse Geol. Meded.*, **49**, 303–77.

Bouckaert, J. and Groessens, E. 1976. *Polygnathus paprothae, Pseudopolygnathus conili, Pseudopolygnathus graulichi:* espèces nouvelles á la limite Dévonian–Carbonifère. *Ann. Soc. Géol. Belg.*, **99**, 587–99, 3 plates.

Bouckaert, J. and Ziegler, W. 1965. Conodont stratigraphy in the Famennian Stage (Upper Devonian) in Belgium. *Mém. Serv. Géol. Belg.*, **5**, 1–40, 5 plates.

Branson, E. B. and Mehl, M. G. 1934. Conodonts from the Grassy Creek Shale of Missouri. *Univ. Missouri Stud.*, **8**, 171–259, 9 plates.

Branson, E. B. and Mehl, M. G. 1934. Conodonts from the Bushberg Sandstone and equivalent formations of Missouri. *Univ. Missouri Stud.*, **8**, 265–299, 3 plates.

Branson, E. B. and Mehl, M. G. 1938. The conodont genus *Icriodus* and its stratigraphic distribution. *J. Paleontol.*, **12**, 156–166, 1 plate.

Branson, E. B. and Mehl, M. G. 1934. A study of Hinde's types of conodonts preserved in the British Museum. *Univ. Missouri Stud.*, **8**, 133–167, 2 plates.

Bryant, W. L. 1921. The Genesee Conodonts with descriptions of New Species. *Bull. Buffalo Soc. Nat. Sci.*, **13**, 1–59, 16 plates.

Bultynck, P. 1970. Revision stratigraphique et paléontologique (Brachiopodes et Conodontes) de la coupe type du Couvinian. *Mém. Inst. Géol. Univ. Louvain*, **26**, 1–152, 39 plates.

Bultynck, P. 1971. Le Silurien Supérieur et le Dévonien Inférieur de la Sierra de Guadarrama (Espagne Centrale), Déuxième partie: assemblages de Conodontes á *Spathognathodus*. *Bull. Inst. R. Sci. Nat. Belg.*, **47**, 1–43, 5 plates.

Bultynck, P. 1976a. Le Silurien Supérieur et le Dévonien Inférieur de la Sierra de Guadarrama (Espagne centrale), Troisieme partie: elements icriodiformes, pelekysgnathiformes et polygnathiformes. *Bull. Inst. R. Sci. Nat. Belg.*, **49** (Sciences de la Terre 5), 1–74, 11 plates.

Bultynck, P. 1976b. Comparative study of Middle Devonian conodonts from North Michigan (USA) and the Ardennes (Belgium–France). In: C. R. Barnes (Ed.), *Conodont Paleoecology, Spec. Paper Geol. Assoc. Can.*, **15**, 119–41.

Carls, P. 1969. Die conodonton des tieferen Unter-Devons der Guadarrama (Mittel-Spanien) und die Stellung des Grenz – bereiches Lochkovium/Pragium nach der rheinischen Gliederung. *Senckenberg. Lethaea*, **50**, 303–355, 14 plates.

Carls, P. and Gandl, J. 1969. Stratigraphie und Conodonten des Unter-Devons der Östlichen Iberischen Ketten (NE–Spanien). *Neues Jahrb. Geol. Paläontol.*, *Abh.*, **132**, 155–218, 6 plates.

Castle, C. 1977. Conodonts from Middle–Upper Devonian boundary beds at Barton Quarry, Torquay. *Proc. Ussher Soc.*, **4** (1), 62.

Castle, C. 1978. Conodont faunas from Babbacombe Cliff, Torquay. *Proc. Ussher Soc.*, **4** (2), 129–134.

Castle, C. 1982. Middle and Upper Devonian conodont biostratigraphy of the Torquay area, South Devon. *Unpublished Ph.D. Thesis*, University of Hull.

Chatterton, B. D. E. 1976. Distribution and paleoecology of Eifelian and early Givetian conodonts from western and northwestern Canada. In: C. R. Barnes (Ed.), *Conodont Paleoecology, Spec. Paper, Geol. Assoc. Can.*, **15**, 143–157.

Clausen, C. D., Leuteritz, K. and Ziegler, W. 1979. Biostratigraphie und Lithofacies der Elstare Mulde (Hower, Mittel- und Liefer Oberdevon) Sauerland, Rheinischeshiefergebirge. *Geol. Jahrb. A.*, **51**, 3–37, 1 plate.

Collinson, C. H. Rexroad, C. B. and Thompson, T. L. 1971. Conodont zonation of the North American Mississippian. *Mem. Geol. Soc. Am.*, **127**, 353–394.

Collinson, C. H., Scott, A. J. and Rexroad, C. B. 1962.

Six charts showing biostratigraphic zones and correlations based on conodonts from the Devonian and Mississippian rocks of the Upper Mississippi Valley. *Circ. Ill. State Geol. Surv.,* **328,** 1–32.

Coward, M. P. and McClay, K. R. 1983. Thrust tectonics of South Devon. *J. Geol. Soc. London,* **140,** 215–228.

Davis, W. E., Jr. 1975. Significance of conodont distribution in the Tully Limestone (Devonian) New York State. *J. Paleontol.,* **49,** 1097–1104.

Dineley, D. L. and Rhodes, F. H. T. 1956. Conodont Horizons in the West and South-West of England. *Geol. Mag.,* **153,** 242–248.

Dreesen, R. 1977. Interspecific morphological relations within the *'quadrantinodosa* stock' (Branson and Mehl, 1934)–(*marginifera* Zone, Upper Devonian). *Ann. Soc. Géol. Belg.,* **99,** 511–529, 2 plates.

Dreesen, R. and Dusar, M. 1974. Refinement of conodont biozonation in the Famenne-type area. In: J. Bouckaert, and M. Streel, (Eds.): *Int. Symp. on Belgian Micropaleontological Limits from Emsian to Viséan, Namur, 1974.* In *Geol. Surv. Belg.,* **13,** 1–36, 7 plates.

Dreesen, R. and Houlleberghs, E. 1980. Evolutionary trends of Famennian icriodids in the Dinant and Vesdre Basins (Conodonts, Belgian Upper Devonian). *Ann. Soc. Géol. Belg.,* **103,** 111–141.

Dreesen, R. and Thorez, J. 1980. Sedimentary environments, conodont biofacies and palaeoecology of the Belgian Famennian (Upper Devonian) – an approach. *Ann. Soc. Géol. Belg.,* **103,** 97–110.

Druce, E. C. 1973. Upper Paleozoic faunal provinces. In: F. H. T. Rhodes (Ed.), *Conodont Paleozoology, Spec. Paper, Geol. Soc. Am.,* **141,** 191–237.

Drummond, M. 1982. The geology of the Brixham, Dartington area, South Devon. *Unpublished Ph.D. Thesis,* University of Newcastle upon Tyne.

Dusar, M. 1977. The Lower Famennian at the south-eastern border of Dinant Basin. *Ann. Soc. Géol. Belg.,* **99,** 565–570.

Dusar, M. and Dreesen, R. 1977. Étude biostratigraphique du Famennian inférieur dans les environs de Theux. *Ann. Soc. Géol. Belg.,* **99,** 543–546, 4 plates.

Evans, M. 1981. A marine fauna from the Dartmouth Beds (Lower Devonian) of Cornwall. *Geol. Mag.,* **118,** 517–523.

Goldring, R., House, M. R., Selwood, E. B., Simpson, S. and Lambert, R. St. J. 1968. Devonian of Southern Britain. In: D. H. Oswald (Ed.), *Int. Symp. on the Devonian System, 1967,* **1,** Alberta Society of Petroleum Geologists, Calgary, 1–14.

Gooday, A. J. 1975. Ostracode ages from the Upper Devonian purple and green slates around Plymouth. *Proc. Ussher Soc.,* **3,** 55–62.

Harvey, J. C. 1967. Conodonts from Veryan Bay, Cornwall. *Proc. Ussher Soc.,* **1,** 284.

Helms, J. 1959. Conodonten aus dem Saalfelder Oberdevon (Thüringen). *Geologie,* **8,** 634–677, 6 plates.

Hendriks, E. M. L., House, M. R. and Rhodes, F. H. T. 1971. Evidence bearing on the stratigraphical successions in South Cornwall. *Proc. Ussher Soc.,* **2** (4), 270–275.

Hinde, G. J. 1879. On conodonts from the Chazy and Cincinnati Group of the Cambro-Silurian and from the Hamilton and Genesse Shale divisions of the Devonian, in Canada and the United States. *Q. J. Geol. Soc. London,* **35,** 351–369.

House, M. R. 1963. Devonian ammonoid successions and facies in Devon and Cornwall. *Q. J. Geol. Soc. London,* **119,** 1–27.

House, M. R. 1982. The Middle–Upper Devonian Series Boundary and decisions of the International Geological Congress. In: R. Werner and W. Ziegler (Eds,) *Proposal of a Boundary Stratotype for the Lower–Middle Devonian Boundary (partitus Boundary), Cour. Forsch.-Inst. Senckenberg,* **55,** 449–462.

House, M. R. and Dineley, D. L. In press. Devonian Series boundaries in Britain. *Cour. Forsch.-Inst. Senckenberg.*

House, M. R., Richardson, J. B., Chaloner, W. G., Allen, J. R. L., Holland, C. H. and Westoll, T. S. 1977. A correlation of Devonian rocks of the British Isles. *Geol. Soc. London Spec. Rep.,* **8,** 1–110.

House, M. R. and Selwood, E. B. 1966. Palaeozoic palaeontology in Devon and Cornwall. In' K. F. G. Hoskins and C. J. Shrimpton (Eds.) *Present Views of Some Aspects of the Geology of Cornwall and Devon, 150th Anniversary Volume* (for 1964), *R. Geol. Soc. Cornwall,* **48–86.**

House, M. R. and Sevastopulo, G. D. 1984. The Devonian Carboniferous boundary in the British Isles: A summary. In E. Paproth and M. Streel (Eds.), *The Devonian–Carboniferous Boundary Cour. Forsch.-Inst. Senckenberg,* **51,** 52.

House, M. R. and Ziegler, W. 1977. The goniatite and conodont sequences in the early Upper Devonian at Ardorf, Germany. *Geol. Palaeontol.,* **11,** 69–108, 6 plates.

Huddle, J. W. 1934. Conodonts from the New Albany Shale of Indiana. *Bull. Amer. Paleont.,* **21,** No. 72, 1–136, 12 plates.

Isaac, K. P., Turner, P. J. and Stewart, I. J. 1982. The evolution of the Hercynides of central S.W. England. *J. Geol. Soc. London,* **139,** 521–531.

Kirchgasser, W. T. 1970. Conodonts from near the Middle–Upper Devonian boundary in North Cornwall. *Palaeontology,* **13,** 335–354, 4 plates.

Klapper, G. 1971. Sequence within the conodont genus *Polygnathus* in the New York lower Middle Devonian. *Geol. Palaeontol.,* **5,** 59–72, 3 plates.

Klapper, G. 1977. Lower and Middle Devonian sequence in Central Nevada. In: M. A. Murphy, W. B. N. Berry and C. A. Sandberg (Eds.), *Western North America: Devonian, Univ. Calif. Riverside Campus Mus. Contrib.,* **4,** 35–54.

Klapper, G., Philip, G. M. and Jackson, J. H. 1970. Revision of the *Polygnathus varcus* Group (Conodonta, Middle Devonian). *Neues Jahrb. Geol. Paläontol. Mh. 1970, H.* **11,** 650–667, 3 plates.

Klapper, G. and Ziegler, W. 1967. Evolutionary development of the *Icriodus latericrescens* Group (Conodonta) in the Devonian of Europe and North America. *Palaeontographica, Abt. A.,* **127,** 68–83, 4 plates.

Klapper, G. and Ziegler, W. 1979. Devonian conodont biostratigraphy. In: M. R. House, C. R. Scrutton and M. G. Bassett (Eds.), The Devonian System, *Spec. Papers Palaeontol., 23,* 199–224.

Klapper, G. Ziegler, W. and Mashkova, T. V. 1978. Conodonts and correlation of Lower–Middle Devonian boundary beds in the Barrandian area of Czechoslovakia. *Geol. Palaeontol., 12,* 103–115, 2 plates.

Leveridge, B. E, 1974. The tectonics of the Roseland coastal section, South Cornwall. *Unpublished Ph.D. Thesis,* University of Newcastle upon Tyne.

Mashkova, T. V. 1968. Konodonty roda *Icriodus* Branson and Mehl, 1938, iz Borshchovskogo i Chortkovskogo gorizontov Podolii. *Dokl. Akad. Nauk, SSR, 182,* 941–944, 1 plate. (in Russian).

Matthews, S. C. 1962. A Middle Devonian conodont fauna from the Tamar Valley. *Proc. Ussher Soc., 1* (1), 27–28.

Matthews, S. C. 1969. A Lower Carboniferous conodont fauna from East Cornwall. *Palaeontology, 12,* 262–275, 4 plates.

Matthews, S. C. 1970. Conodonts from the Lummaton Shell Bed (Middle Devonian, Torquay). *Proc. Ussher Soc., 2* (3), 170–172.

Matthews, S. C., Sadler, R. M. and Selwood, E. B. 1972. A Lower Carboniferous conodont fauna from Chillaton, south-west Devonshire. *Palaeontology, 15,* 550–568, 3 plates.

Matthews, S. C. and Thomas, J. M. 1974. Lower Carboniferous conodont faunas from north-east Devonshire. *Palaeontology, 17,* 371–385.

Miller, A. K. and Youngquist, W. 1947. Conodonts from the type section of the Sweetland Creek Shale in Iowa. *J. Palaeontol., 21,* 501–517, 4 plates.

Moskalenko, T. A. 1966. First discovery of Late Silurian conodonts in the Zeravshan Range. *Palaeont. Zhurn.,* **1966,** no. 2, 81–92, 1 plate.

Mouravieff, N. A. 1977. Additional conodonts from near the Middle–Upper Devonian boundary in North Cornwall. A progress report. *Proc. Ussher Soc., 4* (1), 63–66.

Muller, K. J. 1956. Die Gattung Palmatolepis. *Abh. Senck. naturf. Ges., 494,* 1–70, 11 plates.

Orchard, M. 1972. The conodont biostratigraphy of the Plymouth Limestones about the Middle–Upper Devonian boundary. *Proc. Ussher Soc., 2* (5), 471–474.

Orchard, M. 1974. Famennian conodonts and cavity infills in the Plymouth Limestone (South Devon). *Proc. Ussher Soc., 3* (1), 49–54.

Orchard, M. 1975. Conodonts, correlation and stratigraphy of the Plymouth Limestones. *Unpublished Ph D Thesis,* University of Hull.

Orchard, M. 1977. Plymouth–Tamar. In: M. R. House et. al. (Eds.), *A Correlation of Devonian rocks in the British Isles, Geol. Soc. London Spec. Rep., 8,* 20–23.

Orchard, M. 1978a. The conodont biostratigraphy of the Devonian Plymouth Limestone, South Devon. *Palaeontology, 21,* 907–955, 9 plates.

Orchard, M. 1978b. Plymouth Limestone. In: C. T. Scrutton (Ed.) *A Field Guide to selected areas of the Devonian of South-west England, Int. Symp. on the Devonian System, Palaeontological Association,* 53–56.

Orchard, M. 1979. On a *varcus* Zone conodont fauna from the Ilfracombe Slates (Devonian, North Devon). *Geol. Mag., 116,* 129–134, 1 plate.

Orr, R. W. and Klapper, G. 1968. Two new conodont species from Middle–Upper Devonian boundary beds of Indiana and New York. *J. Paleontol.* **42,** 1066–1075, 2 plates.

Paproth, E. 1964. Die Untergrenze des Karbons. *C. R. 5éeme Congr. Int. de Stratigraphie et de Géologique du Carbonifère, Paris, 1963,* 611–618.

Paproth, E. 1980. The Devonian–Carboniferous boundary. *Lethaia, 13,* 287.

Paproth, E. and Steel, M. (Eds.) 1984. The Devonian–Carboniferous boundary. *Cour. Forsch.-Inst. Senckenberg, 67,* 1–258.

Pennington, J. J. 1975. The geology of the Argyll Field. In: A. W. Woodland (Ed.), *Petroleum and the Continental Shelf of North-west Europe, 1,* 285–291.

Philip, G. M. and Jackson, J. H. 1967. Lower Devonian subspecies of the conodont *Polygnathus linguiformis* Hinde from southeastern Australia. *J. Paleontol., 41,* 1262–1266.

Poole, E. G. 1977. Stratigraphy of the Steeple Aston Borehole, Oxfordshire. *Bull. Geol. Surv. Gt. Br., 57,* 1–85.

Rhodes, F. H. T. and Dineley, D. L. 1957a. Devonian conodont faunas from South-west England. *J. Paleontol., 31,* 353–369, 2 plates.

Rhodes, F. H. T. and Dineley, D. L. 1957b. Supplementary notes on Devonian conodont faunas from South-west England. *J. Paleontol., 31,* 1175.

Rhodes, F. H. T., Williams, J. A. and Robinson, J. C. 1973. Micromorphologic studies of platform conodonts. In: F. H. T. Rhodes (Ed.) *Conodont Paleozoology, Spec. Paper Geol. Soc. Am., 141,* 117–141.

Riddolls, B. W. 1970a. The origin of calcareous nodules in Upper Devonian Slate near Newton Abbot. *Proc. Ussher Soc., 2* (3), 158–159.

Riddolls, B. W. 1970b. Devonian and Carboniferous geology South and West of Newton Abbot, Devon. *Unpublished Ph.D. Thesis,* University of Exeter.

Sadler, P. M. 1973a. An interpretation of new stratigraphic evidence from South Cornwall. *Proc. Ussher Soc., 2* (6), 535–550.

Sadler, P. M. 1973b. A proposed stratigraphical succession for the Roseland area of South Cornwall. *Unpublished Ph.D. Thesis,* University of Bristol.

Sandberg, C. A. 1976. Conodont biofacies of late Devonian *Polygnathus styriacus* Zone in Western United States. In: C. R. Barnes (Ed.) *Conodont Paleoecology, Spec. Paper Geol. Ass. Can., 15,* 171–186.

Sandberg, C. A. 1979. Devonian and Lower Mississippian conodont zonation of the Great Basin and Rocky Mountains. In: C. A. Sandberg and D. L. Clark (Eds.) *Conodont Biostratigraphy of the Great Basin and Rocky Mountains, Geol. Stud. Brigham*

Young Univ., **26,** 87–106.

Sandberg, and Dreesen, R., 1983. Alternate Late Devonian zonation for shallow-water conodont biofacies. *Abstract Geol. Soc. Am., North Central Section Meet. Madison, Wisconsin,* 220.

Sandberg, C. A. and Dreesen, R., 1984. Late Devonian icriodontid biofacies models and alternate shallow-water conodont zonation. In: D. L. Clark (Ed.), *Conodont Biofacies and Provincialism, Spec. Paper Geol. Soc. Am.,* **196,** 143–178, 4 plates.

Sandberg, C. A. and Gutschick, R. C. 1979. Guide to conodont biostratigraphy of Upper Devonian and Mississippian rocks along the Wasatch Front and Cordilleran Hingeline, Utah. In: C. A. Sandberg and D. L. Clark (Eds.) *Conodont Biostratigraphy of the Great Basin and Rocky Mountains, Geol. Stud. Brigham Young Univ.,* **26,** 107–134.

Sandberg, C. A., Gutschick, R. C., Johnson, J. G., Poole, F. G. and Sando, W. J. 1983. Middle Devonian to late Mississippian geologic history of the overthrust belt region, Western United States. In R. B. Powers (Ed.), *Geologic Studies of the Cordilleran Thrust Belt,* Rocky Mountain Association of Geologists, **2,** 691–719.

Sandberg, C. A., Leuteritz, K. and Brill, S. M. 1978. Phylogeny, speciation and zonation of *Siphonodella* (Conodonta, Upper Devonian and Lower Carboniferous). *Newsl. Stratigr.,* **7,** 102–120.

Sandberg, C. A. and Poole, F. G. 1977. Conodont biostratigraphy and depositional complexes of Upper Devonian cratonic-platform and continental-shelf rocks in the Western United States. In: M. A. Murray, W. B. N. Berry and C. A. Sandberg (Eds.), *Western North America: Devonian. Calif. Univ. Riverside Campus Mus. Contrib.,* **4,** 144–182.

Sandberg, C. A., Streel, M. and Scott, R. A. 1972. Comparison between conodont zonation and spore assemblages at the Devonian–Carboniferous boundary in the Western and Central United States and in Europe. *C.R. 7eme Congr. Int. de Stratigraphie et de Géologique du Caronifére, Krefeld, 1971,* **1,** 179–203, 4 plates.

Sandberg, C. A. and Ziegler, W. 1973. Refinement of standard Upper Devonian conodont zonation based on sections in Nevada and West Germany. *Geol. Palaeontol.,* **7,** 97–122, 5 plates.

Sandberg, C. A. and Ziegler, W. 1979. Taxonomy and biofacies of important conodonts of Late Devonian *styriacus* Zone, United States and Germany. *Geol. Palaeontol.,* **13,** 173–212, 7 plates.

Sannemann, D. 1955. Oberdevonische Conodonten (to II alpha). *Senckenbergiana leth.* **36,** 123–156, 6 plates.

Schmidt, H. 1924. Zwei Cephalopodenfaunen an der Devon–Carbon grenze im Sauerland. *Jahrb. preuB. Geol. Landesamtes,* **44,** 98–171, 3 plates.

Schumacher, D. 1977. Conodont biofacies and paleoenvironments in Middle Devonian–Upper Devonian boundary beds, Central Missouri. In: C. R. Barnes (Ed.) *Conodont Paleoecology, Spec. Paper Geol. Assoc. Can.,* **15,** 159–169.

Scott, A. J. 1961. Three new conodonts from the Louisi-ana Limestone (Upper Devonian) of western Illinois. *J. Paleontol.,* **35,** 1223–1227.

Scrutton, C. T. 1977. Facies variations in the Devonian limestones of eastern South Devon. *Geol. Mag.,* **114,** 165–193.

Scrutton, C. D. (Ed.) 1978. *A Field Guide to Selected Areas of the Devonian of South-west England, Int. Symp. on the Devonian System,* Palaeontological Association, 1–73.

Seddon, G. and Sweet, W. 1971. An ecologic model for conodonts. *J. Paleaontol.,* **45,** 869–880.

Selwood, E. B. 1960. Ammonoids and trilobites from the Upper Devonian and Lowest Carboniferous of the Launceston area of Cornwall. *Palaeontology,* **3,** 153–185, 4 plates.

Selwood, E. B. *et al.,* 1984. Geology of the country around Newton Abbot. *Mem. Br. Geol. Surv.,* Sheet 339, 1–212, 18 plates.

Selwood, E. B., Stewart, I. J. and Thomas, J. M. 1985. Upper Palaeozoic sediments and structure in North Cornwall – a reinterpretation. *Proc. Geol. Assoc.,* **96,** 129–141.

Selwood, E. B., Stewart, I. J., Turner, P. J. and Whiteley, M. J. 1982. The Devonian–Carboniferous transition and its structural setting at Chillaton, West Devon, England. *Geol. Mag.,* **119,** 383–393.

Stauffer, C. R. 1938. Conodonts of the Olentangy Shale. *J. Paleontol.,* **12,** 411–443, 6 plates.

Stauffer, C. R. 1940. Conodonts from the Devonian and associated clays of Minnesota. *J. Paleontol.,* **14,** 417–435, 3 plates.

Smythe, D. K. 1973. Structure of the Devonian Limestone at Brixham. *Proc. Ussher Soc.,* **2,** 617–625.

Stewart, I. J. 1981a. Late Devonian and Lower Carboniferous conodonts from North Cornwall and their stratigraphical significance. *Proc. Ussher Soc.,* **5,** 179–185.

Stewart, I. J. 1981b. The structure, stratigraphy and biostratigraphy of the northeastern margin of Bodmin Moor and adjacent areas. *Unpublished Ph.D. Thesis,* University of Exeter.

Straaten, P. van and Tucker, M. E. 1972. The Upper Devonian Saltern Cove Goniatite Bed is an intraformational slump. *Palaeontology,* **15,** 430–438.

Szulczewski, M. 1971. Upper Devonian conodonts, stratigraphy and facial development in the Holy Cross Mts. *Acta Geol. Polonica,* **21.** 1–129, 34 plates.

Telford, P. G. 1975. Lower and Middle Devonian conodonts from the Broken River Embayment, north Queensland, Australia. *Spec. Pap. in Palaeontol.,* **15,** 1–96, 16 plates.

Thomas, L. A. 1949. Devonian–Mississippian formations of south-east Iowa. *Bull Geol. Soc. Amer.,* **60,** 403–437, 4 plates.

Tucker, M. E. 1969. Crinoidal turbidites from the Devonian of Cornwall and their palaeogeographic significance. *Sedimentology,* **13,** 281–290.

Tucker, M. E. and Straaten, P. van. 1970a. Conodonts and facies on the Chudleigh schwelle. *Proc. Ussher Soc.,* **2** (3), 160–170.

Tucker, M. E. and Straaten, P. van 1970b. Conodonts

from the Upper Devonian of the Saltern Cove–Elberry Cove area. *Proc. Ussher Soc.,* **2** (3), 159.

Ulrich, E. O. and Bassler, R. S. 1926. A classification of the toothlike fossils, conodonts, with descriptions of American Devonian and Mississippian species. *Proc. U.S. Nat. Mus.,* **68,** art. 12, 1–63, 11 plates.

Uyeno, T. T. 1967. Conodont zonation of the Waterways Formation (Upper Devonian) northeastern and central Alberta, *Geol. Surv. Can. Pap.* 67–30, 1–20.

Voges, A. 1959. Conodonten aus dem Unterkarbon I und II (*Gattendorfia-* und *Pericyclus-*Stufe) des Sauerlandes. *Paläontol. Z.,* **33,** 266–314, 3 plates.

Waters, R. A. 1974. Palaeozoic succession and structure between Little Haldon and Dartmoor. *Unpublished Ph.D. Thesis,* University of Exeter.

Weddige, K. 1977. Die Conodonten der Eifel-Stufe in Typusgebiet und in benachbarten Faziesqebieten. *Senkenberg Lethaea,* **58,** 271–419, 6 plates.

Weddige, K. 1982. The Wetteldorf Richtschnitt as boundary stratotype from the view point of conodont stratigraphy. In: R. Werner and W. Ziegler, (Eds.) *Proposal of a Boundary Stratotype for the Lower–Middle Devonian Boundary (partitus Boundary). Cour. Forsch.-Inst. Senckenberg,* **55,** 13–84.

Weddige, K. and Ziegler, W. 1976. The significance of *Icriodus: Polygnathus* ratios in limestones from the type Eifelian, Germany. In: C. R. Barnes (Ed.) *Conodont Paleoecology Spec. Paper Geol. Assoc. Can.,* **15,** 187–199.

Whiteley, M. J. 1981. The faunas of the Viverdon Down area, South-east Cornwall. *Proc. Ussher Soc.,* **5** (2), 186–193.

Williams, J. A. 1970. The conodont faunas of the Baggy and Pilton Beds, North Devon. *Unpublished Ph.D. Thesis,* University of Wales.

Wirth, M. 1967. Zur Gliederung des höheren Paläozoikums (Givet-Namur) im Gebiet des Quinto Real (Westpyrenäen) mit Hilfe von Conodonten. *N. Jb. Geol. Paläontol., Abh.,* **127,** 179–244, 5 plates.

Wittekindt, H. 1966. Zur Conodontenchronologie des Mitteldevons. *Das Mitteldevon des Rheinischen Schiefergebirges, Ein Symp.* In *Fortsch. Geol. Rheinl. Westfalen,* **9,** 621–646, 3 plates.

Young, J. 1880. On a group of fossil organisms termed conodonts. *Proc. Nat. Hist. Soc. Glasgow,* **4,** 5–7, 10, 78, 79..

Youngquist, W. L. 1945. Upper Devonian conodonts from the Independence Shale of Iowa. *J. Paleontol.,* **19,** 355–367, 3 plates.

Youngquist, W. L. 1947. A new Upper Devonian conodont fauna from Iowa. *J. Paleontol.,* **21,** 95–112, plates 24–26.

Zeigler, W. 1956. Unterdevonische Conodonten, insbesondere aus dem Schönauer und dem Zorgensis-Kalk.–Notizbl. hess. Landesamt Bodenforsch., **84,** 93–106, 2 plates.

Ziegler, W. 1962. Taxionomie und Phylogenie Oberdevonischer Conodonten und ihre Stratigraphische Bedeutung. *Abh. Hess. Landesamtes Bodenforsch,* **38,** 1–166, 14 plates.

Ziegler, W. 1966. Eine Verfeinerung der Conodonten-gliederung an der Grenze Mittel /Oberdevon, in: *Das Mittledevon des Rheinischen Schiefergebirges. Ein Symposium. – Fortschr. Geol. Rheinl.-Westf.,* **9,** 647–676, 6 plates.

Ziegler, W. 1969. Eine neue Conodontenfauna aus dem höchsten Oberdevon. *Fortschr. Geol. Rheinl. Westfalen,* **17,** 343–360, 2 plates.

Ziegler, W. 1971. Conodont stratigraphy of the European Devonian. In: W. C. Sweet and S. M. Bergström (Eds.) *Symp. on Conodont Biostratigraphy,* in *Mem. Geol. Soc. Am.,* **127,** 227–284.

Ziegler, W. (Ed.) 1975. *Catalogue of Conodonts II,* Schweizerbart'sche, Stuttgart, 1–404, 25 plates.

Ziegler, W. 1979. Historical subdivision of the Devonian. In: M. R. House, C. R. Scrutton and M. G. Bassett (Eds.) *The Devonian System, Spec. Papers Palaeontol.,* **23,** 23–47.

Ziegler, W. 1982. Conodont age of *Phariceras lunulicosta* Zone. In: R. Werner and W. Ziegler (Eds.); *Proposal of a Boundary Stratotype for the Lower–Middle Devonian Boundary (partitus Boundary) Cour. Forsch.-Inst. Senckenberg,* **55,** 493–496.

Ziegler, W. and Huddle, J. W. 1968. Die *Palmatolepis glabra-*Gruppe (Conodonta) nach der Revision der Typen von Ulrich und Bassler durch J. W. Huddle. *Fortschr. Geol. Rheinl.-Westfalen,* **16,** 377–386.

Ziegler W. and Klapper, G. 1964. In: W. Ziegler, G. Klapper and M. Lindström, 1964. The validity of the name *Polygnathus* (Conodonta, Devonian and Lower Carboniferous). *J. Paleontol.,* **38,** 421–423.

Ziegler, W. and Klapper, G. 1982a. The *disparilis* Conodont Zone, the proposed level for the Middle–Upper Devonian boundary. In: R. Werner and W. Ziegler (Eds.), *Proposal of a Boundary Stratotype for the Lower–Middle Devonian Boundary (partitus-Boundary), Cour. Frosch.-Inst. Senckenberg,* **55,** 463–492.

Ziegler, W. and Klapper, G. 1982b. Subcommission on Devonian stratigraphy: decisions since 1973 and present status. In: R. Werner and W. Ziegler (Eds.), *Proposal of a Boundary Stratotype for the Lower–Middle Devonian Boundary (partitus-Boundary), Cour. Forsch.-Inst. Senckenberg,* **55,** 7–12.

Ziegler, W, Klapper G. and Johnson, J. G. 1976. Redefinition and subdivision of the *varcus* Zone (conodonts, Middle–?Upper Devonian) in Europe and North America. *Geol. Palaeontol.,* **10,** 109–140, 4 plates.

Ziegler, W. and Sandberg, C. A. 1983. *Palmatolepis-*based revision of upper part of standard late Devonian conodont zonation. *Abstract Geol. Soc. Am., North Central Section Meet., Madison, Wisconsin,* 221.

Ziegler, 1984. *Palmatolepis-*based revision of upper part of standard late Devonian conodont zonation. In: D. L. Clark (Ed.), *Conodont Biofacies and Provincialism, Spec. Paper Geol Soc. Am.,* **196,** 179–194, 2 plates.

Ziegler, W. and Sandberg, C. A. 1984a. In: R. Werner and W. Ziegler (Eds.), Proposal of boundary stratotype for the Lower–Middle DevonianBoundary (*partitus Boundary). Important candidate sections for stratotype of conodont-based Devonian–Carboniferous boundary*. Cour. Forsch.-Inst. Senckenberg, **67**, 231–239.

Ziegler, W., Sandberg, C. A. and Austin, R. L. 1974. Revision of *Bispathodus* Group (Conodonta) in the Upper Devonian and Lower Carboniferous. *Geol. Palaeontol.*, **8**, 97–112, 3. plates.

5

The Carboniferous System: Part 1 – Conodonts of the Dinantian Subsystem from Great Britain and Ireland

W. J. Varker and G. D. Sevastopulo

5.1. HISTORY OF CONODONT STUDIES

The first record of British Dinantian conodonts was by Moore (1863), in his description of the palaeontology of mineral veins in the Carboni- ferous Limestone. The number of early records, however, was very small (e.g. Young, 1880a, 1880b; Hinde, 1879, 1900; Smith, 1900) and it was not until the 1960s (Fig. 5.1) that the number of research workers and publications dramatically

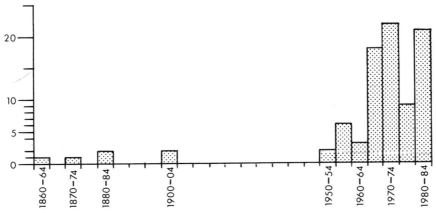

Fig. 5.1 – Histogram showing the number of publications referring to British and Irish Dinantian conodonts in five-year intervals.

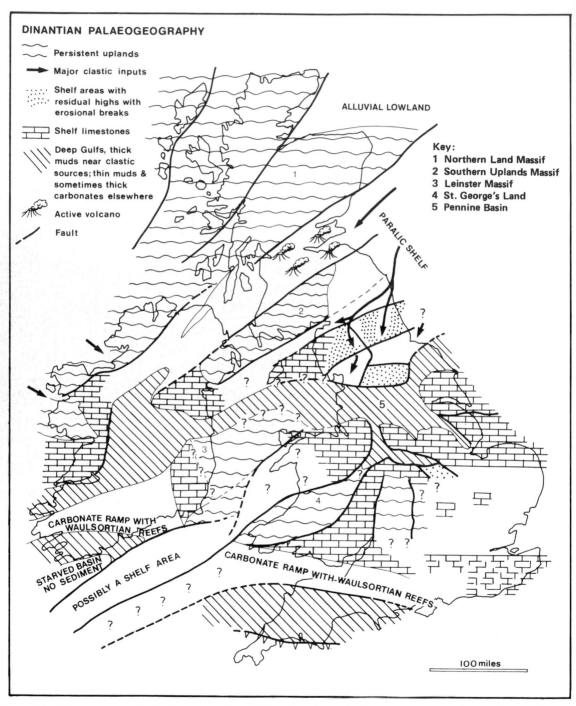

Fig. 5.2 – A generalized palaeogeography of Dinantian times. Evidence suggests that the position of the coastlines, particularly those of St. George's Land, fluctuated widely throughout the Dinantian Subperiod. Map compiled by Dr. D. Moore.

increased. This trend, which started at least ten years later than in Germany, where the first conodont zonation of Lower Carboniferous rocks had been made, and considerably later than in the USA, reached its peak during the early 1970s. Probably the earliest influential work during this recent period was the description of the conodonts of the Dinantian succession of the Avon Gorge, Bristol, by Rhodes *et al.* (1969), which together with a relatively small number of other publications dominated Dinantian conodont research in Britain and Ireland. The preponderance of shallow-water sequences in the British Dinantian Subsystem and a palaeogeography (Fig. 5.2) which led to numerous isolated areas of deposition, resulted in a multitude of zones which may appear confusing to those not familiar with the succession. The situation has been further complicated by the fact that after many years of relative stability the accepted chronostratigraphy of the British Dinantian Subsystem has also recently undergone substantial revision (George *et al.*, 1976).

Since the number of published and unpublished works on Dinantian conodonts is large, it has been necessary to subdivide this section both regionally and on the basis of subject.

(a) Regional Conodont Studies (Fig. 5.3)

In view of the strongly regional nature of the Dinantian succession, which accumulated in a series of distinct provinces dominated by the positive feature of St. Geroge's Land (see Fig. 5.2), descriptions of faunas which are of primarily regional significance are considered under the accepted palaeogeographic headings. For clarification of the age of faunas mentioned in the following sections, reference should be made to the section on conodont zonation (5.4).

(i) *South-west Province*

The first reference to Dinantian conodonts from the South-west Province was by Dineley and Rhodes (1956), who recorded sixteen productive horizons from various localities ranging from South Devon to the Mendips and ranging in age from the Lower Frasnian Stage to near the top of the Tournaisian Series.

Within the South-west Province, faunas from the Culm facies of Devon and Cornwall are considered separately wherever possible since, in addition to environmental and faunal differences, the structural setting of Devon and Cornwall is also very different from that of the carbonate area further north.

House and Butcher (1962) reported two conodont faunas associated with the Winstow Cherts at Chudleigh in South Devon; these were further discussed by Matthews (1969b). The lower of the two faunas was considered to resemble Voges' (1960) *Siphonodella crenulata* Zone, which, in the opinion of Matthews (1969a, p. 277), had in turn been wrongly assigned a cuIIα age on the cephalopod-based Dinantian standard. The higher of the two faunas was confidently assigned to Voges' *anchoralis* Zone and demonstrated a coincidence of *Scaliognathus* and siphonodellids which had not been encountered in North America. Matthews (1961, 1969a) described another fauna of this age from the siliceous sequence around St. Mellion in East Cornwall. This fauna, which had first been referred to in an abstract (Matthews, 1961), consisted of forms typical of Voges' *anchoralis* Zone, even to the extent of containing specimens of the Upper Devonian genus *Palmatolepis*. Austin and Matthews (1968) recorded two conodont faunas from the Boscastle district of Cornwall, the lower of which was dated as cuIIδ on the goniatite scheme (*Cavusgnathus–Apatognathus* Zone of Austin, 1973b) whereas the upper was considered to correlate with cuIIIβ (*Mestognathus beckmanni–Gnathodus bilineatus*). Seven further publications have dealt with Dinantian conodonts from Devon and Cornwall. Matthews and Thomas (1968, 1974) described faunas, including mixed assemblages of cuII and cuIII age from North-east Devon; Matthews *et al.* (1972) described a prolific fauna of approximately *anchoralis* Zone age from Chillaton, South-west Devon. The doubt implied in the dating of the latter fauna arose from the absence of the three primary indices recommended by Voges for the recognition of the *anchoralis* Zone, in spite of the presence of the very restricted *Dollymae hassi*, which had previously only been found in the

Fig. 5.3 – Generalized geological map, showing the distribution in Britain and Ireland of rocks of Dinantian age and the location of some cited works.

upper part of the *anchoralis* Zone in Germany. Austin (in Beer and Fenning, 1976) named a few conodonts from a borehole at Southern Tors. A series of eleven conodont zones (Fig. 5.4) was established for the Dinantian succession of South-west England by Stewart (1981a). Stewart (1981b) also considered the stratigraphic significance of faunas from late Devonian and Lower Carboniferous horizons in the Launceston district of North Cornwall. Finally, using abundant siphonodellids, Selwood *et al.* (1982) were able to recognize the Devonian–Carboniferous boundary in borehole material from the inverted limb of a fold in a major thrust sheet at Chillaton, West Devon.

The British Geological Survey (then the Institute of Geological Sciences) drilled a deep borehole at Cannington Park, Somerset (Knap Farm Borehole) to examine the Upper Palaeozoic sequence of that area and the ensuing report (*Institute of Geological Sciences Report, 82/5,* 1982) included a description of the biostratigraphy (Mitchell, *et al.,* 1982). Conodonts were described covering a range from the Devonian–Carboniferous boundary to just above the *anchoralis* Zone, over a depth range from 1100 to 400 m.

The South-west Province also includes the carbonate area of the Mendips and South Wales. The description of conodonts from the Avon Gorge and other areas by Rhodes *et al.* (1969) was the first publication to deal with this classic area, except for brief previews of that paper (Austin *et al.,* 1966; Austin, 1968b). Austin and Rhodes (1969) published a description of a fused assemblage of four apatognathids and one *Spathognathodus scitulus* collected from a relatively unfossiliferous horizon high in the Avon Gorge succession and interpreted it as the remains of a single conodont-bearing animal. Austin and Davies (1984) provided additional information of conodont occurrence in South Wales.

The unpublished Ph.D. Thesis of Butler (1972) formed the basis of a major paper (Butler, 1973), in which he described the conodont faunas of the Lower Limestone Shale and Black Rock Groups from the Eastern Mendips, where the succession is considerably thicker than in the Avon Gorge. Of particular interest was the pres-

ence of *Scaliognathus anchoralis* and a number of other closely associated forms, including *Dollymae bouckaerti,* which compared closely with faunas which had already been described (Groessens, 1977) from Tn_{3c} in Belgium and which were not known from what was by then considered to be the incomplete Avon Gorge succession (see also Matthews and Butler, 1974). Further records from the Mendips are contained in Austin and Davies (1984).

Another publication from the same approximate area and year was the description of the faunas of *Patrognathus variabilis–S. plumulus* and *Siphonodella–Polygnathus inornatus* age from a temporary roadside exposure at Tintern, Monmouthshire (now Gwent), by Austin and Hill (1973). In this paper the authors concentrated on the possible phylogenetic relationships between species of *Spathognathodus* and *Clydagnathus* and illustrated a growth series in *Patrognathus variabilis.*

The two remaining publications relating to the South-west Province both significantly modified the established view of Dinantian stratigraphy and palaeogeography. Bassett and Jenkins (1977) presented spore and conodont evidence suggesting that the Skrinkle Sandstone of Pembrokeshire, of Old Red Sandstone facies and traditionally regarded as being late Devonian in age, is of lowermost Dinantian age, in its upper parts, with a conodont fauna including *Patrognathus variabilis* and *Bispathodus aculeatus plumulus.* Mitchell and Reynolds (1981) recorded a conodont fauna characteristic of the *Siphonodella–Polygnathus inornatus* Zone from the outlier at Lilleshall, Shropshire, and in so doing extended the South-west Province so far northwards that it virtually splits St. George's land in two and overlaps the most southerly outcrops of the Pennine Basin (see Fig. 5.2).

(ii) *Ireland*

The earliest references to conodonts in the Dinantian rocks of Ireland (Smyth, 1950; Robbie, 1955; Fowler, 1955) were records of (Brigantian) forms found in the course of general stratigraphic investigations. The first study specifically con-

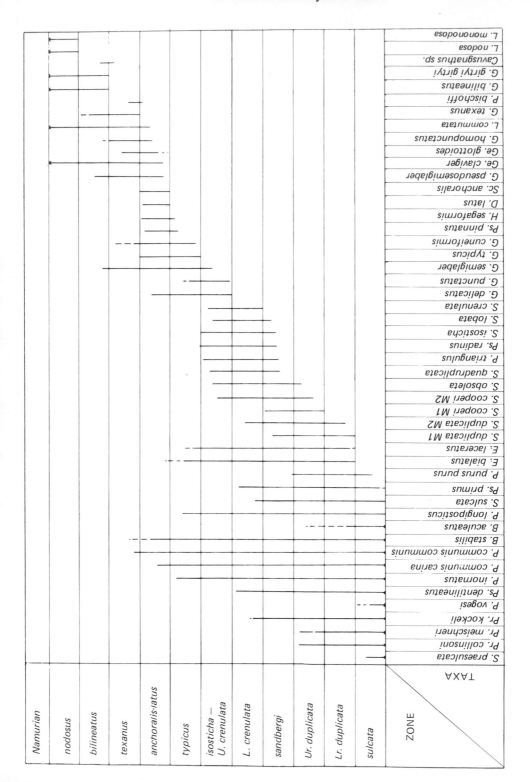

Fig. 5.4 — Ranges of Dinantian conodonts from Cornwall. Information provided by Dr. I. J. Stewart.

cerned with conodonts appearing in an unpublished M.Sc. Thesis (Johnson, 1967) on late Dinantian and early Namurian faunas from the Counties Clare and Leitrim. Several publications by Austin and co-workers between 1968 and 1975 described isolated faunas and more complete sequences of faunas from several regions. Papers dealing with isolated faunas include the following: Austin (1968c), with two faunal lists from mid-Dinantian horizons from Midleton, County Cork, and Askeaton, County Limerick; Austin and Aldridge (1969), with lists of two further mid-Dinantian faunas, from the Kingscourt outlier, County Meath; Hill (1971), which included the first record of *Scaliognathus anchoralis* in Ireland; Austin and Groessens (1972), with references to the occurrence of *Dollymae bouckaerti* and *Eotaphrus (Spathognathodus) bultynki;* Austin (1974), which includes lists of two late Dinantian faunas from Counties Leitrim and Meath, as well as references to several other faunas. Descriptions of sequences of faunas are contained in the following: Aldridge *et al.* (1968), in which the fauna of late Dinantian goniatite-bearing beds in County Leitrim is compared with those of similar age from brachiopod-bearing limestones of North Wales; Austin *et al.* (1970b), which lists and illustrates faunas from several horizons of early to late Dinantian age from around the Shannon Estuary; Austin and Mitchell (1975), in which are listed and illustrated faunas from mid to late Dinantian horizons from Counties Fermanagh and Tyrone. Austin and Husri (1974) provided further details of late Dinantian faunas from County Leitrim and early to late Dinantian faunas from around the Shannon estuary. Austin and Davies (1984) provide a map of the Hill localities.

Matthews and Naylor (1973) described (Courceyan) conodont faunas from the dominantly mudrock basinal sequences of Ringabella, the Old Head of Kinsale and Bantry, County Cork, as well as the more limestone-rich section of Whiting Bay, County Waterford. Work on faunas from this South Munster Basin and from its northern margin has continued and references to the conodont faunas are to be found in Clayton *et al.* (1982), George *et al.* (1976), Naylor *et al.* (1974, 1983), Sevastopulo and Naylor (1981), Sevastopulo (1982) and Naylor *et al.* (1974).

The well-known Courceyan section at Hook Head, County Wexford, has been the subject of study for a number of years. Sleeman *et al.* (1974) provided the first outline of the distribution of conodonts through the section, but more detailed information, with illustrations of the fauna and the description of a new taxon, is to be found in Johnston and Higgins (1981). Courceyan faunas from the neighbouring Wexford outlier were listed by Sleeman *et al.* (1983), and Keeley (1983) outlined the distribution of conodonts in the Courceyan–Asbian succession from the nearby Carrick-on-Suir syncline, to the north-west of Hook Head. The latter faunas are treated in greater detail in an unpublished Ph.D. Thesis (Keeley, 1980). Three further studies deal with Courceyan conodonts from the south of the country; Clayton *et al.* (1977) listed faunas of early Courceyan age from South County Kilkenny, in an unpublished M.Sc. Thesis Jones (1977) described the faunas from a borehole in South County Kilkenny and Clayton *et al.* (1980) described faunas from a borehole at Ballyvergin, County Clare.

Conodonts from the Irish Midlands have been described in several unpublished or only partially published theses. Johnston (1976) recorded and illustrated Courceyan faunas from many areas and established a zonal scheme; Marchant (1978) included details of the distribution of conodonts in the Courceyan–Arundian rocks of the Dublin region; and Polgar (1980) described Courceyan and Chadian conodont faunas from a borehole near Rinn River, County Leitrim. Lastly, Marchant *et al.* (1984) attempted to correlate the conodont, foraminiferal and spore zonal schemes for the Irish Courceyan Stage.

There have been few conodonts studies from the North and North-west of Ireland. Apart from those of Austin and Mitchell (1975) and records in George *et al.* (1976), the only published works are Browne (1981), who described Asbian-aged faunas from County Sligo, and Morris *et al.* (1981), who listed Courceyan faunas from near Carrickallen, County Leitrim.

(iii) *Pennine Basin*

Reference to Fig. 5.2 indicates that the Pennine Basin, which for convenience also includes North Wales, is bounded to the south by the northern coastline of St. George's Land and to the north by the Northern Pennine block system and the Lake District. In terms of the South-west Province zonation, the succession in this area ranges from the non-sequence below the *Mestognathus beckmanni– Polygnathus bischoffi* Zone to the top of the Dinantian Subsystem and, within this range, is complete. Difficulties have arisen in the past since the zonal scheme for this area was not published until 1981 (Metcalfe 1981; see also 5.4), in contrast with the situation in the South-west Province, where the Rhodes *et al.* scheme (1969) was among the vanguard of publications for that area.

The earliest records of Dinantian conodonts from the Pennine Basin well illustrate the difficulties which result from the differing and often extensive time required for publication. The earliest reference was a description of Visean faunas from Flintshire (and also Ireland) by Aldridge *et al.* (1968) in which correlations were made with the then unpublished Rhodes *et al.* (1969) scheme. In contrast, Reynolds (1970) who also described a fauna from Flintshire in his study of the Gronant Borehole (Institute of Geological Sciences) correlated his results with the work of Bischoff (1957), Voges (1959, 1960), Collinson *et al.* (1962) and Boogaert (1967) but did not refer to Rhodes *et al.* (1969).

Austin (1968a) recorded conodonts from isolated horizons in the North of England, three of which were in the Pennine Basin whereas the remaining two were associated with the boundary between the basin and the Northern Pennine Blocks. Morris (1969) published a short communication of considerable interest, since he recorded a *Scaliognathus anchoralis* fauna from limestones in North Staffordshire which indicated that a gap occurred in the conodont sequence established by Rhodes *et al.* (1969) for the South-west Province. In a further short paper, Austin and Aldridge (1973) described faunas from two localities in North Wales and the Isle of Man, the first record

of conodonts associated with diagnostic zonal goniatites of B_2 or P_1 age.

As part of his major study of Namurian conodonts from the South and Central Pennines, Higgins (1975) included horizons from the Dinantian and Westphalian Series. The only zone of relevance to the present chapter is the *Gnathodus girtyi collinsoni* Zone of the Brigantian Stage, which had been established by Rhodes *et al.* (1969) and was recognized by Higgins (1975, p. 13) from Matlock and from the Tansley and Highoredish boreholes.

Metcalfe and Leeder (1979) described various aspects of the limestone sequence obtained from the St. Helen's Well Borehole, Eshton, including the conodont faunas of the upper limestone member. Although the faunas were sparse, they were adequate for correlation with the *Mestognathus beckmanni– Polygnathus bischoffi* Zone of Rhodes *et al.* (1969) and thus to assign a Chadian age to the sequence. Metcalfe (1980) correlated faunas from the Raygill Quarry Limestone of Lothersdale with the *Gnathodus homopunctatus* and *Lochriea commutata* Zones of the Craven Lowlands and suggested that, in view of the similarity of the faunas with those of the Embsay Limestone of the Skipton Anticline, the strata in Raygill Quarry should be assigned to the Embsay Limestone. Other work relating to the Pennine Basin includes that of Miller and Austin (unpublished), which was referred to in Austin (1974, Chart 1), and the Ph.D. Thesis of Metcalfe (1976). Much of the information from the latter forms the basis of Metcalfe's (1981) zonal scheme for the Craven Lowlands reviewed later this chapter (5.4).

(iv) *Northern Pennines*

The Dinantian rocks of the Northern Pennines are very different from those of the Pennine basin. They lie unconformably on a Lower Palaeozoic basement broken by major faults which influenced Dinantian sedimentation. Uplifted blocks (Alston, Askrigg, the Isle of Man and the Northern Lake District) developed thin limestones with non-sequences; the intervening trough sequences (Kendal, Barnard Castle, Penrith, Northumberland and Solway) are thicker with clastic intercalations and few or no non-sequences. Late Courceyan spores occur in the basal clastics in the troughs and on the Northern Lake District block. The overlying limestones are of Chadian age in the troughs, whence they gradually encroached onto the adjacent blocks. A widespread Asbian limestone covers blocks and troughs alike and is succeeded by cyclothems of Brigantian age, the Yoredale Group.

The earliest record of conodonts from this area was by Johnson (1959), who recorded their presence in the Four Fathom, Great and Little Limestones of the Yoredale Group from the Roman Wall District of the Northumberland Trough. Since the top of the Dinantian Subsystem is located between the Four Fathom and Great Limestones (Johnson *et al.*, 1962, p. 344), only those specimens recorded from the Four Fathom Limestone are relevant to this chapter. The first paper dealing specifically with Dinantian conodonts from the Northern Pennines was a review of the genus *Apatognathus* (Varker, 1967), which is surprisingly abundant and varied in these horizons, where it represents over 10% of the total fauna. Facies control was considered (Varker, 1967, p. 138) to be a possible determining factor in the distribution of this genus. Varker (1968) described the numerical distribution of conodonts through the Yoredale Limestones and recorded a commonly repeated pattern in which the greatest concentration of elements was in the upper third of each limestone, irrespective of thickness. Further records of Yoredale conodonts have been given by Rhodes *et al.* (1969).

Conodont faunal lists amongst others, were included, in the field guide to the boundary stratotypes of the Carboniferous Stages in Britain, for the 1981 field meeting of the Subcommission on Carboniferous Stratigraphy (Ramsbottom, 1981). These lists were provided by a number of conodont workers who were not individually identified in the guide; they relate to the Asbian and Brigantian Stages as far as the North of England is concerned but also included a faunal list for the Arundian Stage of Hobby Horse Bay in Pembrokeshire. It is also intended to publish full faunal descriptions of the Carboniferous

stratotypes of Northern Europe, including conodonts of the Dinantian stratotypes (Varker *et al.*, in press).

The zonal scheme of Higgins and Varker (1982), based on the Dinantian sequence in Ravenstonedale, Cumbria, is reviewed in **5.4** of this chapter.

Other work on Dinantian conodonts from the North of England region (see Fig. 5.3) includes that of Varker (1964), who has worked primarily on Asbian and Brigantian horizons, Austin and Ramsbottom (unpublished, referred to by Austin 1974, Chart 1, p. 6 under the heading 'Settle District') and Swift (unpublished), who has worked on faunas of late Arundian–early Brigantian age from the Isle of Man. The latter work includes the record of a single specimen of *Embsaygnathus* (see plate 5.6), from the Derbyhaven beds (late Arundian).

(v) *Scotland*

In view of the strong Scottish influence in several of the very earliest references to Dinantian conodonts, it is surprising that so few papers have referred to Scottish faunas in more recent years. Following Young's (1880a, 1880b) early discussions on conodonts, the first references specifically to Scottish Dinantian conodonts were by Smith (1900), who described faunas from the 'Carboniferous Limestone' of the West of Scotland and Hinde (1900), who concentrated on localities from the Midland Valley. Hinde's specimens have been redescribed and refigured by Clarke (1960), who included additional material from the John Smith Collection (British Geological Survey, Edinburgh), as well as his own collections, together with specimens provided by Dr. E. D. Currie and Professor (then Dr.) G. Y. Craig. (See also Craig, 1952.) Only those horizons up to and including the Top Hosie Limestone are of Dinantian age and therefore of relevance to this chapter. Craig (1954) had earlier recorded conodonts in the Top Hosie Shale in his description of the palaeoecology of this horizon from a locality near Kilsyth. Many of the taxa included in these Scottish works have been the subject of considerable revision since publication. Rhodes *et al.* (1969) and Austin and

Davies (1984) reported conodonts from the Harden Burn section in Roxburgh.

(b) Phylogenetic Studies of Dinantian Conodonts

A considerable number of publications, rather than being regional in their aspect, are essentially phylogenetic studies of Dinantian conodonts. They range from studies of individual genera or species to intercontinental biostratigraphic studies. In view of the evolutionary nature of such studies, they are dealt with in approximate order of publication.

One of the earliest papers was also one of the most general in subject, since Higgins (1965) considered the significance of conodonts in the Carboniferous System of Europe. On a more specific level, Austin et al. (1967) described the value of conodonts in the recognition of the Devonian–Carboniferous boundary. They paid particular attention to Great Britain, where problems had traditionally arisen over the virtual lack of Dinantian cephalopods in almost every region except in the culm facies of Devon and Cornwall, and they saw conodonts as being a means of international correlation between the cephalopod-bearing and non-cephalopod-bearing facies (see also Austin et al., 1970a, 1970b).

Rhodes and Austin (1971) later published a review of the Carboniferous conodont faunas of Europe, in which the Dinantian correlations were based on the then recently published zonal scheme for the Avon Gorge (Rhodes et al., 1969). They also included a consideration of specific boundary problems, and the regional and ecological factors controlling faunal contrasts, as well as phylogenetic studies and the problem of homeomorphy. Druce et al. (1972) also carried out cluster analysis of the same (Rhodes et al., 1969) faunas in an attempt to reconstruct statistically the original multielement assemblages of British Dinantian conodonts. Two further phylogenetic papers appeared at about this same time (Austin and Groessens, 1972; Austin, 1973a) which contained little specific reference to British Dinantian conodonts, but heralded a flood of papers in which the increasing knowledge of conodont distribution was applied to stratigraphic problems.

Austin et al. (1973) concentrated on the recognition and correlation of the Tournaisian–Viséan boundary of Belgium with North America and Britain, especially in the light of new information provided by foraminifera. The Caninia Dolomite of the Avon Gorge section is of V_{2a} age whilst Caninia Oolite rests non-sequentially on strata of highest Tournaisian (Tn_{3c}) or lowest Viséan age. In the following year, Austin (1974) published an important summary paper on the biostratigraphic distribution of conodonts in Great Britain and the Republic of Ireland, in which there was an attempt to give complete coverage of Dinantian faunas known at that time. In this paper the conodonts occurring at Dinantian stratigraphic boundaries were also discussed. This was followed by a more specific discussion on the biostratigraphic limitations of conodonts, with particular reference to the base of the Carboniferous System (Austin and Barnes, 1973).

Conodont ecology and the possibility of ecological control over their distribution had been mentioned in several papers before Matthews and Naylor (1973) proposed that this was a major factor in the world-wide distribution of siphonodellids in the Lower Carboniferous. Conodont ecology was also the subject of a paper by Austin (1976), who considered evidence from Great Britain and Ireland and its implications in West European Dinantian conodont studies. In the following year, Rhodes and Austin (1977) discussed ecologic and zoogeographic factors in the biostratigraphic utilization of conodonts in their general description of provincialism, etc., but with only occasional references to the Dinantian rocks of the UK or Ireland. Higgins (1981) outlined the distribution of conodonts in relation to the palaeogeography of late Viséan–Namurian times, including Brigantian distributions as a preamble to his world-wide review of Namurian provincialism. Austin and Davies (1984) have recently provided a substantial account of the problems associated with Dinantian conodont biofacies, which are reviewed later in this chapter (see p. 188).

It is fitting that a review of this sort should conclude with a subject which has occupied the minds of conodont specialists and of micropalaeontologists in general ever since the first discovery of conodonts. Briggs *et al.* (1983) described a specimen of an elongate soft-bodied animal complete with conodont apparatus near its anterior end, from the Lower Carboniferous of the Edinburgh district, Scotland. The morphology of the platform elements suggests *Clydagnathus?* cf. *cavusformis*.

5.2 DEPOSITORY OF COLLECTIONS OF IMPORTANCE

(a) British Geological Survey, Keyworth

A large conodont collection is housed in the Keyworth Office of the British Geological Survey, including the Dinantian material of Butler (1973), Higgins (1975), Metcalfe (1981), Austin and Mitchell (1975), Selwood *et al.* (1982) and Stewart (1981b), plus all Reynolds' published and unpublished material, including the faunas from the Cannington Park Borehole, Barry Island, etc. Most of the figured material of Matthews and his co-workers is also at the British Geological Survey.

(b) University Departments

The Department of Geology at the University of Southampton houses the collections of Austin and his co-workers, including the material from the Avon Gorge. However, in the near future, all figured specimens will be deposited at the British Museum.The Department of Geology, University of Exeter, houses the collections of former postgraduate students. The figured apatognathids, plus all the material relating to Higgins and Varker (1982), are housed in the micropalaeontology collection in the Department of Geology at the University of Sheffield.

Those figured specimens prefaced by TCD are from the extensive collections at Trinity College, Dublin, which houses most of the published Irish Dinantian material except for that of Browne (1981), which is at Queen's University, Belfast, and that of Austin and his co-workers, which is at the University of Southampton.

The Druce collection of Rhodes *et al.* (1969) is at present located at Cornell University. Much of the collection of the late S. C. Matthews is housed

in the Department of Geology at the University of Bristol. Varker's Dinantian collection from the North of England is housed in the Department of Earth Sciences at the University of Leeds.

(c) The British Museum (Natural History)

Specimens illustrated by Rhodes *et al.* (1969) and Von Bitter and Austin (1984) are housed at the British Museum (Natural History).

5.3 DINANTIAN STRATIGRAPHY

The IUGS Subcommission on Carboniferous stratigraphy recognizes the Dinantian and Silesian Subsystems as subdivisions of the Carboniferous System applicable to Western Europe. The Dinantian—Silesian Subsystem boundary does not coincide with the Mississippian—Pennsylvanian boundary recognized in North America. The Dinantian Subsystem is subdivided into the Tournaisian and Viséan Series in Western Europe. There is as yet no formal agreement as to further subdivision into stages (see Bouroz *et al.*, 1978, for discussion).

Vaughan and Garwood dominated the early work on the stratigraphy of the British Dinantian succession. Vaughan (1905, p. 264) had designated the Lower Carboniferous as 'Avonian' because of what he regarded as the completeness of the Avon Gorge sequence at Bristol and had further produced the much-used zonal scheme based, he supposed, upon the evolutionary lineages of corals and brachiopods. At about the same time Garwood was carrying out an investigation into the limestones of the North of England, resulting in a preliminary faunal zonation (Garwood, 1907), based also upon corals and brachiopods. Garwood later elaborated this work, acknowledged the importance of Vaughan's (1905) paper and included a correlation of his own zones from the North of England with those of Vaughan from the Avon Gorge (Garwood, 1913, p. 452).

This faunal zonation proved to be so successful that it became the foundation on which Dinantian stratigraphy was based for the following sixty years, in spite of the difficulties experienced away from the Bristol district and in spite of the many criticisms and subsequent redefinitions of zonal boundaries. Indeed, Ramsbottom (1973, p. 568) believed that the advance of Carboniferous stratigraphy was hampered by the success of the scheme, since during this period little attention was paid to other aspects of the Lower Carboniferous succession, particularly to details of lithology and their interpretation. Correlation with other regions, including Belgium, had been very difficult because of general faunal and facies differences. The coral—brachiopod zonation was therefore eventually superseded by a series of divisions based upon major cycles of deposition (Ramsbottom, 1973), all except the uppermost of which were characterized by major transgressions at their bases, followed by progressively shallowing sequences and often ending with evidence of emergence. The uppermost division consisted of numerous minor transgressions and regressions. George et al. (1976) later erected six regional stages, which coincided closely with the Ramsbottom cycles and which were designed to be applied throughout Britain. A minor revision of these stages was suggested by Ramsbottom and Mitchell (1980) following the work of Conil et al. (1977, 1980) in Belgium. They proposed the reinstatement of the Tournaisian Series, (approximately equivalent to the Courceyan Stage which was to be eliminated) and its subdivision into the Ivorian and Hastarian Stages. These proposals have not received unanimous acceptance in Britain and the reader is referred to the original papers. The stages outlined in the various correlation schemes and diagrams in this chapter are based on those of George et al. (1976) unless otherwise stated.

As a result of the examination of the depositional history of the Dinantian rocks of Britain it became apparent that the Avon Gorge succession is incomplete, with several major non-sequences, which Ramsbottom (1973) considered to occur at major cycle boundaries. This discovery was of particular importance to conodont workers since Rhodes et al. (1969) had only recently published their description of the British Avonian conodont faunas and their zonal scheme had been accepted, albeit with some reservations, as the framework for numerous other conodont publications.

5.4 CONODONT ZONATION

(a) Published Zonations

The description by Rhodes et al. (1969) of the conodont faunas of the Avon Gorge had a strong influence on later research since, as already stated, this work preceded a spate of publications which appeared in the late 1960s and early 1970s, in addition to being primarily concerned with the section which had been considered since the time of Vaughan as the type area for the Lower Carboniferous in the South-west Province.

The Avon Gorge at Bristol exposes almost 1000 m of predominantly carbonate sediments and offers continuous exposure from the uppermost Old Red Sandstone (Devonian) horizons to the highest beds of Vaughan's D Zone. This sequence yielded 25,000 conodont specimens from 600 samples, the location of which are outlined in Rhodes et al. (1969, pp. 21–30). The large number of species present (167, representing 29 genera) enabled Rhodes et al. (1969, pp. 35–46) to erect 14 conodont assemblage zones and thus to achieve their prime aim of establishing a means of correlation with the rest of Europe and elsewhere in the world, particularly the USA. The almost total lack of cephalopods in the Avon section, combined with the provincialism of the corals and brachipods, rendered the conodont zones of great importance. Samples were also taken from the north crop of the South Wales Coalfield, as well as from a number of other areas, mainly to establish the top three conodont assemblage zones, since the equivalent horizons in the Avon Gorge are represented largely by non-calcareous measures. Unfortunately, Rhodes et al. (1969) found that, although they could correlate the Avon Gorge succession with that of the Mississippi Valley or with West Germany on the basis of general faunal sequences, there was no detailed correspondence between their conodont zones and those already established in the two other regions. They believed that the newly established zones provided a useful method of correlation throughout the British 'Avonian'.

Difficulties were soon experienced in the application of these zones, particularly in the upper part of the succession, and some researchers (Ziegler, 1971; Matthews and Naylor, 1973) expressed concern over the scheme. For example, Matthews and Naylor (1973), in their description of the Lower Carboniferous conodont faunas of Southwest Ireland, strongly criticized (Matthews and Naylor, 1973, 342–346) the 'Avonian' zonal scheme, in particular what they described as the 'thinness' of the evidence and the failure of Rhodes *et al.* to produce confirmation of the zonal arrangements proposed. They also severely criticized the correlations made by Rhodes *et al.* with Germany and the Mississippi Valley.

By this time Austin (1973b) had in press a modification of the British Avonian conodont zonation. This had become possible mainly because of the greatly increased information from, and understanding of, Lower Carboniferous faunas from other regions. It is the modified scheme of eleven assemblage zones which is outlined below (also see Fig. 5.5 and Table 6). New names are presented where revision of taxa has been published since 1973. Multielement taxa are also used where these are known. Doubt over the status of those Dinantian taxa referred to the genus *Apatognathus,* following the multielement work by Nicoll (1980) in the Devonian System, is indicated by the use of inverted commas. Similar doubt is expressed over the status of those species remaining in the genus *Spathognathodus* following its partial revision.

1. *Patrognathus variabilis–Bispathodus aculeatus plumulus* Assemblage Zone

Characteristic species: *Patrognathus variabilis* Rhodes *et al., Bispathodus aculeatus plumulus* (Rhodes *et al.*), *Pseudopolygnathus vogesi* (Rhodes *et al.* and, on the north crop of South Wales *Clydagnathus gilwernensis* Rhodes *et al.*

Limits: the base of this assemblage zone was not defined but it probably corresponds with the first appearance of *P. variabilis* Rhodes *et al.* The upper limit coincides with the oldest stratigraphic occurrence of *Polygnathus inornatus inornatus* Branson and Mehl, *Polygnathus lobatus lobatus* Branson and Mehl, and the genus *Siphono-*

della. George *et al.* (1976) recognized a nonsequence between this zone and the one above.

2. *Siphonodella–Polygnathus inornatus* Assemblage Zone

Characteristic species: *Polygnathus inornatus ininornatus* Branson and Mehl, *Polygnathus lobatus lobatus* Branson and Mehl, *Polygnathus lobatus inflexus* Rhodes *et al., Polygnathus inornatus rostratus* Rhodes *et al, Siphonodella isosticha* (Cooper).

Limits: the base of this zone is marked by the first appearance of *Siphonodella isosticha* (Cooper), *P. inornatus inornatus* Branson and Mehl, *P. lobatus lobatus* Branson and Mehl, and *P. inornatus rostratus* Rhodes *et al.* The top of the zone is marked by the first appearance of *'Spathognathodus'* cf. *robustus* (Branson and Mehl), *Dispathodus aculeatus aculeatus* (E. R. Branson) and *B. aculeatus anteposicornis* (Scott).

3. *'Spathognathodus'* cf. *robustus–Bispathodus aculeatus aculeatus* Assemblage Zone

Characteristic species: *'S.'* cf. *robustus* (Branson and Mehl), *'S.' elongatus* (Branson and Mehl), *B. aculeatus aculeatus* (E. R. Branson), *'S.' crassidentatus* (Branson and Mehl) and *B. aculeatus anteposicornis* (Scott).

Limits: the base of this zone is marked by the first occurrence of *'Spathognathodus'* cf. *robustus* (Branson and Mehl), *B. aculeatus aculeatus* (E. R. Branson) and *B. aculeatus anteposicornis* (Scott). The top of the zone is marked by the first appearance of *Bispathodus costatus* (E. R. Branson).

4. *Bispathodus costatus–Gnathodus delicatus* Assemblage Zone

Characteristic species: *B. costatus* (E. R. Branson), *B. spinulicostatus* (E. R. Branson), *Hindeodus?* cf. *cristulus* (Youngquist and Miller) *'S.' cyrius* (Cooper), *'S.' crassidentatus* (Branson and Mehl), *G. delicatus* Branson and Mehl, *Ligonodina beata* Rhodes *et al., Hindeodella corpulenta* Branson and Mehl, *H. subtilis* Ulrich and Bassler. A number of other species are regarded as characteristic but were restricted to either the Avon Gorge section or to the north crop of the South Wales Coalfield.

Limits: the base of this assemblage zone is marked by the first appearance of *B. costatus* (E. R. Branson) and *H?* cf. *cristulus* (Youngquist and Miller). The top of the assemblage zone is recognized by the incoming of abundant *Pseudopolygnathus multistriatus* Mehl and Thomas and by the replacement of *G. delicatus* Branson and Mehl by *G. semiglaber* (Bischoff) and *G. antetexanus* Rexroad and Scott, which is considered to be a junior synonym of *Gnathodus typicus* Cooper by Lane *et al.* (1980).

5. *Polygnathus mehli* (*lacinatus* of Rhodes *et al.*, 1969)–*Pseudopolygnathus* cf. *longiposticus* Assemblage Zone

Characteristic species: abundant *Pseudopolygnathus* cf. *longiposticus* (Branson and Mehl), *Polygnathus mehli* Thompson, *G. semiglaber* (Bischoff), *G. delicatus* Branson and Mehl, *Hindeodus pulcher* (Branson and Mehl), *Gnathodus simplicatus* Rhodes *et al.*, *G. avonensis* Rhodes *et al.*

Limits: the base of the zone is marked by the first appearance of *Polygnathus mehli* Thompson.

6. *Gnathodus antetexanus–Polygnathus mehli* Assemblage Zone

Characteristic species: zone of maximum abundance of *Polygnathus mehli* Thompson, *'Apatognathus' geminus* (Hinde), *'Apatognathus' scalenus* Varker, *'Apatognathus' petilus* Varker, *Hindeodus?* cf. *cristulus* (Youngquist and Miller) and *G. antetexanus* Rexroad and Scott.

Limits: the lower limit of the zone is marked by the latest appearance of *Pseudopolygnathus* cf. *longiposticus* (Branson and Mehl). The upper limit of the zone is marked by the oldest occurrence of *Mestognathus beckmanni* Bischoff. Ramsbottom (1973) and George *et al.* (1976) recognized a further non-sequence between this zone and the one above.

7. *Mestognathus beckmanni–Polygnathus bischoffi* Assemblage Zone

Characteristic species: *Mestognathus beckmanni* Bischoff, *Hindeodus?* cf. *cristulus* (Youngquist and Miller), *Polygnathus bischoffi* Rhodes *et al.*,

'Apatognathus' scalenus Varker, *'A.' petilus* Varker and *'A.' geminus* (Hinde).

Limits: in the Avon Gorge section the base of this zone is marked by a non-sequence, below which is the *Gnathodus antetexanus–Polygnathus* Assemblage Zone. A further non-sequence was also recognized within this zone by Austin (1973b). The upper limit of the zone is not accurately defined since it is overlain by a sequence without conodonts represented entirely by the Clifton Down Mudstone.

8. *Cavusgnathus–'Apatognathus'* Assemblage Zone

Characteristic species: Austin (1973b) merged three of the Rhodes *et al.* (1969) zones to form this assemblage zone which typically contains *'Apatognathus' libratus* Varker, *Cavusgnathus unicornis* Youngquist and Miller, *C. charactus* Rexroad, *C. cristatus* Branson and Mehl, *M. beckmanni* Bischoff, *Hindeodus cristulus* (Youngquist and Miller).

Limits: the lower limit is not defined but may be recognized by the reappearance of conodonts above the Clifton Down Mudstone sequence in which conodonts were absent. The upper limit is marked by the first appearance of *Gnathodus bilineatus* (Roundy). According to Ramsbottom (1973) and George *et al.* (1976) this zone contains two further non-sequences in the Avon Gorge section. Von Bitter and Austin (1984) recently proposed a *Taphrognathus transatlanticus* Zone based on the range of *T. transatlanticus*.

9. *Mestognathus beckmanni–Gnathodus bilineatus* Assemblage Zone

Characteristic species: *Mestognathus beckmanni* Bischoff, *Cavusgnathus unicornis* Youngquist and Miller, *'Spathognathodus' scitulus* (Hinde), *'Apatognathus' bladus* Rhodes *et al.*, *Hibbardella abnormis* Branson and Mehl, *Lochriea commutata* (Scott), *Gnathodus girtyi girtyi* Hass, *G. bilineatus* (Roundy).

Limits: the base of this zone is marked tentatively at the first appearance of *Gnathodus bilineatus* (Roundy). The top of the zone is marked by the incoming of *Lochriea mononodosa* (Rhodes *et al.*).

10. *Lochriea mononodosa* Assemblage Zone
Characteristic species: *Gnathodus girtyi simplex* Rhodes *et al.*, *G. girtyi girtyi* Hass, *G. bilineatus* (Roundy), *G. homopunctatus* Ziegler, *Lochriea mononodosa* (Rhodes *et al.*), *L. commutata* (Branson and Mehl), *Mestognathus neddensis* Rhodes *et al.*, *M. bipluti* Higgins.
  Limits: the lower limit is marked by the first appearance of *L. mononodosa* (Rhodes *et al.*). The upper limit is marked by the first appearance of *Gnathodus girtyi collinsoni* Rhodes *et al.*

11. *Gnathodus girtyi collinsoni* Assemblage Zone
Characteristic species: *Gnathodus girtyi collinsoni* Rhodes *et al.*, *G. girtyi simplex* Dunn, *G. girtyi girtyi* Hass, *G. bilineatus* (Roundy), *Lochriea mononodosa* (Rhodes *et al.*), *L. nodosa* (Bischoff), *Subbryantodus stipans* Rexroad, *S. subaequalis* Higgins.
  Limits: the lower limit is marked by the first appearance of *Gnathodus girtyi collinsoni* Rhodes *et al.* The upper limit is not defined.

Following the work of Rhodes *et al.* (1969) and Austin (1973b), the next zonal scheme was that of Metcalfe (1981) for the Dinantian and early Namurian succession of the Craven Lowlands of the North of England. Metcalfe's work was carried out in the knowledge of the major non-sequences in the Avon Gorge section at Bristol and was published as a more complete alternative to the earlier scheme, although recognizing that the exposed Craven succession does not extend down to the base of the Dinantian Subsystem. This sequence nevertheless exceeds 2000 m in thickness and has yielded to Metcalfe over 16,000 specimens belonging to seventy-three species and subspecies and referable to twenty-five genera. Much of the succession consists of alternations of shale or mudstone and limestone with occasional thin impersistant sandstones.
  Metcalfe's six local-range zones are based on the first appearances of species and are outlined below (see also Fig. 5.4). Sample location is outlined in Metcalfe (1981, p. 4 and Tables 1–16).

1. *Pseudopolygnathus minutus* Local-range Zone
Characteristic species: *Pseudopolygnathus minutus* Metcalfe, *Polygnathus mehli* Thompson, *Clydagnathus? hudsoni* Metcalfe, *Cloghergnathus rhodesi* Austin and Mitchell, *Cloghergnathus cravenus* Metcalfe, *Cloghergnathus globenskii* Austin and Mitchell.
  Limits: the lower limit of this zone is not exposed. The upper limit is marked by the first appearance of *Mestognathus beckmanni* Bischoff. Metcalfe considered this zone, which occupies the Haw Bank Limestone and Skipton Castle Limestone at the base of the exposed Craven succession, to equate with the non-sequence above the *Gnathodus antetexanus–Polygnathus mehli* Assemblage Zone of the South-west Province and is thus not represented in the Avon Gorge.

2. *Mestognathus beckmanni–Polygnathus bischoffi* Local-range Zone
Characteristic species: *Mestognathus beckmanni* Bischoff, *M.* cf. *beckmanni* (*M. groessensi* of Belka, 1983), *Polygnathus bischoffi* Rhodes *et al.*, *Pseudopolygnathus minutus–Polygnathus bischoffi* transitions, *Hindeodus pulcher* (Branson and Mehl), *Gnathodus pseudosemiglaber* Thompson and Fellows, (upper part only).
  Limits: the lower limit is marked by the first appearance of *Mestognathus beckmanni* Bischoff. The upper limit is marked by the first occurrence of *Gnathodus homopunctatus* Ziegler. Metcalfe (1981, p. 7) considered this zone to correlate well with the zone of the same name in the Avon Gorge although his correlation chart (Metcalfe, 1981, p. 15) equates it rather with the non-sequence below the Gulley Oolite.

2a. *Gnathodus pseudosemiglaber* Local-range Sub-zone
Characteristic species: *Gnathodus pseudosemiglaber* Thompson and Fellows. Metcalfe (1981, p. 7) stressed that, since this form had been recorded from several horizons in the Dinantian

Subsystem, this subzone was to be regarded as being of only local significance.

Limits: the lower limit is recognized by the first appearance of *G. pseudosemiglaber* within the *Mestognathus beckmanni–Polygnathus bischoffi* Local-range Zone. The upper limit is marked by the incoming of *Gnathodus homopunctatus* Ziegler.

3. *Gnathodus homopunctatus* Local-range Zone

Characteristic species: *Gnathodus homopunctatus* Ziegler, *Polygnathus bischoffi* Rhodes *et al.* (lower part only), *Patrognathus capricornis* (Druce) (lower part only), *Gnathodus antetexanus* Rexroad and Scott.

Limits: the lower limit is marked by the first appearance of *G. homopunctatus* Ziegler. The upper limit is marked by the first appearance of *Lochriea commutata* (Branson and Mehl). Unlike the situation in Belgium, *Lochriea commutata* appears consistently later than *Mestognathus beckmanni* in the Craven Lowlands and has therefore been used as a local zonal indicator. This zone occupies most of the Embsay Limestone in the local succession.

4. *Lochriea commutata* Local-range Zone

Characteristic species: *Lochriea commutata* (Branson and Mehl) and *Gnathodus homopunctatus* Ziegler.

Limits: the lower limit is marked by the first appearance of *L. commutata* and the upper limit may be recognized by the first appearance of *Gnathodus bilineatus* Roundy. Foraminiferal evidence suggests that this zone appears at the same horizon in the Craven Lowlands as it does in Belgium, and Metcalfe considered it to correlate with the *Cavusgnathus–'Apatognathus'* Zone of the Avon Gorge and to occupy much of the Arundian Stage, all the Holkerian Stage and the lower half of the Asbian Stage.

4a. *Gnathodus girtyi* Local-range Subzone

Characteristic species: *Gnathodus homopunctatus* Ziegler, *Lochriea commutata* (Branson and Mehl) and *Gnathodus girtyi* Hass.

Limits: the lower limit is marked by the first

appearance of *G. girtyi* whilst the upper limit is the top of the zone to which this subzone belongs. This species is known to occur at lower stratigraphic levels elsewhere, but in the Craven Lowlands its first appearance is consistently close to the top of the *L. commutata* Zone, thus enabling it to be used in local correlation.

5. *Gnathodus bilineatus* Local-range Zone

Characteristic species: *Gnathodus bilineatus* (Roundy), *G. homopunctatus* Ziegler, *G. girtyi* Hass and *Lochriea commutata* (Branson and Mehl).

Limits: the lower limit is marked by the first appearance of *G. bilineatus,* and the upper limit occurs at the first appearance of *Lochriea nodosa* (Bischoff). The base of the zone occurs within the Asbian Stage and the zone as a whole correlates with the combined *Mestognathus beckmanni– Gnathodus bilineatus* and *Lochriea mononodosa* zones of the Avon Gorge.

6. *Lochriea nodosa* Local-range Zone

Characteristic species: *Lochriea nodosa* (Bishoff), *L. commutata* (Branson and Mehl) (lower part), *Gnathodus girtyi* Hass and *G. bilineatus* (Roundy) (lower part).

Limits: the lower limit of this zone is marked by the first appearance of *L. nodosa* but the upper limit is undefined.

A second Dinantian conodont zonal scheme for northern England was published by Higgins and Varker (1982) soon after that of Metcalfe. Higgins and Varker based their scheme on the important sequence in Ravenstonedale, Cumbria, which had been designated by Garwood (1913, p. 451) as his type area for the Lower Carboniferous of the North of England. This sequence, which is approximately 1500 m in thickness, provides the most complete Dinantian succession within the Northern Pennines, with what appears to be an almost continuous record of sedimentation from the Courceyan Stage to the Namurian Series. The lowest unit of the Ravenstonedale sequence is represented by the Pinskey Gill Formation which lies with gross unconformity on steeply inclined

Silurian Bannisdale Slates, below the Shap Conglomerate. Conodont faunas from these beds had already been separately described and details of the succession and sampled horizons from this part of the sequence are outlined by Varker and Higgins (1979, Fig. 1, p. 358). Above the Shap Conglomerate the Ravenstonedale succession is variable but dominated by limestones. Details of the upper part of this successsion, plus the location of all the Ravenstonedale conodont samples, are outlined by Higgins and Varker (1982, Figs. 2–6).

Higgins and Varker (1982) recognized the following four conodont faunas, of which the upper three were named and defined as formal zones.

1. Fauna A
Characteristic species: *Bispathodus aculeatus aculeatus* (Branson and Mehl) and *Clydagnathus unicornis* Rhodes *et al.*

Limits: neither of the limits is clearly defined since these beds are unconformable on the underlying Silurian beds and are overlain by the barren conglomerate. This fauna was thus not defined as a formal zone. Higgins and Varker (1982) were nevertheless able to correlate Fauna A with the *costatus–Gnathodus delicatus* Assemblage Zone of Rhodes *et al.* (1969).

2. *Taphrognathus* Zone
This is a partial range zone occurring in the upper part of the Stone Gill Beds and in the Coldbeck Beds.
Characteristic species: *Taphrognathus varians* Branson and Mehl, *Cloghergnathus carinatus* Higgins and Varker, *'Spathognathodus' scitulus* (Hinde) and *'Apatognathus' cuspidatus* Varker.

Limits: the lower limit of this zone is marked by the first appearance of *Taphrognathus varians* and *Cloghergnathus carinatus* and the upper limit is marked by the last occurrence of *Taphrognathus varians*.

This fauna is not represented in the Avon Gorge since it was considered to correlate with the non-sequence at the base of the Chadian Stage. It does occur in Ireland with *Mestognathus beck-*

manni Bischoff. The *Taphrognathus* Zone also correlates broadly with the *Bactrognathus–Taphrognathus* Zone in the upper part of the Burlington Formation of the Upper Mississippi Valley.

3. *Cloghergnathus* Zone
This assemblage zone occurs in the Scandal Beck Limestone and the *Michelinia grandis* beds.
Characteristic species: *Cloghergnathus carinatus* Higgins and Varker, *'Spathognathodus' scitulus* (Hinde), *'Apatognathus' asymmetricus* Higgins and Varker, and *'Apatognathus scandalensis'* Higgins and Varker.

Limits: the lower limit of this zone is marked by the incoming of the two species of *'Apatognathus'*. The upper limit is not precisely defined since it is marked by the incoming of the barren Ashfell Sandstone. The appearance of *Magnilaterella robusta* Rexroad and Collinson, and *Lochriea singularis* (Hass) at the base of the *Michelinia grandis* Beds allowed the subdivision of this zone locally into two subzones but since both of these species were known to have longer ranges elsewhere it was considered by Higgins and Varker (1982, p. 154) that this might merely reflect environmental changes at the base of the *Michelinia grandis* Beds. The fauna of the *Cloghergnathus* Zone is thus not distinctive and was regarded by Higgins and Varker (1982) as an interregnum between the disappearance of *Taphrognathus* and the appearance of *Cavusgnathus*.

According to George *et al.* (1976) this part of the sequence is largely missing in the Avon Gorge or is represented by non-conodont-bearing strata (Austin, 1973b). The interval was considered by Higgins and Varker to compare closely with the *Taphrognathus varians–'Apatognathus'* interval in the Upper Mississippi Valley (Collinson *et al.*, 1962) which occupies the Warsaw, Salem and Lower St. Louis Formations.

4. *Cavusgnathus* Zone
This zone includes the highest beds of the Ashfell Sandstone and at least the lowest beds of the Ashfell Limestone and therefore, according to George *et al.* (1976), spans the Arundian–Holkerian boundary.

Characteristic species: *Cavusgnathus regularis* Youngquist and Miller, *C. unicornis* Youngquist and Miller, *Neoprioniodus scitulus* (Branson and Mehl), *'Spathognathodus' scitulus* (Hinde), *Magnilaterella robusta* Rexroad and Collinson, *'Apatognathus' libratus* Varker.

Limits: the lower limit is marked by the appearance of *Cavusgnathus regularis* and *C. unicornis*. The upper limit is not defined.

This fauna was considered by Higgins and Varker (1982) to correlate well with the lower part of the *Cavusgnathus–'Apatognathus'* Zone of the Avon Gorge and also with the *'Apatognathus' scalenus–Cavusgnathus* Zone of the Upper Mississippi Valley (Collinson *et al.*, 1962). Austin and Davies (1984) correlate the zone with a level at least as low as the Goblin Coombe Oolite in the Avon Gorge.

A scheme of five biozones was established for the Lower Carboniferous succession at Hook Head, County Wexford, Ireland, by Johnston and Higgins (1981). This sequence consists of two formations (Sleeman *et al.*, 1974) of which the lower, the Porter's Gate Formation, is 41.5 m in thickness and the upper, the Hook Head Limestone Formation, is 335.5 m thick. The latter contains the 25 m thick Bullockpark Bay Member 124 m above its base.

1. *Polygnathus spicatus* Partial-range Biozone
Characteristic species: *P. spicatus* E. R. Branson, *Patrognathus variabilis* Rhodes *et al.*

Limits: the lower limit was defined by the base of the succession. The top of the zone occurs at the lowest occurrence of *Polygnathus inornatus* and the last occurrence of *P. spicatus* in the highest bed of the Houseland Member.

2. *Polygnathus inornatus* Local-range Biozone
Characteristic species: *P. inornatus* Branson and Mehl, *P. communis communis* Branson and Mehl.

Limits: the base and top of this zone are defined by the entire local range of the eponymous species.

Above the *P. inornatus* Local-range Biozone there is a horizon with no diagnostic conodonts.

3. *Pseudopolygnathus multistriatus* Local-range Biozone
Characteristic species: this local-range biozone may be divided into two parts of approximately equal thickness. The lower part has relatively low conodont densities with *Ps. multistriatus* Mehl and Thomas and *Polygnathus communis communis* Branson and Mehl, the only common forms. The upper part coincides with the Bullockpark Bay Dolomite Member and includes, in addition to those species found also in the lower part, *Clydagnathus unicornis* Rhodes *et al.*, *Bispathodus aculeatus aculeatus* (E. R. Branson), *B. aculeatus plumulus* (Rhodes *et al.*), *B. aculeatus anteposicornis* (Scott), and *Prioniodina oweni* Rhodes *et al.*

Limits: The base is marked by the incoming of *Ps. multistriatus*. The top of this local-range biozone is marked by the first appearance of *Polygnathus communis carina*.

4. *Polygnathus communis carina* Local-range Biozone
Characteristic species: *P. communis carina* association with *Pseudopolygnathus multistriatus* Mehl and Thomas.

Limits: the base of this biozone is marked by the appearance of *Polygnathus communis carina*. The top is marked by the occurrence of small numbers of *Polygnathus mehli latus*.

5. *Polygnathus mehli latus* Partial-range Biozone
Characteristic species: *P. mehli latus* Johnston and Higgins in small numbers, associated with species common in the biozone below.

Limits: this partial-range biozone occupies that part of the sequence from 103.3 m above the top of the Bullockpark Bay Member to the top of the section. Its base is defined by the incoming of *P. mehli latus*.

(b) A Conflated Dinantian Conodont Zonation for Great Britain and Ireland

The following notes are provided as an explanation and justification for the biostratigraphical framework presented in Fig. 5.5. In Belgium the Hastarian

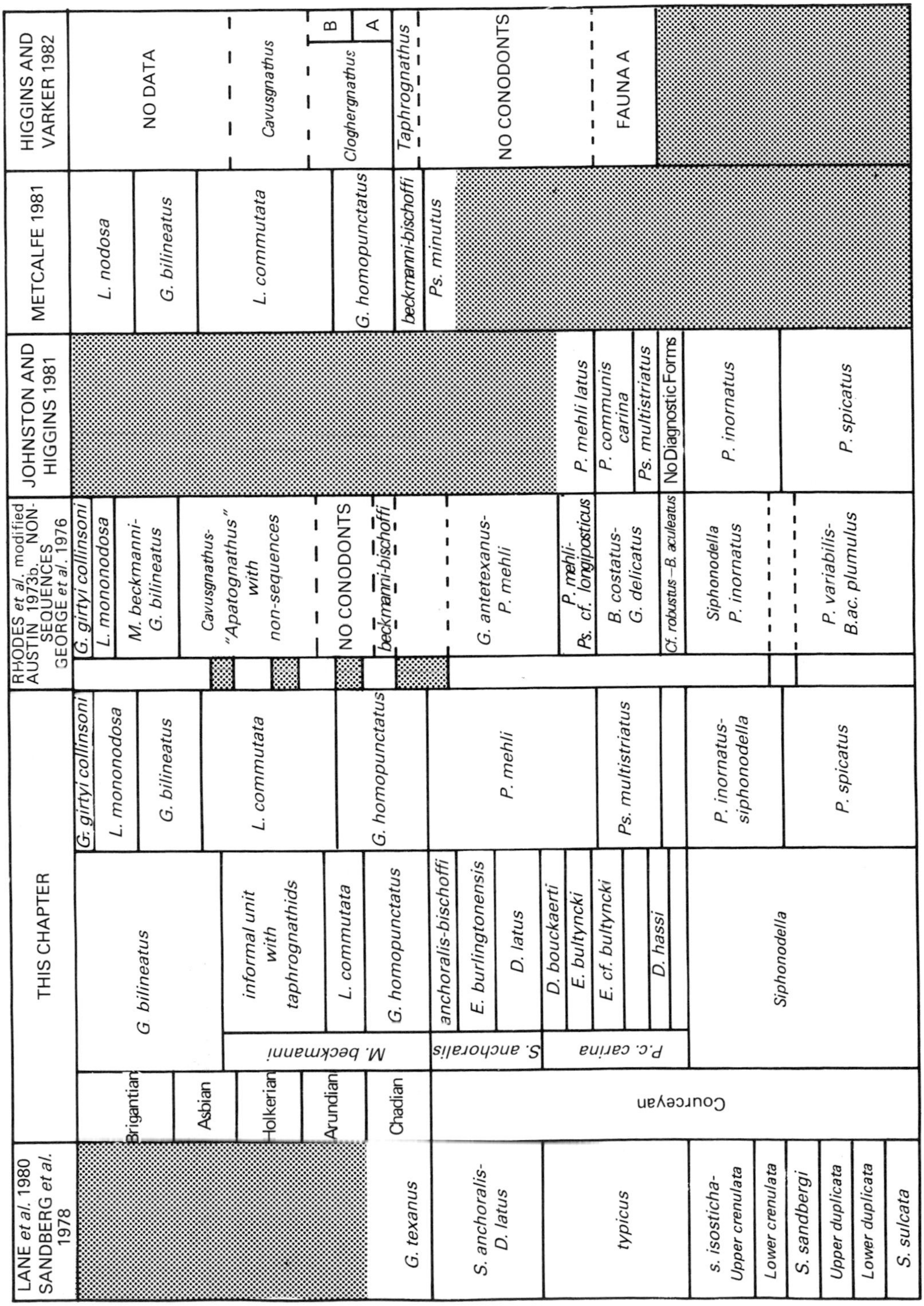

Fig. 5.5 — General correlation diagram for published Dinantian conodont zonal schemes considered in this work.

Stage is coincident with the *Siphonodella* Zone, characterized by advanced siphonodellids such as *S. obsoleta* and *S. cooperi*; this suggests that most of the zone is to be correlated with the Lower *crenulata* and *isosticha*–Upper *crenulata* Zone of Sandberg *et al.* (1978). In the basinal sequence of South-west England, Selwood *et al.* (1982) have been able to distinguish all the Sandberg *et al.* siphonodellid zones, apart from the *sandbergi* Zone. In contrast, in the South Munster Basin of Ireland, the early part of the Courceyan Stage is represented by shallow-marine sandstones and siphonodellids first appear in the *crenulata* Zone.

The base of the Ivorian Stage in Belgium is identified by the base of the *carina* Zone (note that this zone was proposed by Groessens (1977) as an Acrozone and that, in many sections of the Dinant Syncline, the horizon of incoming of *P.c. carina* is substantially higher than that of the disappearance of the siphonodellids). *P.c. carina* is common on the northern margins of the basinal developments in South-west England and Ireland, but it is usually found as reworked specimens in the basin proper. *Dollymae hassi* is rare but it has been found in the basinal sequences (reworked) in South-west England and on the margin of the South Munster Basin. In Belgium the base of the *Eotaphrus* cf. *bultyncki* Subzone is recognized by the first appearance of the eponymous taxon. This subzone has been identified on the margin of the South Munster Basin and further north in Ireland and Britain (but see the comments on the nomenclature of *Eo.* cf. *bultyncki* below), although not in the basinal sequences. The *bultyncki* and *bouckaerti* subzones are lineage subzones, in that their bases are identified by the first occurrences of eponymous species in the lineage *Prioniodina oweni*, (=*Eo.* cf. *bultyncki*), *Eo. bultyncki*, *Dollymae bouckaerti*. Both subzones have been recognized around the margins of (and to the north of) the basinal developments in South-west Ireland and in South-west England, but they are generally reworked within the basinal sequences proper. The base of the *anchoralis* Zone was defined by the first appearance of *Scaliognathus anchoralis* which Groessens (1977) suggested was derived from *Dollymae bouckaerti*. Recent proposals on the

phylogeny of *Scaliognathus* (Lane and Ziegler, 1983) identify *S. preanchoralis* Lane, Sandberg and Ziegler, as the immediate ancestor of *S. anchoralis*, but new information from South-west Ireland (Brenda Thornbury, personal communication) suggests that the ranges of *S. anchoralis* and *Do. bouckaerti* are unlikely to overlap. The *D. latus* Subzone, identified by the presence of the eponymous taxon, has been found both on the margins of and in the basinal developments of South-west England and South-west Ireland but *Eotaphrus burlingtonensis*, which is used to recognise the *burlingtonensis* Subzone in the upper part of its range above the disappearance of *Doliognathus latus*, has only been found in the Mendips and at Cannington Park.

The zonal framework appropriate to regions north of the basinal sequences of South-west England and Ireland incorporates elements of the schemes proposed by Austin (1973b), Johnston (1976) and Johnston and Higgins (1981). The earliest zone, the *spicatus* Assemblage Zone, is characterized by the eponymous species as well as by *Bispathodus aculeatus aculeatus*, *B. a. plumulus*, *Clydagnathus gilwernensis*, *C. unicornis*, *Patrognathus variabilis* and *Pseudopolygnathus dentilineatus*. None of these species is confined to this zone and *P. spicatus* does not consistently occur throughout. Its use in correlation is limited although it has broad biostratigraphical–ecological significance. The succeeding *Polygnathus inornatus–Siphonodella* Assemblage Zone is characterized by *P. inornatus*, *Psuedopolygnathus dentilineatus* and rare *Siphonodella cooperi*, *S. isosticha*, *S.* cf. *isosticha* and *S. obsoleta* with *Elictognathus* and *Gnathodus punctatus*. The base is defined by the first appearance of *P. inornatus* which, however, is known to range very much lower elsewhere, for instance at Cannington Park (Mitchell *et al.*, 1982), but in many sections it is clearly coincident with a major facies change. In almost all sections studied, *P. inornatus* and the siphonodellids disappear abruptly and succeeding strata contain an impoverished fauna of long-ranging taxa such as *Bispathodus aculeatus* and *Polygnathus communis*. The earliest occurrence of *Bispathodus costatus* and its descendant *B. spinulicostatus* is towards the top of this stratigraphical interval. The succeeding *Pseudopolygnathus multistriatus* Zone is a lineage zone, the base of which is defined by the first occurrence of the eponymous taxon, which evolved from *B. spinulicostatus*. Other taxa which occur in this zone include *Gnathodus cuneiformis, G. simplicatus, Hindeodus?* cf. *cristulus, Polygnathus communis carina* (not consistently present), *Pseudopolygnathus minutus* in the upper part and in shallow-water facies, *Bispathodus aculeatus* ssp. and *Clydagnathus* sp. A stratigraphically important taxon which also occurs commonly in this and the base of the succeeding zone is *Prioniodina oweni* Rhodes *et al.* Stratigraphically younger forms of this species are identical with *Eotaphrus* cf. *bultyncki* (Groessens but it is not clear whether stratigraphically older forms, in which the basal cavity is less expanded and the cusp is shorter, are present in Belgium. For this reason correlation of the base of the Belgian cf. *bultyncki* Zone is tenuous. The *mehli* Zone is also a lineage zone since its base is defined by the first appearance of *Polygnathus mehli*, which evolved from *Pseudopolygnathus multistriatus*. The older subspecies *P. mehli latus* is restricted to the base of the zone as is *Pseudopolygnathus multistriatus*. Characteristic taxa of the *mehli* Zone include *Pseudopolygnathus minutus, Polygnathus bischoffi* (which first occurs above the base but in the lower part of the zone), *Gnathodus cuneiformis, G. pseudosemiglaber* (which dominates the Waulsortian Reef facies of this age), *G. simplicatus, Cloghergnathus* spp. and *Mestognathus groessensi*. Rare taxa which allow correlation with the basinal biozones include *Eotaphrus* cf. *bultyncki, E. bultyncki* and *D. bouckaerti*, which are restricted to the lower part of the zone, and *S. anchoralis* and *Pseudopolygnathus pinnatus*. The top of the *mehli* Zone is identified by the first occurrence of *Mestognathus beckmanni* or *Gnathodus homopunctatus*. In facies where the latter taxa are absent (for instance in much of the Waulsortian Limestone of Ireland) the upper part of the *mehli* Zone is Chadian in age.

The biostratigraphical framework for the post-Courceyan horizons is based primarily upon the published zonal schemes of Austin (1973b),

Metcalfe (1981) and Higgins and Varker (1982), but it also incorporates other data, published and unpublished. At these horizons the conflated zonal scheme suggested here is similar to that which already exists for Belgium except that several of the important zonal species first appear slightly later over most of Britain and Ireland than in Belgium.

The *homopunctatus* Assemblage Zone is characterized by *Gnathodus texanus, Taphrognathus varians, Cloghergnathus carinatus* and *Mestognathus beckmanni* in addition to the eponymous species, plus a number of apatognathids, of which '*A.*' *cuspidatus* is fairly long ranging and first appears at the base of the zone, whilst '*A.*' *asymmetricus* and '*A.*' *scandalensis* are restricted to the zone. The top of the zone is marked by the incoming of *L. commutata*. In the Avon Gorge this part of the sequence is severely disrupted by non-sequences and horizons without conodonts and within it Austin (1973b) was only able to recognize a poorly delimited *beckmanni–bischoffi* Zone. In Belgium, *G. homopunctatus* and *L. commutata* are the eponymous species of the lower two subzones of the *beckmanni* Zone, which combined occupy much the same time interval as the *homopunctatus* Zone in Britain. It should be added, however, that unpublished work by Stewart (1981a) indicates that, in the Culm facies of the South-west of England, *L. commutata* occurs even earlier than in Belgium and may extend down into the *anchoralis* Zone. Stewart consequently does not recognize a *commutata* Zone in his zonal scheme. Elsewhere in Britain and Ireland the base of the *commutata* Assemblage Zone is recognized by the first appearance of *Cavusgnathus charactus, C. unicornis* and '*Apatognathus*' *libratus*, in addition to the eponymous species, whilst *Cavusgnathus cristatus* and *C. regularis* appear above the base. This is a part of the sequence where Austin (1973b) made a number of modifications to the scheme of Rhodes *et al.* (1969), leaving a broad zone extending from high in the Arundian Stage to mid-Asbian Stage which was characterized by *Cavusgnathus* and apatognathids. The *commutata* Zone is here considered to be more extensive than the similarly named *beckmanni* Subzone of Belgium and extends up to the base of the *bilineatus* Zone.

Gnathodus bilineatus also appears slightly earlier in Belgium, where its zone extends up to the top of the Dinantian Subsystem, occupying the major part of the Warnantian Stage. In Britain and Ireland the base of the *bilineatus* Assemblage Zone is recognized by the first appearance of *G. bilineatus* and *G. girtyi girtyi*, although the latter species can occur slightly earlier, just below the top of the *commutata* Zone. The *bilineatus* Zone does not extend to the top of the Dinantian Subsystem in Britain and Ireland, since the eponymous species is later joined in the Brigantian Stage by several species which permit the recognition of two further zones. The appearance of rather common *Lochriea mononodosa* enables the recognition of the *mononodosa* Assemblage Zone, and in late Brigantian rocks the highest zone is identified by the appearance of *Gnathodus girtyi collinsoni*, a subspecies described by Rhodes *et al.* (1969) and used by them to define the base of the uppermost of their Lower Carboniferous Zones.

Table 5 shows the range of selected British and Irish Dinantian conodont species and correlation between the zonal scheme presented in this publication and that of the Dinantian Subsystem in Belgium (see also Paproth *et al.*, 1983).

5.5 FACIES CONTROL OF DINANTIAN CONODONT FAUNAS IN GREAT BRITAIN

The apparent success of conodont biostratigraphic studies in providing local zonal schemes at many different stratigraphic horizons, particularly where difficulty had previously been experienced using other fossil groups, led to the general belief in the 1950s and early 1960s that conodonts were essentially free from facies control. However, with the rapid increase in the availability of data relating to conodont distribution which occurred during the late 1960s and early 1970s, anomalous distribution patterns were increasingly attributed to the influence of facies. By the mid-1970s, conodont depth zones had been proposed (Austin, 1974, 1976) and facies control was the accepted explanation for the poor correlation between the Dinantian

faunas of the South-west Province and those of the USA and Germany. A clear distinction had been recognized in the Tournaisian Series (Austin and Barnes, 1973; Austin, 1976) between conodonts from shelf environments characterized by *Clydagnathus* and *Patrognathus* and those from basin environments with *Siphonodella* and *Protognathus*. More recent publications have substantiated this distinction, indeed Selwood *et al.* (1982) interpreted their fauna from Chillaton in Devon as representing a position high on the rise slope with a mixing of the faunas from the two regimes.

A similar distinction between conodont faunas of shelf and basin can be demonstrated in later Dinantian horizons. Austin (1976) described a shelf facies characterized by *Cavusgnathus, Mestognathus* and *Taphrognathus* whereas the deeper-water facies were dominated by species of *Gnathodus* and again this distinction has been largely substantiated by later publications. Higgins and Varker (1982) for example proposed *Taphrognathus, Cloghergnathus* and *Cavusgnathus* zones for the Dinantian sequence of Ravenstonedale whilst Metcalfe (1981) found *Gnathodus* to be dominant in a nearby sequence of equivalent age in the Craven Lowlands (see Fig. 5.3). Austin and Davies (1984) further indicate that the facies control of conodonts during the Dinantian Subsystem can also be demonstrated by comparing faunas from rocks deposited in similar facies but of different age. A more recent trend is to consider sedimentological implications and Austin and Davies (1984) outline the relationships between sediment types and conodont genera and go on to apply knowledge of environments of deposition of modern sediments to conodont distribution patterns. Sandberg and Gutschick (1984) have suggested a biofacies model for Lower Carboniferous conodont distribution from deep basin to shoreline in the *Scaliognathus latus* Zone (Fig. 5.6).

PALAEO-TECTONIC SETTING	STARVED BASIN		FORESLOPE		CARBONATE PLATFORM			TIDAL LAGOON AND SABKHA	
				Margin	Outer	Inner			LAND
CONODONT BIOFACIES (I–VII)	I Bispatho-did	II Scaliognathid-doliognathid	III Gnathodid-pseudopolygnathid	IV Eotaphrid	V Hindeodid	VI Pandori-nellinid(?)	VII Mesto-gnathid(?)	
CONODONT ABUNDANCE (specimens/kg)	Low (5–25)	Low to high (10–30)	Low (5–20) to very high (50–650)	Low to high (15–140)	Low (0–20)	Low	?	

Fig. 5.6 – Biofacies model of conodont distribution from deep basin to shoreline in the *Scaliognathus latus* Zone, Lower Carboniferous. Modified after Sandberg and Gutschick (1984).

PLATE 5.1

On this and following plates, except where indicated, all illustrated material represents the pectiniform element of the conodont apparatus.

Patrognathus variabilis Rhodes, Austin and Druce 1969
Plate 5.1, Figs. 1, 4 and 7. Table 6. Diagnosis: a species of *Patrognathus*, having a symmetrical platform with a stout anterior blade bearing denticles of which the most conspicuous is at the posterior, Distinguished from *P. andersoni* by its more rounded basal cavity and a less developed medial trough.
Fig. 1., lateral view; Figs. 4 and 7, upper view stereopair. All TCD25589, ×48. Sample at 370 ft in Munster Base Metals Borehole M76–46, unnamed limestones and sandstone neat Buttevant, County Cork, Ireland, *spicatus* Zone. Specimen courtesy of Karen Campbell.

Polygnathus spicatus E. R. Branson, 1934
Plate 5.1, Figs. 2, 5, 6 and 8. Table 6. Diagnosis: a species of *Polygnathus* with an elongate, nearly asymmetrical platfom, a lanceolate basal cavity and a prominent pseudokeel. Very similar to nearly symmetrical forms of *Polygnathus mehli* but tends to have a more slender elongate platform and stronger ribs, and the flat pseudokeel extends to close to the posterior tip.
Fig. 2, lateral view; Figs. 5 and 8, lower view stereopair; Fig. 6, upper view. All TCD25590. Houseland Sandstone Member, Hook Head, County Wexford, Ireland, *spicatus* Zone.

Pseudopolygnathus dentilineatus E. R. Branson, 1934
Plate 5.1, Figs. 3, 9 and 10. Table 6. Diagnosis: a species of *Pseudopolygnathus* with a subcircular basal cavity as wide as the platform. Very similar to early forms of *Ps. multistriatus* but distinguished by the wider basal cavity which is subcircular rather than elongate posteriorly.
Fig. 3, lateral view; Fig. 9, upper view; Fig. 10, lower view. All TCD25591, ×48. Unnamed basal sandstones and limestones, Whiting Bay, Ardmore, County Waterford, Ireland, *spicatus* Zone.

Polygnathus inornatus E. R. Branson 1934
Plate 5.1, Figs. 11, 14 and 15. Table 6. Diagnosis: a species of *Polygnathus* with slightly to markedly asymmetric platform and small circular aboral cavity. Distinguished from *P. bischoffi* by its less accentuated adcarinal grooves and more elongate platform and from *P. spicatus* in the form of the basal cavity.
Fig. 11, lateral view; Fig. 14, upper view; Fig. 15, lower view. All TCD25592, ×48. Ringmoylan Shale Formation, Ballyquin, Ardmore, County Waterford, Ireland, *inornatus* Zone.

Polygnathus communis communis Branson and Mehl 1934
Plate 5.1, Figs. 12, 16 and 17. Table 6. Diagnosis: a species of *Polygnathus* with subcircular basal cavity and narrow unornamented platform.
Fig. 12, lateral view; Fig. 16, upper view, Fig. 17, lower view; All TCD25593, ×72. Unnamed formation, sample from 100–105 ft in borehole BV14, Ballyvergin, County Clare, Ireland, above *inornatus* Zone and below *multistriatus* Zone. See Clayton *et al.* (1980).

Elictognathus laceratus (Branson and Mehl 1934)
Plate 5.1, Fig. 13. Table 6. Diagnosis: a species of *Elictognathus* with a narrow lateral ridge on the outer side.
Outer lateral view, TCD25594, ×72. Limestones on the western side of the River Bray, Stag's Head, near South Moulton, Devonshire, England, *Siphonodella* Zone. Specimen courtesy of Peter Jackson.

Siphonodella isosticha (Cooper, 1939)
Plate 5.1, Figs. 18 and 19. Table 6. Diagnosis: a species of *Siphonodella* with a pseudokeel; platform unornamented to weakly ornamented with nodes on the inner side. Rostral ridge of the outer side approaching or meeting the margin, in the anterior two-thirds of the platform. The figured specimen is similar to *S. obsoleta* but has a well-developed pseudokeel and a shorter outer rostral ridge.
Fig. 18, lower view; Fig. 19, upper view. Both TCD25595, ×48. Ringmoylan Shale Formation, Ballyquin, Ardmore, County Waterford, Ireland, *inornatus* Zone.

Gnathodus delicatus Branson and Mehl 1938
Plate 5.1, Figs. 20 and 24. Table 6. Diagnosis: a species of *Gnathodus* characterized by a long parapet extending to, or close to, the posterior tip on the inner side and scattered nodes on the outer side of the platform.
Fig. 20, outer lateral view; Fig. 24, upper view. Both TCD25596, × 48. Waulsortian Limestone, Corkbeg Island, Whitegate, County Cork, Ireland, *carina* Zone.

Pl. 5.1]   The Carboniferous System: Part 1   191

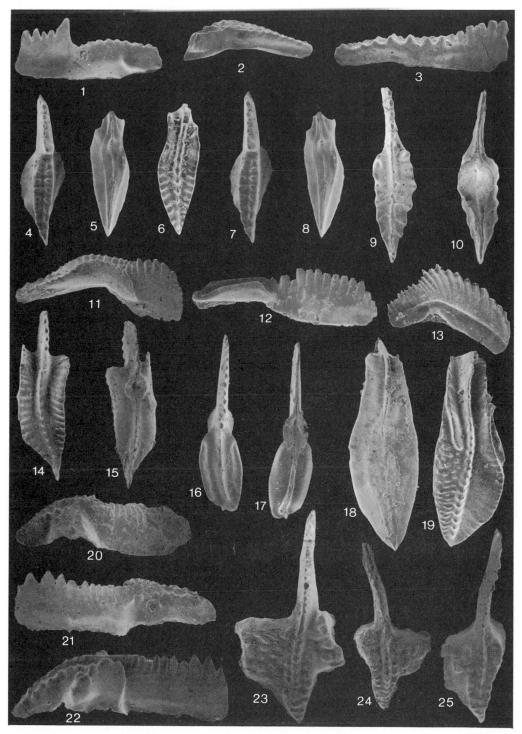

Plate 5.1

Gnathodus cuneiformis Mehl and Thomas 1947
Plate 5.1, Figs. 21 and 25. Table 6. Diagnosis: a species of *Gnathodus* characterized by a long parapet extending to the posterior tip on the inner side and a parapet or row of nodes extending to the posterior tip on the outer side of the carina.
Fig. 21, outer lateral view; Fig. 25, upper view. Both TCD25597, ×48. 8 m above the base of the Ringabella Limestone, Ringabella, County Cork, Ireland, *carina* Zone; *hassi* Subzone.

Gnathodus punctatus (Cooper 1939)
Plate 5.1, Figs. 22 and 23. Table 6. Diagnosis: a species of *Gnathodus* characterized by a short row of nodes or a parapet, convex towards the carina on the inner side. Nodes on the outer side are commonly arranged in radial rows.
Fig. 22, inner lateral view; Fig. 23, upper view. Both TCD25598, ×48. Base of limestone section, Ballygan Quarry, near Carrigaline, County Cork, Ireland, earliest part of *carina* Zone. Specimen courtesy Brenda Thornbury.

PLATE 5.2

Bispathodus aculeatus aculeatus (Branson and Mehl 1934)
Plate 5.2, Figs. 1, 3 and 4. Table 6. Diagnosis: a species of *Bispathodus* with one or a row of lateral nodes or transverse ridges on the right side of the blade that does not extend to the posterior tip. Distinguished from *B. aculeatus plumulus* by the lack of plume-like development of the blade.
Fig. 1, right lateral view; Fig. 3, upper view; Fig. 4, lower view. All TCD25599, ×48. Castle Slate Member, Kinsale Formation, Ardmore, County Waterford, Ireland, *spicatus* Zone. See Clayton *et al.* (1982).

Pseudopolygnathus multistriatus (Mehl and Thomas 1947)
Plate 5.2, Figs. 2, 7 and 8. Table 6. Diagnosis: a species of *Pseudopolygnathus* characterized by a basal cavity which is not as wide as the platform. Platform generally weakly asymmetrical, bearing coarse ribs. Stratigraphically older forms of this species such as the individual in the figure have proportionately larger basal cavities and the left side of the platform poorly developed anterior to the basal cavity. Stratigraphically younger forms have a more symmetrical platform and a relatively smaller basal cavity.
Fig. 2, right lateral view; Fig. 7, upper view; Fig. 8, lower view. All TCD25600, ×48. Ballysteen Limestone Formation, sample from 40–45 ft in the borehole BV14, Ballyvergin, County Clare, Ireland, *multistriatus* Zone. See Clayton *et al.* (1980).

Bispathodus spinulicostatus (E. R. Branson 1934)
Plate 5.2, Figs. 5 and 6. Table 6. Diagnosis: a species of *Bispathodus* with a row of nodes or ridges extending to the posterior tip on the right side of the blade and a row of lateral nodes posterior to the basal cavity on the left side.
Fig. 5, upper view; Fig. 6, lower view. Both TCD25601, ×48. Unnamed formation, sample from 100–105 ft in borehole BV14, Ballyvergin, County Clare, Ireland, above *inornatus* Zone and below *multistriatus* Zone. See Clayton *et al.* (1980).

Polygnathus mehli latus Johnston and Higgins 1981
Plate 5.2, Figs. 9 and 10. Table 6. Diagnosis: a subspecies of *P. mehli* (see below) distinguished by its wider basal cavity and coarser ribs. Distinguished from its likely ancestor *Pseudopolygnathus athus multistriatus* by the presence of flat lips surrounding the basal cavity and the development of a pseudokeel.
Fig. 9, upper view; Fig. 10, lower view. Both TCD25602, ×48. Hook Head Formation (sample 144), Hook Head, County Wexford, Ireland, *mehli* Zone. See Johnston and Higgins (1981).

Polygnathus mehli mehli Thompson 1967
Plate 5.2, Figs. 11, 12, 15 and 18. Table 6. Diagnosis: a species of *Polygnathus* characterized by a narrow lanceolate basal cavity bounded by flat lips which extend posteriorly into a prominent pseudokeel. This common species has quite a varied platform shape including almost symmetrical varieties which resemble the North American holotype. It can be distinguished from *P. mehli latus* but its finer ribs and narrower basal cavity and from the morphologically very similar *P. spicatus* by its generally wider platform.
Fig. 11, upper view; Figs. 12 and 15, lower view stereopair; Fig. 18, inner lateral view. All TCD25603, ×48. Unnamed limestones and shales (sample 19), Druminshin Glebe, County Leitrim, Ireland, *mehli* Zone. See Morris *et al.* (1981).

Pseudopolygnathus minutus Metcalfe 1981
Plate 5.2, Figs. 13, 14 and 19. Table 6. Diagnosis: a species of *Pseudopolygnathus* with a lanceolate, almost symmetrical platform ornamented with ribs.
Fig. 13, upper view; Fig. 14, lower view; Fig. 19, lateral view. All TCD25604, ×48. Waulsortian Limestone, Claremont Strand, Honeth, County Dublin, Ireland. Chadian.

Pl. 5.2]   The Carboniferous System: Part 1   193

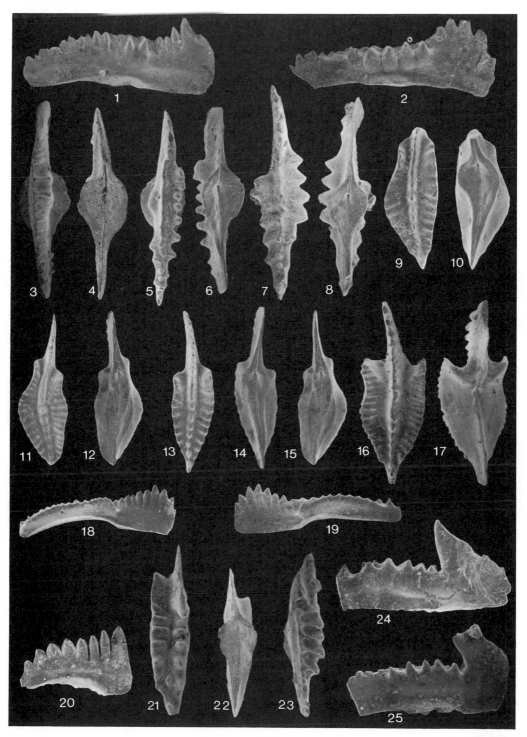

Plate 5.2

Polygnathus bischoffi Rhodes, Austin and Druce 1969
Plate 5.2, Figs. 16 and 17. Table 6. Diagnosis: a species of *Polygnathus* characterized by a slightly curved to nearly symmetrical platform, generally triangular at its posterior end but parallel sided anteriorly, with deep adcarinal grooves and an ornament of fine ribs. In lateral view the platform is strongly arched. The basal cavity is small. Distinguished from its likely ancestor, *Pseudopolygnathus minutus,* by its smaller basal cavity, and finer and more numerous ribs. Specimens transitional in morphology between *P. bischoffi* and *Ps. minutus* are common. Juveniles of both species are indistinguishable.
Fig. 16, upper view; Fig. 17, lower view. Both TCD25605, ×36. Sample from 152 ft in borehole 431, Tynagh Mine, Tynagh, County Galway, Ireland. Chadian. Specimen courtesy of Ennex Ltd.

Hindeodus? cf. *cristulus* (Youngquist and Miller 1949)
Plate 5.2, Fig. 20. Table 6. Diagnosis: Rexroad and Thompson (1979) suggested that this form should be identified as *Hindeodus? (Spathognathodus) regularis.* However, specimens almost always have a single large denticle anterior to the basal cavity.
Lateral view, TCD25606, ×72. Ballysteen Limestone Formation. Sample from 75–80 ft in borehole BV14, Ballyvergin, County Clare, Ireland, *multistriatus* Zone. See Clayton *et al.* (1980).

Clydagnathus unicornis Rhodes, Austin and Druce 1969
Plate 5.2, Figs. 21, 22 and 24. Table 6. Diagnosis: a species of *Clydagnathus* with a blade highest posteriorly, sloping evenly downwards anteriorly. Median trough opens to the anterior. The specimen in Fig. 21 is smaller. Larger specimens have a proportionally longer platform and more nodes.
Fig. 21, upper view, TCD25607, ×72; Fig. 22, lower view, TCD25608, ×48, Fig. 24, lateral view, TCD25607, ×72. Both from unnamed micrites at Beaverton Farm, near Donabate, County Dublin, Ireland. Sample DON 6 (see Marchant, 1978).

Bispathodus aculeatus plumulus Rhodes, Austin and Druce 1969
Plate 5.2, Figs. 23 and 25. Table 6. Diagnosis: distinguished from *B. aculeatus aculeatus* by the plume-like blade, which has its anterior denticles reclined.
Fig. 23, upper view; Fig. 25, right lateral view. Both TCD21035, ×48. Houseland Sandstone Member, Hook Head, County Wexford, Ireland, *spicatus* Zone. Specimen figured by Johnston and Higgins (1981, Fig. 6).

PLATE 5.3
Polygnathus communis carina Hass 1959
Plate 5.3, Figs. 1 and 2. Table 6. Diagnosis: distinguished from *P. communis communis* (Plate 5.1, Figs. 12, 16 and 17) by the ornament of ridges or nodes, usually set at an angle to the carina, on the anterior part of the platform.
Fig. 1, lower view; Fig. 2, upper view. Both TCD25609, ×48. Waulsortian Limestone, Corkbeg Island, Whitegate, County Cork, Ireland, *carina* Zone.

Dollymae hassi Voges 1959
Plate 5.3, Figs. 3 and 4. Table 6. Diagnosis: a species of *Dollymae* with blade bearing two rows of nodes, broadly expanded basal cavity with two ridge-like carinae on the outer side and one on the inner side.
Fig. 3, upper view; Fig. 4, posterior view. Both TCD25610, ×48. 8 m above the base of the Ringabella Limestone, Ringabella, County Cork, Ireland, *carina* Zone; *hassi* Subzone.

Prioniodina oweni Rhodes, Austin and Druce 1969
Plate 5.3, Figs. 5 and 9. Table 5. Diagnosis: straight to curved, slightly arched blade-like form, with a prominent posteriorly directed cusp over slightly expanded basal cavity which in aboral view has a rounded margin reaching the posterior and tapers anteriorly. At least one, commonly two or three, well-defined denticles occur posterior to the cusp. The figured specimen could be identified as *Eotaphrus (Spathognathodus)* cf. *bultyncki* (Groessens, 1977) but stratigraphically older specimens with relatively longer anterior processes and less conspicuous cusps seem to be outside the range of variation found in Belgium. Distinguished from its successor *Eo. bultyncki* by its less expanded basal cavity and number of posterior denticles.
Fig. 5., lateral view; Fig. 9, lower view. Both TCD20347, ×48. Ballysteen Limestone (sample Dunkitt 116/20), Dunkitt Townland, County Kilkenny, Ireland, *multistriatus* Zone. See Keeley (1980). Specimen courtesy of Martin Keeley.

Eotaphrus bultyncki (Groessens 1977)
Plate 5.3, Figs. 6, 10 and 11. Table 6. Diagnosis: a species assigned to *Eotaphrus* by Lane *et al.* (1980) because it was interpreted as the ancestor of *Eotaphrus burlingtonensis.* Characterized by straight to slightly curved anterior blade with upright to reclined denticles, a prominent posteriorly directed cusp and a laterally expanded basal cavity. A single small denticle posterior to the cusp occurs in some specimens.

Pl. 5.3]   The Carboniferous System: Part 1   195

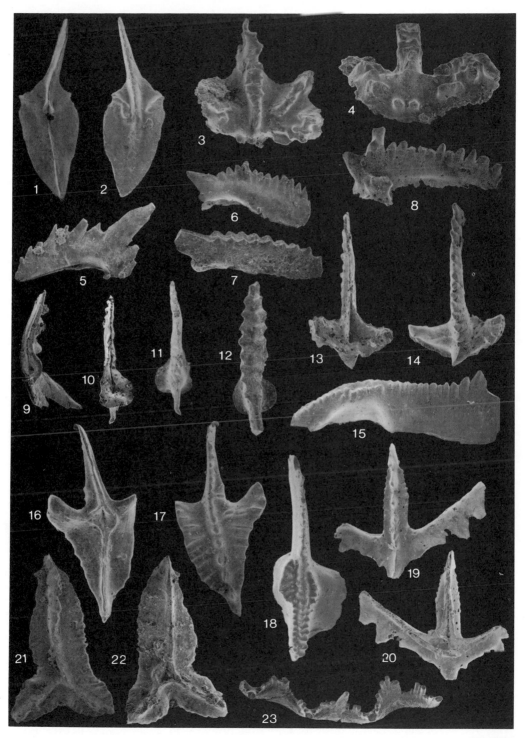

Plate 5.3

Fig. 6, lateral view; Fig. 10, lower view; Fig. 11, upper view. All TCD25611, ×48. Unnamed limestones, Rio Fin Ex borehole BS21, 58.30 m, West of Carrigaline, County Cork, Ireland, *carina* Zone; *bultyncki* Subzone. Specimen courtesy of Rio Fin Ex.

Eotaphrus burlingtonensis Pierce and Langeheim 1974
Plate 5.3, Figs. 7 and 12. Table 6. Diagnosis: a species of *Eotaphrus* characterized by a single anterior process bearing a double row of nodes and a prominent cusp.
Fig. 7, lateral view; Fig. 12, upper view. Both British Geological Survey LZA 6150/2, ×48. Black Rock Limestone, Vallis Vale, Somerset, England, *anchoralis* Zone. Specimen figured by Butler (1973, Plate 58, Figs. 3–5).

Dollymae bouckaerti Groessens 1977
Plate 5.3, Figs. 8, 13 and 14. Table 6. Diagnosis: a species of *Dollymae* characterized by a straight anterior blade and two lateral processes which bear a node, or row of nodes, commonly with a zig-zag pattern. Distinguished from its ancestor, *Eotaphrus bultyncki,* in its more expanded ornamented lateral processes and more subdued denticles on the anterior blade.
Fig. 8, lateral view; Fig. 13, lower view; Fig. 14, upper view. All TCD25612, ×48. Unnamed limestone, Ballygaran Quarry, near Carrigaline, County Cork, Ireland, *carina* Zone; *bouckaerti* Subzone. Specimen courtesy of Brenda Thornbury.

Gnathodus pseudosemiglaber Thompson and Fellows 1970
Plate 5.3, Figs. 15 and 18. Table 6. Diagnosis: a species of *Gnathodus* characterized by a posteriorly expanded carina, a strongly developed short parapet, concave towards the carina, on the inner side and a more subdued parapet or nodes close to the carina on the outer side.
Fig. 15, outer lateral view; Fig. 18, upper view. Both TCD25613, ×36. Sample from 152 ft in borehole 431, Tynagh Mine, Tynagh, County Galway, Ireland. Chadian. Specimen courtesy of Ennex Ltd.

Pseudopolygnathus pinnatus Voges 1959
Plate 5.3, Figs. 16 and 17. Table 6. Diagnosis: a species of *Pseudopolygnathus* characterized by a pinnate extension of the right or left antero-lateral edge of the platform.
Fig. 16, lower view; Fig. 17, upper view. Both TCD25614, ×48. Unnamed limestone, Ballygarvan Quarry, near Carrigaline, County Cork, Ireland, *anchoralis* Zone. Specimen courtesy of Brenda Thornbury.

Scaliognathus anchoralis europensis Lane and Ziegler 1983
Plate 5.3, Figs. 19 and 20. Table 6. Diagnosis: *S. anchoralis* is distinguished from other species of *Scaliognathus* by its anchor-like shape. *S. a. europensis* differs from *S. a. anchoralis* in its larger basal activity and from *S. a. fairchildi* in its wider anterior process with subdued denticulation.
Fig. 19, upper view; Fig. 20, lower view. TCD25615, ×48. Unnamed limestone, Ballygarvan Quarry, near Carrigaline, County Cork, Ireland, *anchoralis* Zone. Specimen courtesy of Brenda Thornbury.

Doliognathus latus Branson and Mehl 1941
Plate 5.3, Figs. 21 and 22. Table 6. Diagnosis: a species of *Doliognathus* with a large postero-lateral process.
Fig. 21, upper view; Fig. 22, lower view. Both TCD25616, ×48. Kersdown Quarry, Bampton, Devonshire, England. Reworked into ?Arundian limestone. Specimen courtesy of Peter Jackson.

Hindeodella segaformis Bischoff 1957)
Plate 5.3, Fig. 23. Table 6. Diagnosis: a species of *Hindeodella* with a zig-zag outline in upper view. According to Chauff (1981), *H. segaformis* represents the Sc. element of *Scaliognathus* spp. Chauff, a multielement conodont species from the Osagean (Lower Carboniferous) in Mid-continent North America and Texas.
Oblique oral view, TCD25617, ×48. Waulsortian Limestone, White Quarry, Ardbraccan, County Meath, Ireland, *anchoralis* Zone.

PLATE 5.4

'Apatognathus' cuspidatus Varker 1967
Plate 5.4, Figs. 1 and 2. Table 6. Diagnosis: a species of *'Apatognathus'* distinguished by its larger denticles on the less steeply inclined posterior bar and an apical cusp which is more than half the bar length.

Pl. 5.4]   The Carboniferous System: Part 1   197

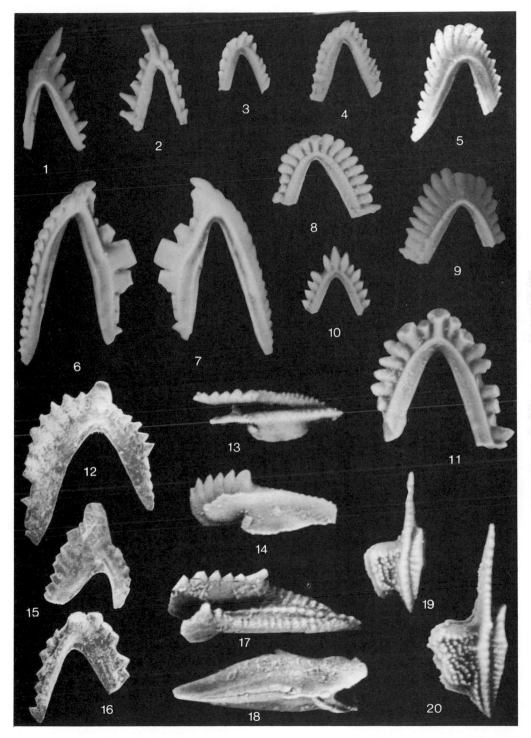

Plate 5.4

Fig. 1. Outer lateral view, holotype 28(6)BB205, ×41; Fig. 2, inner lateral view, 31(3)BB159, ×41. Fig. 1, 1.5 m below the top of the Four Fathom Limestone (Yoredale Group), Borrowdale Beck, Stainmore. Fig. 2, 3.00 m below the top of the Great Limestone (Yoredale Group), Borrowdale Beck, Stainmore. Fig. 1 *girtyi collinsoni* Zone; Fig. 2, base of the Namurian.

'Apatognathus' petilus Varker 1967

Plate 5.4, Figs. 3, 4 and 5. Table 6. Diagnosis: a species of *'Apatognathus'* distinguished by a small apical cusp, a strongly inwardly inclined anterior bar on which the denticles increase in size apically and a posterior bar with uniform denticulation and no inward inclination.
Fig. 3, inner lateral view, 24(4)SW182; Fig. 4, inner lateral view, 35(5)GB110; Fig. 5, outer lateral view, holotype 16(6)MG39. Fig. 3, 1.00 m below the top of the Three Yard Limestone (Yoredale Group), Middlehope Burn, Westgate, Weardale; Fig. 4, 1.50 m below the top of the Gayle Limestone (Yoredale Group), Gayle Beck, Hawes, Wensleydale; Fig. 5, 5.00 m below the top of the Hardraw Scar Limestone (Yoredale Group), Whitfield Gill, Askrigg, Wensleydale, *mononodosa* Zone.

'Apatognathus' scalenus Varker 1967

Plate 5.4, Figs. 6 and 7. Diagnosis: a species of *'Apatognathus'* distinguished by its subequal denticles on the anterior bar and variable denticles including a large bar-cusp on the posterior bar.
Fig. 6, Inner lateral view; Fig. 7, outer lateral view; Both holotype 32(4)BB213, ×41. 2.00 m below the top of the Great Limestone (Yoredale Group), Borrowdale Beck, Stainmore. Base of the Namurian.

'Apatognathus' libratus Varker 1967

Plate 5.4, Figs. 8, 9, 10 and 11. Table 6. Diagnosis: a species of *'Apatognathus'* distinguished by its symmetry and subequal denticles on both limbs.
Fig. 8, inner lateral view, 30(2)BB212; Fig. 9, outer lateral view, 30(2)BB212; Fig. 10, inner lateral view, juvenile specimen 29(5)BB159; Fig.11, inner lateral view, holotype 18(2)MG132. All ×41. Figs. 8 and 9, 3.00 m below the top of the Great Limestone (Yoredale Group), Borrowdale Beck, Stainmore; Fig. 10, from 2.50 m below the top of the Great Limestone, Stainmore; Fig. 11, from the Simonstone Limestone (Yoredale Group), Whitfield Gill, Askrigg, Wensleydale.

'Apatognathus' scandalensis Higgins and Varker 1982

Plate 5.4., Fig. 12. Table 6. Diagnosis: a species of *'Apatognathus'* distinguished by its thin wide-angled bars and bar denticles which are highest near, but not at, the cusp. The denticles of the anterior bar are twice the height of those of the posterior bar.
Inner lateral view, holotype R18, ×60. Sample SB8, Scandel Beck Limestone, Scandel Beck, Ravenstonedale, *homopunctatus* Zone. Figure from Higgins and Varker, 1982, Plate 19, Fig. 10.

Cavusgnathus regularis Youngquist and Miller 1949

Plate 5.4, Figs. 13 and 14. Table 6. Diagnosis: a species of *Cavusgnathus* distinguished by its compact form and regular denticulation of the blade. Older specimens recorded from Ravenstonedale show some difference from this specimen, the main distinction being the larger blade, which extends up to half the length of the platform.
Fig. 13, upper view; Fig. 14, inner lateral view. Both specimen SAD682K1, ×40. Cawdor Quarry, Matlock, *girtyi collinsoni* Zone. Copy of Higgins, 1975 (Plate 8, Figs. 1 and 2).

'Apatognathus' asymmetricus Higgins and Varker 1982

Plate 5.4, Figs. 15 and 16. Plate 6. Diagnosis: a species of *'Apatognathus'* distinguished by its asymmetry, with a laterally thickened anterior bar half the height of the posterior bar, which is thin. Denticles on the posterior bar are fused and twice the height of those on the anterior bar.
Fig. 15, inner lateral view, holotype R21; Fig. 16, inner lateral view, R20. Both ×60. Fig. 15, sample SB9, Scandel Beck Limestone, Fig. 16, sample SB8, Scandel Beck Limestone, *homopunctatus* Zone. Copy of Higgins and Varker (1982, Plate 19, Figs. 7 and 9).

Mestognathus bipluti Higgins 1961

Plate 5.4, Figs. 17 and 18. Table 6. Diagnosis: a species of *Mestognathus* distinguished by its two denticulated anterior parapets.
Figs. 17, upper view; Fig. 18, lower view. Both specimen X249. Both ×56. Sample CYD6, north crop of the South Wales coalfield, Craig-y-Dinas, South Wales. Copy of Rhodes *et al.* (1969, Plate 15, Figs. 15(a) and 15(b)).

Pl. 5.4]   The Carboniferous System: Part 1   199

Gnathodus bilineatus (Roundy 1926)
Plate 5.4, Figs. 19 and 20. Table 6. Diagnosis: this abundant and widespread species is represented in the Dinantian of Britain and Ireland by the subspecies *G. bilineatus bilineatus,* this being joined by *G. bilineatus bollandensis* in the Namurian. *G. bilineatus bilineatus* shows considerable variation in the size and ornamentation of the outer and inner lateral platforms. (See also Plate 6.1).
Fig. 19, upper view, SAD680K15; Fig. 20, upper view, SAD680K16. Both ×40. Basal Namurian, Caldon Low, North Staffordshire. Copy of Higgins (1975, Plate 11, Figs. 1 and 2).

PLATE 5.5

Mestognathus beckmanni Bischoff 1957
Plate 5.5, Figs. 1, 3 and 5. Table 6. Diagnosis: a species of *Mestognathus* with one high anterior blade with six to twelve denticles, a prominent medial trough and a restricted basal cavity which is shallow and occupies the anterior half of the platform.
Fig. 1, upper view; Fig. 3, lower view; Fig. 5, lateral view. All X245, ×60. Sample SCC29, Fall Bay, Gower, South Wales, *homopunctatus* Zone. Figures from Rhodes *et al.* (1969, Plate 15, Figs. 7(b), 7(c) and 7(d)).

Taphrognathus varians Branson and Mehl 1940
Plate 5.5, Figs. 2 and 4. Table 6. Diagnosis:transitional forms are known to occur between this genus and *Cavusgnathus* depending on the position of the anterior blade, which is centrally placed in *Taphrognathus* but moves to the outer lateral position in *Cavusgnathus*. A few specimens previously illustrated bear a short carina in the posterior quarter of the median sulcus and at the present time such specimens are included in *Taphrognathus varians*.
Fig. 2, upper view; Fig. 4, inner lateral view. Specimens R37 and R39, ×60. Sample SG19, Stone Gill Beds, Ravenstonedale, *homopunctatus* Zone. Figures from Higgins and Varker (1982, Plate 18, Figs. 15 and 16).

Cloghergnathus carinatus Higgins and Varker 1982
Plate 5.5, Figs. 6, 8 and 10. Table 6. Diagnosis: a right- and left-sided element with the anterior blade developed on the inner side, a central sulcus containing a short carina at the posterior end and a short blade that does not extend onto the platform. The unit is arched.
Fig. 6, upper view, R29, Fig. 8, upper view, holotype R30; Fig. 10, outer lateral view, holotype R30. All ×60. Fig. 6, sample SG19, Stone Gill Beds, Ravenstonedale; Figs. 8 and 10, sample SB2, Scandel Beck Limestone, Ravenstonedale, *homopunctatus* Zone. Figures from Higgins and Varker (1982, Plate 18, Figs. 1, 2 and 7).

Mestognathus groessensi Belka 1983
Plate 5.5, Figs. 7 and 9. Table 6. Diagnosis: a species of *Mestognathus* with a median carina and an unusually large aboral cavity, described by Rhodes *et al.* (1969) as *Scaphignathus?* sp.B and by Metcalfe (1981) as *Mestognathus* cf. *beckmanni*. Some immature specimens of *M. beckmanni* tend also to have a slightly larger basal cavity than the adults.
Fig. 7, upper view; Fig. 9, lower view. Both X533, ×60. Sample ZL9, Daren Ddu, north crop of South Wales Coalfield, *mehli* Zone. Figures from Rhodes *et al.* (1969, Plate 2, Figs. 12(a) and 12(c)).

Lochriea commutata (Branson and Mehl 1941)
Plate 5.5, Figs. 11 and 12. Table 6. Diagnosis: an abundant species previously described as *Gnathodus commutatus*, with a smooth asymmetrical platform free from ornament and a broad noded carina which may extend beyond the posterior margin of the platform.
Fig. 11, lower view, specimen 56/2/GB113; Fig. 12, upper view, specimen 56/1/GB113. Both ×41. From 2 m below the top of the Gayle Limestone (Yoredale Group), Gayle Beck, Hawes, Wensleydale, *bilineatus* Zone. Stewart (1981a) records this species from the *anchoralis–latus* Subzone to the Namurian.

Lochriea mononodosa (Rhodes, Austin and Druce 1969)
Plate 5.5, Figs. 13, 16, 17, 18 and 20. Table 5. Diagnosis: a species of *Lochriea*, very similar to *L. commutata* but with a single large elongate node on the inner side of the platform. The other side of the platform remains unornamented.
Fig. 13, outer lateral view, holotype N124, ×60; Fig. 17, upper view, holotype, ×60; Fig. 18, lower view, holotype, ×60; Fig. 20, inner lateral view, holotype, ×60; Fig. 16, upper view, specimen 56/4/BB213, ×41. Figs. 13, 17, 18 and 20 sample 3D14/15 from the north crop of the South Wales Coalfield; Fig. 16, from 2 m below the top of the Great Limestone (Yoredale Group), Borrowdale Beck, Stainmore. Figs. 13, 17, 18 and 20, *girtyi collinsoni* Zone; Fig. 16, basal Namurian. Figs. 13, 17, 18 and 20 from Rhodes *et al.* (1969, Plate 19, Figs. 14(a), 14(d), 14(c) and 14(b)).

Gnathodus homopunctatus Ziegler 1960
Plate 5.5, Figs. 14, 15, 19, 21 and 22. Table 6. Diagnosis: a species of *Gnathodus* distinguished by its platform, which occupies the posterior half of the unit and bears on each side an irregular row of nodes, often parallel to the margins of the platform and midway between the margin and the carina.
Fig. 14, outer lateral view, specimen X121, ×60; Fig. 15, upper view, specimen X121, ×60; Fig. 19, inner lateral view, specimen X121, ×60; Fig. 22, lower view, specimen X121, ×60; Fig. 21, upper view, specimen 57/4/GB111, ×41. Figs. 14, 15, 19 and 22, sample from 3D13/15, from the north crop of the South Wales Coalfield; Fig. 21, from 2 m below the top of the Gayle Limestone (Yoredale Group), Gayle Beck, Hawes, Wensleydale. Figs. 14, 15, 19 and 22, *girtyi collinsoni* Zone; Fig. 21, *bilineatus* Zone. Figs. 14, 15, 19 and 22 from Rhodes *et al.* (1969, Plate 19, Figs. 5(a), 5(c), 5(b) and 5(d)).

Pl. 5.5]   The Carboniferous System: Part 1   201

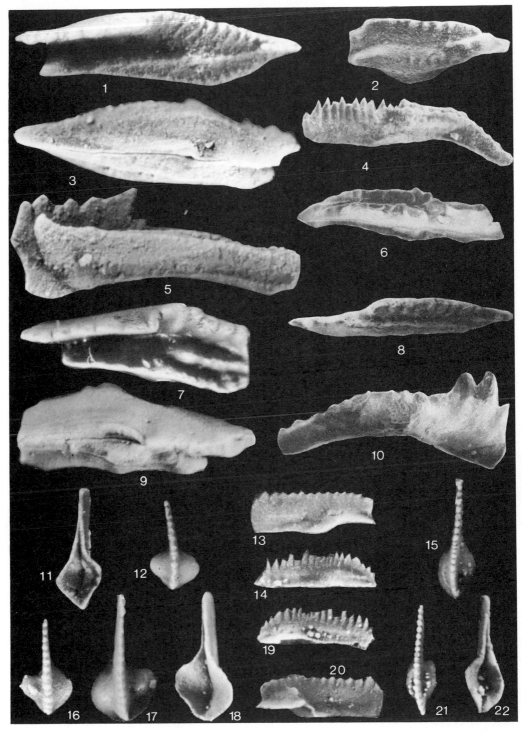

Plate 5.5

PLATE 5.6

Gnathodus girtyi girtyi Hass 1953
Plate 5.6, Figs. 1 and 2. Table 6. Diagnosis: Hass's original description referred to specimens in which the inner side of the platform was transversely ridged in its anterior part and noded in its posterior part. The outer side of the platform does not extend as far anteriorly as the inner and it may be continued to the posterior end as irregular nodes fused to the carina. (See also Plate 6.2).
Fig. 1, upper view, specimen SAD684K26; Fig. 2, upper view, specimen SAD684K25. Both ×40. Cawdor Quarry, Matlock, *girtyi collinsoni* Zone. Figures from Higgins (1975, Plate 10, Figs. 6 and 5).

Gnathodus girtyi collinsoni Rhodes, Austin and Druce 1969
Plate 5.6, Figs. 3 and 4. Table 6. Diagnosis: a subspecies of *Gnathodus girtyi* in which the outer lateral platform completely or almost completely lacks nodular ornament. Unlike *G. girtyi simplex* Dunn, the inner lateral platform stops well short of the posterior end of the unit.
Fig. 3, upper view, specimen SAD684K21; Fig. 4, upper view, specimen SAD684K22. Both ×40. Cawdor Quarry, Matlock. Figures from Higgins (1975, Plate 10, Figs. 1 and 2).

Geniculatus glottoides Voges 1959
Plate 5.6, Figs. 5 and 6. Table 6, Diagnosis: a species of *Geniculatus* distinguished by its great size and the extreme lateral thickening of its bars.
Fig. 5, upper view; Fig. 6, lower view. Both specimen TCD25618, ×24. From the highest limestone bed, member 4, Reenydonagen Formation, Reenydonagen, Bantry Bay, County Cork, Ireland, *commutata* Zone.

Embsaygnathus asymmetricus Metcalfe 1981
Plate 5.6, Figs. 7, 8, 11 and 16. Table 6. Diagnosis: this species is distinguished by its *Polygnathus*-like platform which possesses a posterior bar extension, which curves outwards and then anteriorly in the same plane as the platform. The basal cavity is small and situated posteriorly.
Fig. 7, upper view, holotype MPK1909, ×60; Fig. 8, lower view, holotype, ×60; Fig. 11, upper view, only specimen known from Isle of Man; Fig. 16, lower view; Figs. 7 and 8, sample 24, Embsay Beck, near Skipton, West Yorkshire; Figs. 11 and 16, only specimen known from the Isle of Man DerbyhävenBeds. Figs. 7 and 8, *homopunctatus* Zone; Figs. 11 and 16, *commutata* Zone. Figs. 7 and 8 from Metcalfe (1981, Plate 2, Figs. 2(a) and 2(f)); Figs. 11 and 16 provided by Mr. A. Swift.

Gnathodus texanus Roundy 1926
Plate 5.6, Figs. 9, 10 and 12. Table 6. Diagnosis: a species of *Gnathodus* distinguished by its very narrow platform, the posterior part of which is long and tapered. The inner side does not reach the posterior end of the unit. Ornamentation is limited to a single elongate node or parapet paralleling the carina on the inner side. Generally believed to have evolved from *Gnathodus pseudosemiglaber* by a reduction of the outer platform.
Fig. 9, upper view; Fig. 10, lower view; Fig. 12, lateral view. All specimen LZA6118/1 (HQ35), ×30. Black Rock Group, Halecombe Quarry, Frome, Somerset. Figures from Butler (1973, Plate 56, Figs. 32, 33 and 31).

Neoprioniodus singularis (Hass 1953)
Plate 5.6, Fig. 13. Table 6. Diagnosis: a species of *Neoprioniodus* with a long slender blade-like anterior denticle and a short down-curved posterior bar. The denticles become rapidly and regularly shorter towards the posterior. All are slender and inwardly curved. This is probably the Ne element of *Lochriea commutata*.
Inner lateral view, specimen SAD684K5, ×40. From loc. CA3, Cawdor Quarry, Matlock, *girtyi collinsoni* Zone. Figure from Higgins (1975, Plate 3, Fig. 11).

Cavusgnathus charactus Rexroad 1957
Plate 5.6, Figs. 14 and 15. Table 6. Diagnosis: a species of *Cavusgnathus* distinguished by the form of its relatively short anterior blade, which has four to eight denticles of relatively uniform size, its bluntly crenulate oral platform surface, which has a median posterior carina, and the regularly concave lower surface of the unit.
Fig. 14, outer lateral view; Fig. 15, upper view. Both specimen X61, ×45. Sample HAR13, Lower Algal Limestone, Harden Burn, Roxburgh. Figures from Rhodes *et al.* (1969, Plate 13, Figs. 7(e) and 7(a)).

Patrognathus capricornis (Druce 1969)
Plate 5.6, Fig. 17. Table 6. Diagnosis: a species of *Patrognathus* which is bowed in oral view, with a median free anterior blade approximately equal in length to the platform. Platform ornament consists of rounded nodes on the inner side and elongate nodes or transverse ridges on the outer side. The nodes fuse at the sharply pointed posterior end of the platform.
Upper view, specimen MPK1946, ×50. Sample 207, Embsay Limestone, Embsay Beck, Skipton, West Yorkshire, *homopunctatus* Zone. Figure from Metcalfe (1981, Plate 9, Fig. 1(a)).

Pl. 5.6]   The Carboniferous System: Part 1   203

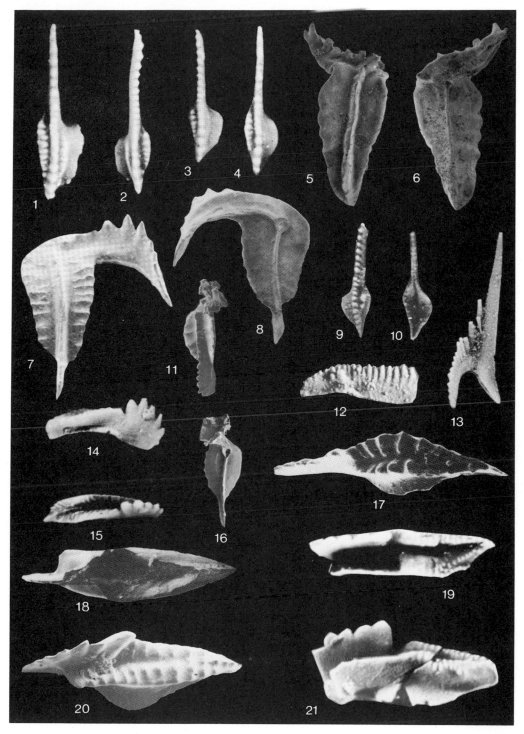

Plate 5.6

Cavusgnathus unicornis Youngquist and Miller 1949

Plate 5.6, Figs. 18 and 20. Table 6. Diagnosis: a species of *Cavusgnathus* distinguished by its conspicuously large posterior denticle on the anterior blade, its large, slightly asymmetrical aboral cavity and its posteriorly tapering platform with transverse ridges.

Fig. 18, lower view; Fig. 20, upper view. Both specimen MPK1905, ×50. Sample 10B, Lower Bowland Shales, Banks Gill, West Yorkshire, *girtyi collinsoni* Zone. Figures from Metcalfe (1981, Plate 1, Figs 3(c) and 3(a)).

Cavusgnathus cristatus Branson and Mehl 1940

Plate 5.6, Figs. 19 and 21. Table 6. Diagnosis: a species of *Cavusgnathus* in which a deep trough is developed for most of the length of the platform, obstructed by a short, poorly developed carina at the posterior end. Transverse ridges extend into the trough. This species differs from *C. convexus* in that the basal cavity does not extend to the posterior extremity of the unit.

Fig. 19, upper view; Fig. 21, inner lateral view. Both specimen X64, ×45. Sample 3D22, Craig-y-Dinas on the north crop of the South Wales Coalfield. Figures from Rhodes *et al.* (1969, Plate 14, Figs. 3(a) and 3(c)).

5.6 REFERENCES

Aldridge, R. J., Austin, R. L. and Husri, S. 1968. Viséan Conodonts from North Wales and Ireland. *Nature (London)*, **219**, 255–258.

Austin, R. L. 1968a. Five Viséan conodont horizons in the North of England. *Geol. Mag.*, **105**, 367–371.

Austin, R. L. 1968b. New conodont horizons in Southwest England. *Proc. Ussher Soc.*, **1** (6).

Austin, R. L. 1968c. Conodont faunas from the Waulsortian Reef Limestone at Askeaton and from the Cork Red Marble at Midleton. *Sci. Proc. R. Dublin Soc., Ser. A*, **9**, 107–114.

Austin, R. L. 1973a. Phylogeny and homeomorphy of conodonts in the Lower Carboniferous. In F. H. T. Rhodes (ed.), *Conodont Paleozoology, Spec. Paper Geol. Soc. Am.*, **141**, 105–116, 1 plate.

Austin, R. L. 1973b. Modification of the British Avonian Conodont zonation and a reappraisal of European Dinantian conodont zonation and correlation. *Ann. Soc. Géol. Belg.*, **96**, 523–532.

Austin, R. L. 1974. The biostratigraphic distribution of conodonts in Great Britain and the Republic of Ireland. In: J. Bouckaert and M. Streel (Eds.), *Int. Symp. on Belgian Micropaleontological Limits from Emsian to Viséan, Namur, 1974*, **3**, Geological Survey of Belgium, 1–17, 1 plate.

Austin, R. L. 1976. Evidence from Great Britain and Ireland concerning West European Dinantian conodont paleoecology. In: C. R. Barnes (Ed.), *Conodont Paleoecology, Spec. Paper Geol. Assoc. Can.*, **15**, 201–224.

Austin, R. L. and Aldridge, R. J. 1969. Lower Carboniferous (C Zone) conodonts from County Meath, Ireland. *Sci. Proc. R. Dublin Soc., Ser. A.*, **3**, 231–236.

Austin, R. L. and Aldridge, R. J. 1973. Conodonts from horizons with *Goniatites crenistria* Phillips in North Wales and the Isle of Man. *Geol. Mag.*, **110**, 37–42, 2 plates.

Austin, R. L. and Barnes, C. 1973. The biostratigraphic limitation of conodonts with particular reference to the base of the Carboniferous. *Bull. Soc. Belge. Géol. Paleontol. Hydrol.*, **92**, 351–374.

Austin, R. L., Conil, R., Dolby, G., Lys, M., Paproth, E., Rhodes, F. H. T., Streel, M., Utting, J. and Weyer, D. 1970a. Les couches de passage du Devonien au Carbonifère de Hook Head (Irlande) au Bohlen (DDR). *Colloq. sur la Stratigraphie du Carbonifère, Liège*, in *Congr. Collq. Univ. Liege*, **55**, 167–177.

Austin, R. Conil, R. and Husri, S. 1970b. Correlation and age of the Dinantian rocks north and south of the Shannon, Ireland. *Colloq. su la Stratigraphie du Carbonifère, Liège.*, in *Congr. Colloq. Univ. Liège*, **55**, 179–192, 2 plates.

Austin, R. L., Conil, R. and Rhodes, F. H. T. 1973. Recognition of the Tournaisian–Viséan boundary in North America and Britain. *Ann. Soc. Géol. Belg.*, **96**, 165–188, 2 plates.

Austin, R. L. and Davies, R. B. 1984. Problems of recognition and implications of Dinantian conodont biofacies in the British Isles. In D. L. Clark (Ed.), *Conodont Biofacies and Provincialism, Spec. Paper Geol. Soc. Am.*, **196**, 195–228, 3 plates.

Austin, R. L., Druce, E. C. and Rhodes, F. H. T. 1966. British Lower Carboniferous conodont faunas and their value in correlation. *Bull. Am. Assoc. Pet. Geol.*, **50**, 604.

Austin, R. L., Druce, E. C., Rhodes, F. H. T. and Williams, J. A. 1967. The value of conodonts in the recognition of the Devonian–Carboniferous boundary, with particular reference to Great Britain. *C. R. 6ème Congr. Int. de Stratigraphie et de Géologique du Carbonifère, Sheffield, 1967*, 431–444, 1 plate.

Austin, R. L. and Groessens, E. 1972. The origin and evolution of the Middle Dinantian conodont genera *Doliognathus, Dollymae, Scaliognathus* and *Staurognathus,* and related forms. *Ann. Soc. Géol. de Belg.*, **95**, 229–238, 1 plate.

Austin, R. L. and Hill, P. J. 1973. A Lower Avonian (K Zone) conodont fauna from near Tintern, Monmouthshire, Wales. *Geol. Palaeontol.*, **7**, 123–129, 2 plates.

Austin, R. L. and Husri, S. 1974. Dinantian Conodont Faunas of County Clare, County Limerick and County Leitrim. In: J. Bouckaert and M. Streel (Eds.), *Int. Symp. on Belgian Micropaleontological Limits from Emsian to Viséan, Namur, 1974*, **3**, Geological Survey of Belgium, 18–69, 15 plates.

Austin, R. L. and Matthews, S. C. 1968. In: Edmonds *et al.* (Eds.) *Geology of the Country around Okehampton, Mem. Geol. Surv. Gt. Br.*, **324**, 13–15.

Austin, R. L. and Mitchell, M. 1975. Middle Dinantian platform conodonts from County Fermanagh and County Tyrone, Northern Ireland. *Bull. Geol. Surv. Gt. Br.*, **55**, 43–54, 2 plates.

Austin, R. L. and Ramsbottom, W. H. C. Unpublished. Conodonts from Settle.

Austin, R. L. and Rhodes, F. H. T. 1969. A conodont assemblage from the Carboniferous of the Avon Gorge, Bristol. *Palaeontology*, **12**, 400–405.

Bassett, M. G. and Jenkins, T. B. H. 1977. Tournaisian conodont and spore data from the Uppermost Skrinkle Sandstones of Pembrokeshire, South Wales. *Geol. Palaeontol.*, **11**, 121–134, 2 plates.

Beer, K. E. and Fenning, P. J. 1976. Geophysical anomalies and mineralisation at Sourton Tors, Okehampton, Devon. *Inst. Geol. Sci. Rep.*, **76/1**, 1–38.

Belka, Z. 1983. Evolution of the Lower Carboniferous conodont genus *Mestognathus*. *Acta Geol. Pol.*, **33**, 73–84.

Bischoff, G. 1957. Die Conodonten-Stratigraphie des rheno-herzynischen Unter-karbons mit Berucksichtigung der *Wocklumeria*-Stufe und der Devon/Karbon-Grenze. *Abh. Hess. Landesamtes. Bodenforsch.*, **19**, 1–64, 6 plates.

Boogaert, H. A. van Adrichem, 1967. Devonian and Lower Carboniferous conodonts of the Cantabrian Mountains (Spain) and their stratigraphic application. *Leidse Geol Meded.*, **39**, 129–192.

Bouroz, A., Einor, D. L., Gordon, M., Meyen, S. V. and Wagner, R. H. 1978. Proposals for an international chronostratigraphic classification of the Carboniferous. *C. R. 8ème Int. Congr. de Stratigraphie et de*

Geologique du Carbonifère, Moscow, 1975, 36–69.

Branson, E. B. and Mehl, M. G. 1934. Conodonts of the Grassy Creek Shale of Missouri. *Univ. Missouri Stud.,* **8,** 171–259, 9 plates.

Branson, E. B. and Mehl, M. G. 1934. Conodonts from the Bushberg Sandstone and equivalent formations of Missouri. *Univ. Missouri Stud.,* **13,** 128–148, 2 plates.

Branson, E. B. and Mehl, M. G. 1938. Conodonts from the Lower Mississippian of Missouri. In E. B. Branson, *et al.,* Stratigraphy and paleontology of the Lower Mississippian of Missouri. *Univ. Missouri Stud.,* **13,** 128–148, 2 plates.

Branson, E. B. and Mehl, M. G. 1941b. Conodonts from the Keokuk Formation. *Denison Univ., Sci. Lab. J.,* **35,** 179–188, 1 plate.

Branson, E. B. and Mehl, M. G. 1941. New and little known Carboniferous conodont genera. *J. Paleontol.,* **15,** 97–106, 1plate.

Briggs, D. E. G., Clarkson, E. N. K. and Aldridge, R. J. 1983. The conodont animal. *Lethaia,* **16,** 1–14.

Browne, A. N. 1981. The conodont faunas of the Lower Carboniferous Glencar and Dartry Formations of County Leitrim, and of comparable stratigraphic horizons in Northern Ireland. *Unpublished M.Sc. Thesis,* Queen's University, Belfast.

Butler, M. 1972. Conodont faunas and stratigraphy of certain Tournaisian sections in the Bristol Mendip area. *Unpublished Ph.D. Thesis,* University of Bristol.

Butler, M. 1973. Lower Carboniferous conodont faunas from the Eastern Mendips, England. *Palaeontology,* **16,** 477–517, 4 plates.

Chauff, K. M. 1983. Multielement conodont species and ecological interpretation of the Lower Osagean (Lower Carboniferous) conodont zonation from the Mid-continent North America. *Micropaleontology,* **29,** 404–429, 3 plates.

Clarke, W. J. 1960. Scottish Carboniferous conodonts. *Trans. Edinburgh Geol. Soc.,* **18,** 1–31, 5 plates.

Clayton, G., Colthurst, J. R. J., Higgs, K., Jones, G. L. and Keegan, J. B. 1977. Tournaisian miospores and conodonts from County Kilkenny. *Geol. Surv. Irel. Bull.,* **2,** 99–106.

Clayton, G., Johnston, I. S., Sevastopulo, G. D. and Smith, D. G. 1980. Micropalaeontology of a Courceyan (Carboniferous) borehole section from Ballyvergin, County Clare, Ireland. *J. Earth Sci. R. Dublin Soc.,* **3,** 81–100.

Clayton, G., Keegan, J. B. and Sevastopulo, G. D. 1982. Palynology and Stratigraphy of late Devonian and early Carboniferous rocks, Ardmore, County Waterford, Ireland. *Pollen and Spores,* **24,** 511–521.

Collinson, C. W., Scott, A. J. and Rexroad, C. B. 1962. Six charts showing biostratigraphic zones, and correlations based on conodonts from Devonian and Mississippian rocks of the Upper Mississippi Valley. *Ill. State Geol. Surv., Circ.* **328,** 1–32.

Conil, R., Groessens, E. and Pirlet, H. 1977. Nouvelle charte stratigraphique du Dinantien type de la Belgique. *Ann. Soc. Géol. Nord,* **96,** 363–371.

Conil, R., Longerstaey, P. J. and Ramsbottom, W. H. C.

1980 (dated 1979). Materiaux pour l'etude micropaleontologique du Dinantien de Grande-Bretagne. *Mém. Inst. Géol. Univ. Louvain,* **30,** 1–186, 30 plates.

Cooper, C. L. 1939. Conodonts from a Bushberg-Hannibal horizon in Oklahoma. *J. Paleontol.,* **13,** 379–422, 9 plates.

Craig, G. Y. 1952. A comparative study of the ecology and palaeoecology of *Lingula. Trans Edinburgh Geol. Soc.,* **15,** 110–120.

Craig, G. Y. 1954. The palaeoecology of the Top Hosie Shale (Lower Carboniferous) at a locality near Kilsyth. *Q. J. Geol. Soc. London,* **110,** 103–119.

Dineley, D. L. and Rhodes, F. H. T. 1956. Conodont horizons in the West and South-west of England. *Geol. Mag.,* **93,** 242–248.

Druce, E. C. 1969. Devonian and Carboniferous conodonts from the Bonaparte Gulf Basin, northern Australia. *Austral. Bur. Min. Resources Bull.,* **98,** 1–242, 43 plates.

Druce, E. C., Rhodes, F. H. T. and Austin, R. L. 1972. Statistical analysis of British Carboniferous conodont faunas. *J. Geol. Soc. London,* **128,** 53–70.

Dunn, D. L. 1965. Late Mississippian conodonts from the Bird Spring Formation in Nevada. *J. Paleontol.,* **39,** 1145–1150, 1 plate.

Fowler, A. 1955. The zonal sequence of the Carboniferous rocks of South-east Tyrone. *Bull. Geol. Sur. Gt. Br.,* **8,** 38–43.

Garwood, E. J. 1907. Notes on the faunal succession in the Carboniferous Limestone of Westmorland and neighbouring portions of Lancashire and Yorkshire. *Geol. Mag.,* **44,** 70–74.

Garwood, E. J. 1913. The Lower Carboniferous succession in the North-west of England. *Q. J. Geol. Soc. London,* **68,** 449–596.

George, T. N., Johnson, G. A. L., Mitchell, M., Prentice, J. E., Ramsbottom, W. H. C., Sevastopulo, G. D. and Wilson, R. B. 1976. A correlation of Dinantian rocks in the British Isles. *Geol. Soc. London Spec. Rep.,* **7,** 1–87.

Groessens, E. 1977. Distribution de Conodontes dans le Dinantien de la Belgique. In: J. Bouckaert and M. Streel (Eds.), *Int. Symp. on Belgian Micropaleontological Limits from Emsian to Viséan, Namur, 1974,* **17,** Geological Survey of Belgium, 1–193.

Hass, W. H. 1953. Conodonts of the Barnett Formation of Texas. *U.S. Geol. Surv. Prof. Pap.,* **286,** 1–47, 3 plates.

Higgins, A. C. 1961, Some Namurian conodonts from North Staffordshire. *Geol. Mag.,* **98,** 210–224, 3 plates.

Higgins, A. C. 1965. The significance of conodonts in the Carboniferous of Europe. *Proc. Subcommission on Carboniferous Stratigraphy, Sheffield, 1965,* 69–75.

Higgins, A. C. 1975. Conodont zonation of the late Viséan–early Westphalian strata of the South and Central Pennines of Northern England. *Bull. Geol. Surv. Gt. Br.,* **53,** 1–90, 18 plates.

Higgins, A. C. 1981. The distribution of conodonts in relation to the palaeogeography of late Viséan–Namurian times. In: J. W. Neale and M. D. Brasier

(Eds.), *Microfossils from Recent and Fossil Shelf Seas*, Ellis Horwood, Chichester, Sussex, 37–51.

Higgins, A. C. and Varker, W. J. 1982. Lower Carboniferous conodont faunas from Ravenstonedale, Cumbria. *Palaeontology, 25*, 145–166, 2 plates.

Hill, P. J. 1971. Carboniferous conodonts from Southern Ireland. *Geol. Mag., 108*, 69–71.

Hinde, G. J. 1879. On conodonts from the Chazy and Cincinnati Group of the Cambro–Silurian and from the Hamilton and Genesee Shale divisions of the Devonian, in Canada and the United States. *Q. J. Geol. Soc. London, 35*, 351–369.

Hinde, G. J. 1900. Notes and descriptions of new species of Scotch Carboniferous conodonts. *Trans. Nat. Hist. Soc. Glasgow, 5*, 338–346, 2 plates.

House, M. R. and Butcher, N. E. 1962. Excavations in the Devonian and Carboniferous rocks of the Chudleigh area, South Devon. *Proc. Ussher Soc., 1*, 28–29.

Johnson, G. A. L. 1959. The Carboniferous stratigraphy of the Roman wall district in Western Northumberland. *Proc. Yorks. Geol. Soc., 32*, 83–130.

Johnson, G. A. L., Hodge, B. L. and Fairbairn, R. A. 1962. The base of the Namurian and of the Millstone Grit in North-eastern England. *Proc. Yorks. Geol. Soc., 33*, 341–362.

Johnson, R. J. 1967. Conodonts from the Viséan of North-west County Clare, Eire. *Unpublished M.Sc. Thesis*, University of London.

Johnston, I. S. 1976. The conodont biostratigraphy of some Lower Carboniferous (Courceyan Stage) rocks of Central Ireland. *Unpublished Ph.D. Thesis*, University of Dublin.

Johnston, I. S. and Higgins, A. C. 1981. Conodont faunas from the Lower Carboniferous rocks at Hook Head, County Wexford. *J. Earth Sci. R. Dublin Soc., 4*, 83–96.

Jones, G. H. 1977. The stratigraphy and palaeontology of a Courceyan borehole section near Callan, County Kilkenny. *Unpublished M.Sc. Thesis*, University of Dublin.

Keeley, M. L. 1980. The Carboniferous geology of the Carrick-on-Suir syncline, Southern Ireland. *Unpublished Ph.D. Thesis*, University of Dublin.

Keeley, M. L. 1983. The stratigraphy of the Carrick-on-Suir syncline, Southern Ireland. *J. Earth Sci. R. Dublin Soc., 5*, 107–120.

Lane, H. R., Sandberg, C. A. and Ziegler, W. 1980. Taxonomy and phylogeny of some Lower Carboniferous conodonts and preliminary standard post-*Siphonodella* zonation. *Geol. Palaeontol., 14*, 117–164.

Lane, H. R. and Ziegler, W. 1983. Taxonomy and Phylogeny of *Scaliognathus* Branson and Mehl 1941 (Conodonta, Lower Carboniferous). *Senckenberg. lethaea, 64*, 199–225.

Marchant, T. R. 1978. The Stratigraphy and Micropalaeontology of the Lower Carboniferous (Courceyan–Arundian) of the Dublin Basin, Ireland. *Unpublished Ph.D. Thesis*, University of Dublin.

Marchant, T. R., Sevastopulo, G. D. and Clayton, G. 1984. Preliminary correlation of Irish Tournaisian

conodont, foraminiferal and miospore zonal schemes. *C. R. 9ème Congr. Int. de Stratigraphie et de Géologique du Carbonifère, Washington and Champaign–Urbana, 1979, 2*, 282–288.

Matthews, S. C. 1961. A Carboniferous conodont fauna from Callington, east Cornwall. *Abstracts Proc. Conf. on the Geology and Geomorphology of South-west England, in Trans. R. Geol. Soc. Corn.,* 13–14.

Matthews, S. C. 1969a. A Lower Carboniferous conodont fauna from East Cornwall. *Palaeontology, 12*, 262–275, 5 plates.

Matthews, S. C. 1969b. Two conodont faunas from the Lower Carboniferous of Chudleigh, South Devon. *Palaeontology, 12*, 276–280, 1 plate.

Matthews, S. C. and Butler, M. 1974. Siphonodellid conodonts in the Lower Carboniferous. *C.R. Congr. Int. de Stratigraphie et de Géologique du Carbonifère, Krefeld, 1971, 3*, 409–414.

Matthews, S. C. and Naylor, D. 1973. Lower Carboniferous conodont faunas from South-west Ireland. *Palaeontology, 16*, 335–380, 4 plates.

Matthews, S. C., Sadler, P. M. and Selwood, E. B. 1972. A Lower Carboniferous conodont fauna from Chillaton, South-west Devonshire. *Palaeontology, 15*, 550–568, 3 plates.

Matthews, S. C. and Thomas, J. M. 1968. Conodonts from the Dinantian of North-east Devon. *Proc. Ussher Soc., 2*, 262–275.

Matthews, S. C. and Thomas, J. M. 1974. Lower Carboniferous conodont faunas from North-east Devon. *Palaeontology, 17*, 371–385, 2 plates.

Mehl, M. G. and Thomas, L. A. 1947. Conodonts from the Fern Glen of Missouri. *Denison Univ., J. Sci Lab., 40* (2), 3–20, 1 plate.

Metcalfe, I. 1976. The conodont biostratigraphy of the Lower Carboniferous sediments of the Skipton Anticline and Craven Lowlands. *Unpublished Ph.D. Thesis*, University of Leeds.

Metcalfe, I. 1980. Conodont faunas and the age of the Raygill Quarry Limestones (Embsay Limestone), Lothersdale, Yorkshire. *Proc. Yorks. Geol. Soc., 43*, 169–178, 1 plate.

Metcalfe, I. 1981. Conodont zonation and correlation of Dinantian and early Namurian strata of the Craven Lowlands of Northern England. *Inst. Geol. Sci. Rep., 80/10*, 1–70, 19 plates.

Metcalfe, I. and Leeder, M. R. 1979. Palaeontology and petrography of the St. Helen's Well Borehole, Eshton, Yorkshire. *Trans. Leeds Geol. Assoc., 9*, 53–60.

Miller, J. and Austin, R. L. Unpublished. Conodonts from Clitheroe.

Mitchell, M. and Reynolds, M. J. 1981. Early Tournaisian rocks at Lilleshall, Shropshire. *Geol. Mag., 118*, 669–702.

Mitchell, M., Reynolds, M. J., Laloux, M. and Owens, B. 1982. Biostratigraphy of the Knap Farm Borehole at Cannington Park, Somerset. *Inst. Geol. Sci. Rep., 82/5*, 9–17.

Moore, C. 1863. On the palaeontology of mineral veins, and on the secondary age of some mineral veins in the Carboniferous limestone. *Rep. Br. Assoc. Adv. Sci.*, 82–83.

Morris, P. G. 1969. Carboniferous conodonts in the South-western Pennines. *Geol. Mag.*, **106**, 497–499.

Morris, J. H., Howard, D. W., Sevastopulo, G. D. and Williams, C. T. 1981. An occurrence of Tertiary Olivine–Dolerite Sills in Lower Carboniferous (Courceyan) rocks near Carrigallen, County Leitrim. *J. Earth Sci. R. Dublin Soc.*, **4**, 39–52.

Naylor, D., Jones, P. C. and Matthews, S. C. 1974. Facies relationships in the Upper Devonian–Lower Carboniferous of South-west Ireland and adjacent areas. *Geol. J.*, **9**, 77–96.

Naylor, D., Reilly, T. A., Sevastopulo, G, D. and Sleeman, A. G. 1983. Stratigraphy and structure in the Irish Variscides. In: P. L. Hancock (Ed.), *The Variscan Fold Belt in the British Isles*, Adam Hilger, Bristol, 20–46.

Nicoll, R. S. 1980. The multielement genus *Apatognathus* from the late Devonian of the Canning Basin, Western Australia. *Alcheringa*, **4**, 133–152.

Paproth, E. *et al.* 1983. Bio- and lithostratigraphic subdivisions of the Dinantian in Belgium, a review. *Ann. Soc. Géol. Belg.*, **106**, 185–239.

Pierce, R. W. and Langenheim, R. L., jr. 1974. Platform conodonts of the Monte Cristo Group, Mississippian, Arrow Canyon Range, Clark County, Nevada. *J. Paleontol.*, **48**, 149–169, 4 plates.

Polgar, R. 1980. The stratigraphy and micropalaeontology of a borehole in the Carboniferous rocks of Knockadrinan Townland, County Leitrim. *Unpublished M.Sc. Thesis*, University of Dublin.

Ramsbottom, W. H. C. 1973. Transgressions and regressions in the Dinantian: a new synthesis of British Dinantian stratigraphy. *Proc. Yorks. Geol. Soc.*, **39**, 567–607.

Ramsbottom, W. H. C. (Ed.) 1981. *Field Guide to the Boundary Stratotypes of the Carboniferous Stages in Britain, Proc. Subcommission on Carboniferous Stratigraphy*, Leeds, 1–146.

Ramsbottom, W. H. C. and Mitchell, M. 1980. The recognition and division of the Tournaisian Series in Britain. *J. Geol. Soc. London*, **137**, 61–63.

Rexroad, C. B. 1957. Conodonts from the Chester Series in the type area of southwestern Illinois. *Illinois Geol. Surv. Rept. Invest.*, **199**, 43 pp., 4 plates.

Rexroad, C. B. and Collinson, C. 1963. Conodonts from the St. Louis Formation (Valmeyeran series) of Illinois, Indiana, and Missouri. *Ill. State Geol. Surv. Circ.*, **355**, 28 pp., 2 plates.

Rexroad, C. B. and Scott, A. J. 1964. Conodont zones in the Rockford Limestone and the lower part of the New Providence Shale (Mississippian) in Indiana. *Indiana Geol. Surv. Bull.*, **30**, 1–54, 3 plates.

Rexroad, C. B. and Thompson, T. L. 1979. A spathognathodont lineage of Mississippian conodonts. *Lethaia*, **12**, 235–243.

Reynolds, M. J. 1970. A Lower Carboniferous conodont fauna from Flintshire, North Wales. *Bull. Geol. Surv. Gt. Br.*, **32**, 1–19, 34 plates.

Rhodes, F. H. T. 1954. The zoological affinities of conodonts. *Biol. Rev.*, **29**, 419–452.

Rhodes, F. H. T. and Austin, R. L. 1971. Carboniferous conodont faunas of Europe. In: W. C. Sweet and S. M. Bergström (Eds.), *Symp. on Conodont Biostratigraphy*, in *Mem. Geol. Soc. Am.*, **127**, 317–352.

Rhodes, F. H. T. and Austin, R. L. 1977. Ecologic and Zoogeographic factors in the biostratigraphic utilisation of conodonts. In: E. G. Kauffman and J. E. Hazel (Eds.), *Concepts and Methods of Biostratigraphy*, Dowden, Hutchinson and Ross, 365–396.

Rhodes, F. H. T., Austin, R. L. and Druce, E. C. 1969. British Avonian (Carboniferous) conodont faunas, and their value in local and intercontinental correlation. *Bull. Br. Mus. (Nat. Hist.), Geol., Suppl.*, **5**, 1–313, 31 plates.

Robbie, J. A. 1955. The Carboniferous rocks of Edendork, County Tyrone. *Bull. Geol. Surv. Gt. Br.*, **8**, 21–37.

Roundy, P. V. 1926. Part II. The Micro-fauna, in Mississippian formations of San Saba County, Texas. *U.S. Geol. Surv. Prof. Pap.*, **146**, 5–23, 4 plates.

Sandberg, C. A. and Gutschick, R. C., 1984. Distribution, microfauna and source-rock potential of Mississippian Delle Phosphatic Member of Woodman Formation and equivalents, Utah and adjacent States. In: J. Woodward, F. F. Meissner and J. L. Clayton (Eds.) *Hydrocarbon Source Rocks of the Greater Rocky Mountain Region: Denver, Colorado*, Rocky Mountain Association of Geologists, 135–178, 8 plates.

Sandberg, C. A., Ziegler, W., Leuteritz, K and Brill, S. M. 1978. Phylogeny, speciation and zonation of *Siphonodella* (Conodonta, Upper Devonian and Lower Carboniferous). *Newsl. Stratigr.*, **7**, 102–120.

Selwood E. B., Stewart, I. J., Turner, P. J. and Whiteley, M. J. 1982. The Devonian-Carboniferous transition and its structural setting at Chillaton, West Devon, England. *Geol. Mag.*, **119**, 383–393.

Sevastopulo, G. D. 1982. Age and depositional setting of Waulsortian Limestones in Ireland. In K. Bolton, H. R. Lane, and D. V. Le More (Eds.) *Symp. on the Palaeoenvironmental Setting and Distribution of the Waulsortian Facies*, El Paso Geological Society and University of Texas, El Paso, 65–79.

Sevastopulo, G. D. and Naylor, D. 1981. Erratic Carboniferous boulders in Bantry Bay, County Cork. *Geol. Surv. Irel. Bull.*, 79–84.

Sleeman, A. G., Higgs, K. and Sevastopulo, G. D. 1983. The stratigraphy of the late Devonian–early Carboniferous rocks of South County Wexford. *Geol. Surv. Irel. Bull.*, **3**, 141– 158.

Sleeman, A. G., Johnston, I. S., Naylor, D. and Sevastopulo, G. D. 1974. The stratigraphy of the Carboniferous Rocks of Hook Head, County Wexford. *Proc. R. Ir. Acad., Sect. B*, **74**, 227–243.

Smith, J. 1900. Conodonts from the Carboniferous Limestone strata of the West of Scotland. *Trans. Nat. Hist. Soc. Glasgow*, **5**, 336–338.

Smyth, L. B. 1950. The Carboniferous System in North County Dublin. *Q. J. Geol. Soc. London*, **105**, 295–326.

Stewart, I. J. 1981a. *Unpublished Ph.D. Thesis*, University of Exeter.

Stewart, I. J. 1981b. Late Devonian and Lower Carboniferous conodonts from North Cornwall and their stratigraphical significance. *Proc. Ussher Soc.,* **5,** 179–185.

Swift, A. Unpublished. Dinantian conodonts from the Isle of Man.

Thompson, T. L. 1967. Conodont zonation of Lower Osagean rocks (Lower Mississippian) of south-western Missouri. *Missouri Geol. Surv. and Water Res., Rept. Inv.,* **39,** 1–88, 6 plates.

Thompson, T. L. and Fellows, L. D. 1970. Stratigraphy and conodont biostratigraphy of Kinderhookian and Osagean (Lower Mississippian) rocks of South-western Missouri and adjacent areas. *Mo. Geol. Surv. Water Resour.,* **45,** 1–263, 8 plates.

Ulrich, E. O. and Bassler, R. S. 1926. A classification of the toothlike fossils, conodonts, with descriptions of American Devonian and Mississippian species. *Proc. U.S. Nat. Mus.,* **68,** art. 12; 1–63, 11 plates.

Varker, W. J. 1964. The conodont faunas and stratigraphy of the Yoredale Series in the Askrigg and Alston regions. *Unpublished Ph.D. Thesis,* University of Sheffield.

Varker, W. J. 1967. Conodonts of the genus *Apatognathus* Branson and Mehl from the Yoredale Series of the North of England. *Palaeontology,* **10,** 124–141, 2 plates.

Varker, W. J. 1968. Conodont distribution in Yoredale Limestones (D_2-E_1) of the North of England. *Trans. Leeds Geol. Assoc.,* **7,** 275–290.

Varker, W. J. *et al.* In press. Carboniferous stratotypes of Northern Europe. *Spec. Publ. Yorks. Geol. Soc.*

Varker, W. J. and Higgins, A. C. 1979. Conodont evidence for the age of the Pinskey Gill Beds of Ravenstone-dale, North-west England. *Proc. Yorks. Geol. Soc.,* **42,** 357–369, 1 plate.

Vaughan, A. 1905. The palaeontological sequence in the Carboniferous Limestone of the Bristol area. *Q. J. Geol. Soc. London,* **61,** 181–385.

Voges, A. 1959. Conodonten aus dem Unterkarbon I und II (Gattendorfia- und *Pericyclus*-Stufe) des Sauer-landes. *Paläontol. Z.,* **33,** 266–314, 3 plates.

Voges, A. 1960. Die Bedeutung der Conodonten fur Stratigraphie des Unterkarbons I und II (Gaten-dorfia- und *Pericyclus*-Stufe) im Sauerland. *Fortschr. Geol. Rheinl. Westfalen,* **3,** 197–228.

Von Bitter, P. H. and Austin, R. L. 1984. The Dinantian *Taphrognathus transatlanticus* Conodont Range Zone of Great Britain and Atlantic Canada. *Palaeontology,* **27,** 95–111, 3 plates.

Young, J. 1880a. Notes on Scottish Carboniferous micro-zoa and the methods by which they may be collected and mounted. *Trans. Edinburgh Geol. Soc.,* **3,** 300–302.

Young, J. 1880b. On a group of fossil organisms termed conodonts. *Proc. Trans. Nat. Hist. Soc. Glasgow,* **4,** 5–7, 10, 78, 79.

Youngquist, W. and Miller, A. K. 1949. Conodonts from the Late Mississippian Pella beds of south-central Iowa. *J. Paleontol.,* **23,** 617–622, 1 plate.

Ziegler, W. 1971. Review of Rhodes, Austin and Druce, 1969. *Zentralbl. Geol. Paläontol,,* *Teil II,* **5,** 365–369.

Ziegler, W. 1960. Die Conodonten aus den Geröllen des Zechsteinkonglomerates von Rossenray (südwestlich Rheinberg/Niderrhein). *Fortschr. Geol. Rheinl.- Westf.,* **6,** 1–16, 4 plates.

6

The Carboniferous System:
Part 2 – Conodonts of the
Silesian Subsystem from
Great Britain and Ireland

A. C. Higgins

6.1 HISTORY OF CONODONT STUDIES

Silesian conodonts from Europe are poorly known but probably best known in the British area, particularly from the Namurian Series. Until the 1960s, the records principally consisted of incidental references to their presence, mainly in geological survey publications, in works having a much broader scope. From the 1960s onwards, systematic study of Namurian faunas has led to a zonation, mainly based on the Craven Basin (Higgins, 1961, 1967, 1975; Ramsbottom et al., 1979), which is applicable to much of Western Europe; little is known of the Westphalian faunas, nothing of Stephanian faunas and no zonation exists for these latter. The dearth of information reflects in part the slower rate of evolution of the Silesian conodont animal compared with that of the Dinantian and in part the nature of Silesian rocks (Fig. 6.1) which are principally shales and sandstones of mixed marine and non-marine origin, less suitable for study than carbonate

sequences. A summary of the early phase of conodont studies is given by Rhodes and Austin (1971).

The first record of British Silesian faunas was from Scotland where Smith (1907) recorded conodonts from the Upper Coal Measures (Westphalian C). Also recorded from Scotland were conodonts from Skipsey's Marine Band and other Westphalian C horizons by Currie et al. (1973). From early Westphalian B, Manson (1957) listed conodonts from a marine band in the Anthraconaia modiolaris Zone of the Midland Valley of Scotland. Clarke (1960) produced the first systematic study of Silesian conodonts in Britain with his work on the conodont faunas of the Upper Limestone Group (Arnsbergian), the Passage Group (Alportian?, Kinderscoutian) and Skipsey's marine band (Westphalian C) in the Midland Valley of Scotland. This paper was of great significance in showing the great similarity between early Namurian faunas and the latest faunas from the Dinantian, and the major differences between these faunas and those of the later Namurian.

In England, Mitchell and Stubblefield (1941) recorded conodonts from the Westphalian rocks of the Leicestershire and South Derbyshire Coalfields as did Mitchell and Crookall (1942, 1945) from the Warwickshire and South Staffordshire

Coalfields, Edwards and Stubblefield (1948) from the Derbyshire and Nottinghamshire Coalfields; Stevenson and Mitchell (1955), Stubblefield and Calver (1955), Mitchell (1954) and Eden (1954) recorded conodonts from the Midlands Coalfields. Edwards (1954) recorded faunas from the Clowne Marine Band (Westphalian B) in Derbyshire and

Fig. 6.1 – Outcrop and subcrop map of the Silesian rocks (Namurian Series) of Great Britain and Ireland.

Marine Band (Westphalian B) in Derbysgire and Nottinghamshire, Earp and Magraw (1955) from Tonge's now *Amaliae* Marine Band (Westphalian A) and Magraw (1957) recorded faunas from various marine bands in Lancashire, Derbyshire and Yorkshire. From South Wales, Ramsbottom (1952) and Woodland *et al.* (1957) noted the presence of conodonts. The first systematic treatment of Westphalian faunas from England including faunas from the Westphalian A marine bands, typified by *Gastrioceras subcrenatum* and *G. listeri*, was that of Higgins (1962, 1975) which referred to two conodont biozones. Matthews and Moore (1967) recorded and named some conodont species from the *Gastrioceras listeri* horizon of North Devon. Although not figured, the fauna appears to be closely similar to that of the same horizon described by Higgins (1962, 1975). Austin (1972) figured faunas from the *G. listeri* marine band in Lancashire. In summary, conodont faunas appear to be widespread in the Westphalian rocks of Britain and offer considerable potential for recognition of the marine horizons.

Namufian faunas were first recorded from the Colsterdale Marine Beds of Namurian age from Yorkshire (Dunham and Stubblefield, 1945). Stevenson and Mitchell (1955) recorded the presence of conodonts from the Namurian rocks of the Midlands. Higgins (1961) described and figured a well-preserved and abundant fauna from the *Cravenoceras leion* Zone, the basal zone of the Silesian Subsystem, from North Staffordshire and in 1962 and 1975 erected a zonation of Namurian faunas from the Craven Basin, consisting of five zones and four subzones. This sequence, a basin facies fauna, contrasted to a small extent with the shelf faunas described by Varker (1964) from Yoredale limestones of Northern England which are distinctive in the presence of abundant representatives of the genus *Apatognathus* (Varker, 1967). An attempt to summarize the environmental similarities and differences was made by Higgins (1981a, 1981b). Metcalfe (1981) described early Namurian faunas from the Craven Lowlands of Northern England, and Austin (1972) discussed some systematic problems by reference to Chokierian—Marsdenian faunas of Ireland. Aldridge *et al.*

(1968) listed faunas from the Pendleian Stage of Ireland, and Rhodes *et al.* (1969) recorded faunas from the Upper Limestone Group of Scotland. Reynolds (1977), using Higgins' zonation. listed a sequence of faunas from the Duffield Borehole, Derbyshire.

6.2 LOCATION OF COLLECTIONS OF IMPORTANCE

Few Silesian collections are easily available for further study but the major ones can be located. The collections of Higgins, including all the type and figured specimens from his 1975 study have been deposited with the British Geological Survey. Type and figured material from the *Cravenoceras leion* Zone (Higgins, 1961) is curated in the British Museum Collections. Clarke's (1960) material from the Namurian and Westphalian rocks of Scotland is located at the Department of Geology, University of Edinburgh. Specimens from Ireland (Austin, 1972) are in the collections of the Department of Geology, University of Southampton. Metcalfe's figured specimens from the early Namurian Bowland Shales of Lancashire and Yorkshire are deposited with the British Geological Survey, as are Reynolds' (1977) specimens from his Duffield Borehole study.

6.3 DEFINITION OF BOUNDARIES AND INTERNAL DIVISION OF THE SILESIAN SUBSYSTEM

The Silesian Subsystem is currently divisible into three series, Namurian, Westphalian and Stephanian, although a recent decision by the Subcommission of Carboniferous Stratigraphy to accept a new Mid-Carboniferous boundary at the appearance of the conodont species *Declinognathodus noduliferus* will divide the Namurian Series into two parts and necessitate its revision. The Namurian Series is divided into seven stages Pendleian—Yeadonian (Table 7), the Westphalian Series into four stages, Westphalian A—D, and the Stephanian Series also into four stages Cantabrian and Stephanian A—C. The effective type area for the Namurian Series is Great Britain, particularly the Craven

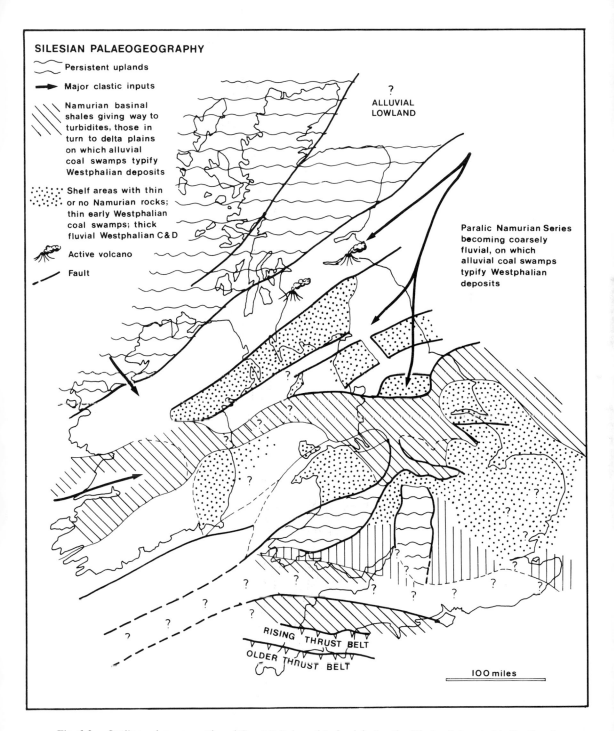

Fig. 6.2 – Outline palaeogeography of Great Britain and Ireland during the Silesian Subperiod indicating the major basins of deposition and principal positive areas. (Compiled by Dr. D. Moore).

Basin, and proposed boundary stratotypes for the stages have been described by Ramsbottom (1981). Up to and including the Kinderscoutian Stage, the sequence in the Craven Basin is largely marine but with non-marine intercalations. Higher in the Namurian Series and particularly in the Westphalian Series the marine horizons (marine bands) become less common and in the Stephanian Series they are unknown. Consequently the precision with which correlation can be affected in marine sequences becomes less as the Silesian Subsystem is ascended.

Since the work of Bisat (1924), Silesian biostratigraphy has been dominated by goniatite study. The proposed boundary stratotypes of Ramsbottom (1981) are based on the appearance of characteristic goniatite species. Supplementing, and in non-goniatite sequences, replacing the goniatites in the Namurian Series are spores (Owens et al., 1977) and conodonts (Higgins, 1975). In the Westphalian Series, non-marine bivalves have been used to great effect, based on the zonal scheme of Trueman (1954) and Trueman and Weir (1946), together with spores (Owens et al., 1977) and plants (Dix, 1934; Crookall, 1955). In the Stephanian Series, spores and plants provide a means of correlation, but rocks of this age are probably poorly represented in Great Britain. The biostratigraphy of the Silesian Subsystem has been excellently documented by Ramsbottom et al. (1978).

The palaeogeography of Great Britain during Silesian times was complex (Fig. 6.2). Deposition was controlled by transgressions, which Ramsbottom (1977) argues were eustatic in origin, and by tectonic activity. Tectonic activity is seen in the south in Devon and Cornwall, which was a part of the Variscan foredeep accumulating great thicknesses of flysch sediments and subsequently folded and metamorphosed by the Variscan orogenic movements. The Carboniferous succession in this area is still poorly known. To the north was St. George's Land which was progressively inundated during the Namurian Epoch but became land during the Westphalian Epoch and which was periodically uplifted throughout the Silesian Epoch. In Northern England, two tilted fault

blocks, the Askrigg and Alston Blocks, were positive areas throughout the Silesian Subperiod, receiving little sediment and, according to Ramsbottom (1977), these were frequently areas of non-deposition. Still further north was the Southern Uplands High and in Northern Scotland an extensive positive area was probably land throughout Silesian times. The centres of deposition were mainly between these positive areas, in basins and troughs which were interconnected; These were the Craven Basin, Stainmore Trough, Midland Valley of Scotland, the Leinster Basin and Shannon Trough in Ireland. As shown by Ramsbottom et al. (1978) the sequences, and particularly the marine beds in the basins, vary considerably and, therefore, affect to a high degree the completeness of the conodont record. Tectonic and eustatic activity also produce environmental changes whose effects are currently poorly understood but which must affect the zonal scheme. The zonal scheme presented is deliberately broad in an attempt to make it applicable throughout the British Isles and Ireland and, where facies control is suspected, it has been highlighted. However, facies control of the faunas is not a serious drawback in their use for correlation purposes since few species are totally restricted to any one environment.

6.4 CONODONT ZONATION

The zonation used is basically that of Higgins (1975), slightly modified to take into account more recent work, but comparing it with those of other researchers, e.g. Metcalfe (1981). This section also takes into account what is known of the faunas in Northern England, much of which is unpublished, which is principally of shelf faunas and shows some differences when compared with the basinal faunas of the Craven Basin to the south.

(a) Kladognathus—Gnathodus girtyi simplex Zone Characteristic species include Gnathodus bilineatus bilineatus, Gnathodus girtyi girtyi, G. girtyi intermedius, Lochriea commutata, P. nodosus, L. mononodosa, Neoprioniodus spathatus and Kladognathus macrodentatus.

The lower limit of the zone is marked by the appearance of *Gnathodus girtyi simplex* and the upper limit by the appearance of *Gnathodus bilineatus bollandensis.*

Probably the most distinctive and widespread group of species in this zone are *Paragnathodus nodosus. Lochriea commutata* and *L. monoondosa.* As an easily recognized internationally acceptable zone, the recognition of a *P. nodosus* Zone is attractive. However, within the Craven Basin it is possible to recognize a *Kladognathus– Gnathodus girtyi simplex* Zone and, since this coincides with the basal beds of the Silesian Subsystem it seems preferable to recognize this rather than amend it before further work on the *Gnathodus girtyi* complex has been completed. *P. nodosus* appears slightly below the base of the Silesian Subsystem within the P_{2b} Zone of the Brigantian Stage.

The upper limit of the zone is marked by the incoming of *Gnathodus bilineatus bollandensis* and by the disappearance of *Gnathodus homopunctatus, Kladognathus macrodentatus* and *Neoprioniodus peracutus* and of the genus *Mestognathus.*

The zone embraces the Pendleian Stage in the Craven Basin (Higgins, 1975; Reynolds, 1977). It also occurs in the Pendleian Stage in County Leitrim, Ireland (Aldridge *et al.,* 1968) and in the basal Pendleian Great Limestone of Stainmore, Northern England (Varker, 1964) and its equivalent in North Yorkshire, the Main Limestone. The faunas in Northern England differ slightly from those of the basin faunas to the south, in the presence of *Apatognathus scalenus, A. cuspidatus* and *A. petilus* (Varker, 1967). The genus *Apatognathus* typifies the shallow-water faunas of Northern England although, in other respects, the remaining fauna is identical with that in the basinal environments.

In addition, unpublished data from the Stainmore Trough point to the presence of this zone in the Stonedale limestones and Belsay Dene Limestone respectively. These two limestones, occurring in the Upper Pendeleian *C. malhamense* Zone (E_{1c}), include species of *Apatognathus* amongst otherwise typical Pendleian faunas.

In the Midland Valley of Scotland, Clarke (1960) described similar apatognathids in rich faunas from the lower part of the Upper Limestone Group.

(b) Gnathodus bilineatus bollandensis Zone

This zone encompasses the *G. bilineatus bollandensis–C. naviculus* Zone and the lower (Arnsbergian) part of the *I. minutus* Subzone of Higgins (1975). The abrupt faunal change apparent in some late Arnsbergian sections led Higgins (1975) to associate the *Idiognathoides* (now *Rhachistognathus*) faunas with the overlying *Declinognathodus* faunas. However, more recent work by Higgins and a better appreciation of the significance of faunas of this age outside Britain has led to this revision. The zone consists of two parts of which the lower part is the longer time period.

Characteristic species of the lower part of the zone consist of *G. bilineatus bollandensis, G. bilineatus bilineatus, P. nodosus* and *L. mononodosa, G. girtyi girtyi, G, girtyi intermedius* and *C. naviculus* do not extend beyond the *Cravenoceratoides nitidus* Zone (E_{2b}), whereas the previously named species may extend up to the top of the *Nuculoceras nuculum* Zone (E_{2c}).

Characteristic species of the upper part of the zone include *G. bilineatus bollandensis, G. bilineatus bilineatus* and *Rhachistognathus minutus.*

The lower limit of the zone is marked by the appearance of *Gnathodus bilineatus bollandensis.* The base of the upper part is marked by the appearance of *Rhachistognathus minutus* and the disappearance of *P. nodosus* and *L. mononodosa.* The upper limit of the zone is marked by the appearance of *Declinognathodus noduliferus.*

This zone is well known in the Craven Basin (Higgins, 1975; Reynolds, 1977). The upper part only is known from Edale, Derbyshire (Higgins, 1975) and the Duffield Borehole (Reynolds, 1977) where it occurs in the *Nuculoceras nuculum* Subzone as beds with *Rhachistognathus minutus.* It is also present in the proposed stratotype section for the Chokierian Stage at Gill Beck near Cowling in Yorkshire (Ramsbottom, 1981) but in this section *Rh. minutus* has not been recorded.

G. bilineatus bollandensis Zone is also present in Northern England in the Stainmore Trough where Varker (1964) and Varker and Austin (1974) recorded a typical fauna together with *Adetognathus unicornis* from the Mirk Fell Beds. The latter species was recorded from the Throckley Borehole by Reynolds (1968), also occurring in early Arnsbergian rocks. Also recorded in these faunas is *Spathognathodus scitulus,* a species which does not occur in the Craven Basin. The fauna of the Peasah Wood Limestone includes *G. bilineatus bollandensis* and *G. bilineatus bilineatus.* Further north, in the Northumberland Trough, unpublished faunas from the Corbridge Limestone (E$_{2a}$) and Newton Limestone (E$_{2b}$) are typical of the *G. bilineatus bollandensis* Zone except for the presence of species of *Apatognathus* and *S. scitulus.* The absence of *Rh. minutus* from these northern sections tends to confirm the contention of Ramsbottom (1977) that the *Nuculoceras nuculum* Zone is absent north of the Craven Basin because of erosion or non-deposition.

Still further north, in the Midland Valley of Scotland, Clarke described faunas from the Castlecary Limestone, probably of early Arnsbergian age, which include *G. bilineatus* and *Cavusgnathus* sp.

(c) Declinognathodus noduliferus Zone

This zone is equivalent to the *Idiognathoides noduliferus–Streptognathodus lateralis* Zone of Higgins (1975), except for the lower part of the range of *Rhachistognathus minutus* which is included in the underlying zone. It corresponds to the Chokierian and Alportian stages.

Characteristic species include *Declinognathodus noduliferus inaequalis, D. noduliferus noduliferus, D. noduliferus japonicus, D. lateralis* and *Neognathodus bassleri. Rhachistognathus minutus* is known to occur up to the top of the Chokierian Stage in Belgium (Higgins and Bouckaert, 1968) but does not appear to extend beyond the *Homoceras subglobosum* Zone in Britain (Higgins, 1975).

The lower limit of the zone is marked by the appearance of *Declinognathodus noduliferus* and the upper limit by the appearance of *Idiogna-*

thoides corrugatus. Declinognathodus noduliferus japonicus does not appear until the beginning of the Alportian Stage and may prove a useful guide to that level.

The changes at the base of the Chokierian Stage are one of the most important events in the history of the Carboniferous conodonts (Higgins, 1982; Ramsbottom *et al.,* 1983). *Declinognathodus noduliferus,* whose appearance marks this change, has been chosen as the guide fossil to identify the proposed Mid-Carboniferous boundary (Lane *et al.,* in press). In the majority of sections, only *Rhachistognathus minutus* crosses the boundary although in Belgium (Higgins and Bouckaert, 1968) and, in the Craven Basin (unpublished data), *Gnathodus bilineatus bollandensis* has been recorded from both the Chokierian and the Alportian stages.

This zone occurs extensively in the Craven Basin (Higgins, 1975; Reynolds, 1977), possibly in the Midland Valley of Scotland (Clarke, 1960), and in Ireland where Austin (1972) recorded rich faunas from both the Chokierian and the Alportian stages in County Clare.

(d) Idiognathoides corrugatus–Idiognathoides sulcatus Zone

This zone was described by Higgins (1975) and does not require modification. It corresponds to the Kinderscoutian Stage.

Characteristic species include *Idiognathoides corrugatus, Id. sulcatus, Id. sinuatus, Declinognathodus noduliferus, D. noduliferus japonicus, Idiognathoides macer* and *D. lateralis.*

The lower limit is taken at the appearance of *Idiognathoides sulcatus* and *Id. corrugatus* and the upper limit at the appearance of the genus *Idiognathodus.*

This zone is widespread in the Craven Basin (Higgins, 1975). It also occurs in the Whitehouse Limestone on the Alston Block in Northern England (unpublished data) and in early Kinderscoutian horizons in County Clare in Ireland (Austin, 1972).

Species of the genus *Declinognathodus,* as in the underlying zone, are still the most abundant and diverse ones in this zone but the important new entrants, species of *Idiognathoides*, are usually represented.

(e) *Idiognathoides sinuatus–Idiognathodus primulus* Zone

This zone was described by Higgins (1975) and is not modified. It includes the Marsdenian, Yeadonian and early Westphalian A Stages. Characteristic species include *Idiognathoides corrugatus*, *Id. sinuatus*, *Id. sulcatus* and *Idiognathodus primulus* and *I. delicatus*. The lower limit is marked by the appearance of the genus *Idiognathodus*, represented by the primitive species *Idiognathodus primulus*. The upper limit is marked by the appearance of *Idiognathoides sulcatus parva*.

This zone is very broad and will undoubtedly be divisible with further study. It is characterized by abundant representatives of the genus *Idiognathoides*, particularly *Id. corrugatus* and *Id. sinuatus*, whereas *Declinognathodus* is poorly represented. In the early Marsdenian Stage, one horizon yields large numbers of specimens morphologically identical with *Id. sulcatus sulcatus* except for the possession of an outer anterior node. These specimens were referred to *D. noduliferus japonicus* by Higgins (1975) but may well be a variant of *Id. sulcatus sulcatus*. If the latter interpretation is correct, the genus *Declinognathodus* does not occur above the Kinderscoutian Stage in Britain. There also exist in this zone occasional specimens of the genus *Neognathodus* which are difficult to speciate but with larger collections it should be possible to relate them to the more numerous specimens in North American collections. The genus *Idiognathodus* is represented by the simple *I. primulus* and the more complex forms referred to the generalized species *I. delicatus*. This zone is present throughout the Craven Basin (Higgins, 1975; Austin, 1972).

(f) *Idiognathoides sulcatus parva* Zone

This zone was described by Higgins (1975) from abundant faunas occurring in the *Gastrioceras listeri* Zone of early Westphalian A age.

Characteristic species include *Idiognathoides sulcatus parva*, *Id. sulcatus sulcatus*, *Id. corrugatus*, *Id. sinuatus* and *Idiognathodus delicatus*.

Its lower limit is marked by the appearance of *Idiognathoides sulcatus parva* but its upper limit is unknown.

The zone is widespread in the Craven Basin (Higgins, 1975) and has been recorded from North Devon (Matthews and Moore, 1967). The specimens from the latter locality are no longer available for study but Matthews and Moore described three forms which could be interpreted as typical of this horizon. The first form was referred to *Gnathodus liratus* which is superficially similar to *Id. sulcatus parva*. The second is the idiognathoidid component which is generally referred to *I. delicatus* and the third to *Polygnathodella* (now *Idiognathoides*) which is probably the *Id. corrugatus–Id. sinuatus* group of species.

(g) Later Westphalian Faunas

Numerous records of later Westphalian faunas exist (see Section 6.1) but few list or figure the species present. Clarke (1960) figured specimens from Skipsey's Marine Band, of Westphalian C age, from the Midland Valley of Scotland. These include *I. delicatus* (*I.* cf. *magnificus* of Clarke (1960)) and *Idiognathoides corrugatus* (*Polygnathodella tenuis* of Clarke (1960)), but further study is needed before zonal possibilities are realized.

6.5 FACIES CONTROL OF THE CONODONT FAUNAS

Biofacies studies of Silesian conodonts are few and only generalizations can be offered at this stage. Studies by Ramsbottom (1969) and Calver (1969) show that the marine faunas in the Silesian Subsystem are cyclic within each marine horizon and Ramsbottom *et al.* (1978) suggested that the overall control on the faunas is eustatic sea-level changes. Varker (1968) also suggested that rate of deposition could affect relative abundances within the Silesian Subsystem. What is the relative importance of these factors?

Insufficient data are available to determine the effects of transgressions and regressions on the conodont faunas but the experience of Higgins (1975) suggests that conodonts can occur in any phase of marine band; variation in composition of the late Namurian faunas, e.g. idiognathodid as opposed to idiognathoidid-dominated faunas, suggests that depth of water may be a controlling factor. Similarly in the early Namurian faunas, species such as *Gnathodus bilineatus* and *Gnathodus girtyi* appear to be controlled in their distribution by environmental factors. In this respect, sea-level changes may be an important factor, since the disappearance of *Gnathodus girtyi* from the British area occurs in the late Arnsbergian Stage, at a time which Ramsbottom *et al.* (1978) suggest was a time of widespread regression. This change also coincides with the brief appearance of *Rhachistognathus minutus,* the only species representing a genus which is common in the shallow epiconti-

nental seas of North America at this time. Similarly, in the shallow seas which covered the Askrigg and Alston Blocks in early Namurian time the genus *Apatognathus,* unknown in the Craven Basin to the south, is an important element of the faunas.

Cyclicity is more apparent in the Yoredale Limestones described by Varker (1968) where he described the variations in abundance obtained by measuring the number of conodonts per kilogram in closely sampled sections. In successive limestones he convincingly demonstrated an increase in abundance, reaching a peak close to the highest bedding plane followed by a sharp decrease in the highest beds. It is not clear what the cause of this is but the rate of deposition might be a possibility; sea-level change may also play a part.

PLATE 6.1
All figured specimens are deposited in the British Museum (Natural History)

Gnathodus bilineatus bilineatus (Roundy 1926)
Plate 6.1, Figs. 1 and 2. Pectiniform element. Table 7. Diagnosis: unit asymmetric having a long blade and a subrectangular outer platform whose oral surface is covered with parallel rows of nodes which may be fused to form ridges. Inner side of platform longer than inner and covered with transverse ridges. Blade continued to posterior end as a carina. Cup widest at anterior end.
Figured specimens:upper views, ×40. Pendleian Stage, *Cravenoceras leion* Zone, loc. CH3 of Higgins (1975).

Cavusgnathus naviculus (Hinde 1900)
Plate 6.3, Fig. 3. Pectiniform element. Table 7. Diagnosis: unit asymmetric having a long platform and a short outer blade, half of which extends onto the platform. The blade is crested, highest at the posterior end reducing in height gradually to the anterior. Typically, the upper surface of the platform is covered by more than one row of nodes on each side with a shallow median trough separating the rows. Cup elongate, wider but shorter on the inner than the outer side.
Figured specimen: inner lateral view, ×40. Pendleian Stage, *Cravenoceras leion* Zone, loc. CH3 of Higgins (1975).

Gnathodus bilineatus bollandensis Higgins and Bouckaert 1968
Plate 6.1, Figs. 4 and 5. Pectiniform element. Table 7. Diagnosis: unit asymmetric having a long blade, narrow, rounded to subrectangular outer platform whose upper surface is smooth to weakly noded. Inner side of platform longer than outer, covered by transverse ridges.
Figured specimens: upper views, ×40. Arnsbergian Stage, *Cravenoceratoides nitidus* Zone, loc. ED9 of Higgins (1975).

'Spathognathodus' campbelli Rexroad 1957
Plate 6.1, Fig. 6. Pectiniform element. Table 7. Diagnosis: unit subsymmetrical, blade-like, oral margin of denticle row convex in lateral view, slightly indented about one third from posterior end. Carina denticles slightly thickened laterally. Cup narrow, occupying posterior half of unit, very low, slightly expanded near middle of unit. Cup shallow.
Figured specimen: inner lateral view, ×40. Brigantian Stage, loc. CA1 of Higgins (1975).

Lochriea mononodosa Rhodes (Austin and Druce, 1969)
Plate 6.1, Figs. 7, 8, 11 and 12. Pectiniform element. Table 7. Diagnosis: unit asymmetric. Cup semicircular slightly longer but narrower on outer than inner side, upper surface convex. Inner side of cup bears one or two nodes. Carina consists of slightly thickened discrete denticles. Figure 11 shows the reticulate microstructure on the tips of the carinal nodes and Fig. 1 shows the furrowed microstructure on the cup node.
Figured specimens: upper views, ×40 except for Figs. 11 and 12. Pendleian Stage, *Cravenoceras leion* Zone, loc. CH3 of Higgins (1975).

Pl. 6.1]

The Carboniferous System: Part 2

219

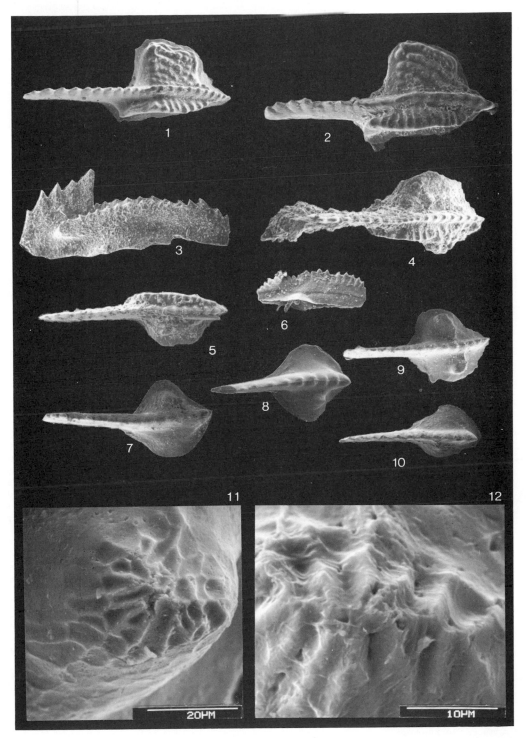

Plate 6.1

PLATE 6.2

Gnathodus girtyi rhodesi Higgins 1975
Plate 6.2, Fig. 1. Pectiniform element. Table 7. Diagnosis: a subspecies of *Gnathodus girtyi* having a platform in which the outer side extends to the posterior end but is restricted anteriorly, and an inner side which is developed anteriorly but does not extend to the posterior end. Carina well developed.
Figured specimen: upper view, ×40. Brigantian Stage, loc. CA3 of Higgins (1975).

Gnathodus girtyi girtyi Hass 1953
Plate 6.2, Fig. 2. Pectiniform element. Table 7. Diagnosis: a subspecies of *Gnathodus girtyi* having weakly developed platform parapets both of which are transversely ridged anteriorly but continued to the posterior as nodes, particularly on the outer side. Carina well developed.
Figured specimen: upper view, ×40. Brigantian Stage, loc. CA 3 of Higgins (1975).

Rhachistognathus minutus (Higgins and Bouckaert 1968)
Plate 6.2, Figs. 3, 4, 5, 6, 7, 8 and 9. Pectiniform element. Figs. 3, 4 and 6, ramiform elements. Table 7. Diagnosis: Figs. 5, 7, 8 and 9, asymmetric unit, platform consisting of two parapets, usually noded, but occasionally transversely ridged, with a deep trough separating the parapets, posterior end pointed. Blade continuation of outer platform parapet, straight and slightly convex in lateral view, shorter than platform. Inner platform parapet does not extend to posterior end in many specimens. Cup asymmetric, better developed on outer side, cavusgnathoid in shape. Figs. 3 and 4, slightly arched in later view, cusp subcentral, five or six discrete subequal denticles posterior to cusp. six to ten fused denticles of unequal size anterior to cusp. Cavity narrow. Fig. 6, long unit with indistinct cusp separating a very short incurved anterior process with up to three denticles from a long posterior process having alternating denticles of two sizes. Bar thickened. Figs. 3 and 4, inner and outer lateral views; Figs. 5, 7, 8 and 9, upper views; Fig. 6, inner lateral view. All ×40. Chokierian Stage, *Homoceras subglobosum* Zone, loc. K12 of Higgins (1975).

Neognathodus bassleri (Harris and Hollingsworth 1933)
Plate 6.2, Fig. 10. Pectiniform element. Table 7. Diagnosis: unit has subsymmetrical platform consisting of two sub-equal parapets, noded or transversely ridged, separated by a median noded carina. Shallow troughs separate the parapets and the carina. Cup gnathodid-like.
Figured specimen: upper view, ×40. Chokierian Stage, *Homoceras subglobosum* Zone, loc. K12 of Higgins (1975).

Declinognathodus noduliferus inaequalis Higgins 1975
Plate 6.2, Figs. 11, 12 and 14. Pectiniform element. Table 7. Diagnosis: unit consists of a platform with two subequal parapets, ridged or noded, separated by a carina which is median at the anterior end but deflected to the outer side halfway or more to the posterior where it merges with the outer parapet. Cup gnathodid in outline.
Figured specimens: upper views, ×40. Chokierian Stage, *Homoceras subglobosum* Zone, loc. K12 of Higgins (1975).

Declinognathodus noduliferus noduliferus (Ellison and Graves 1941)
Plate 6.2, Figs. 13 and 15. Pectiniform element. Table 7. Diagnosis: as for *D. noduliferus inaequalis* except that the carina merges with the outer parapet in the anterior half of the platform. Transitional specimens between the two subspecies are known.
Figured specimens: upper views, ×40. Chokierian Stage, *Homoceras subglobosum* Zone, loc. K12 of Higgins (1975).

Pl. 6.2] The Carboniferous System: Part 2

Plate 6.2

PLATE 6.3

Declinognathodus noduliferus inaequalis (Higgins 1975)
Plate 6.3, Figs. 1 and 4. Pectiniform element. Table 7. Diagnosis: see Plate 6.2.
Figured specimens: upper views, ×40. Chokierian Stage, *Homoceras subglobosum* Zone, loc. K12 of Higgins (1975).

Declinognathodus noduliferus japonicus Igo and Koike 1964)
Plate 6.3, Figs. 2 and 9. Pectiniform element. Table 7. Diagnosis: unit asymmetric, lanceolate platform consisting of two parapets either ridged or noded separated by a median sulcus extending almost to the posterior end. Platform ridges may extend across the sulcus. Blade joins outer platform parapet. One or two nodes present anterior to, and isolated from the outer platform parapet.
Figured specimens: upper views, ×40. Fig. 2, Alportian, *Homoceratoides prereticulatus* Zone, loc. PO2 of Higgins (1975); Fig. 9, Marsdenian Stage, *Reticuloceras gracile* Zone, loc. CH2 of Higgins (1975).

Declinognathodus lateralis (Higgins and Bouckaert 1968)
Plate 6.3, Figs. 3, 5 and 8. Pectiniform element. Table 7. Diagnosis: unit subsymmetric, platform having two subequal parapets, transversely ridged. Blade joins side of platform as a short carina which continues onto platform for up to half its length. Carina median. Cup gnathodid.
Figured specimens: upper views, ×40. Marsdenian Stage, *Reticuloceras gracile* Zone; Figs. 3 and 5, loc. HI1 of Higgins (1975); Fig. 8, loc. CH2 of Higgins (1975).

Idiognathoides sulcatus sulcatus (Higgins and Bouckaert 1968)
Plate 6.3, Fig. 6. Pectiniform element. Table 7. Diagnosis: unit asymmetric, platform consisting of two parapets, noded or ridged but separated by a median sulcus. Blade joins outer parapet. Cup gnathodid.
Figured specimen: upper views, ×40. Marsdenian Stage, *Reticuloceras gracile* Zone, loc. CH2 of Higgins (1975).

Declinognathodus noduliferus noduliferus (Ellison and Graves 1941)
Plate 6.3, Fig. 7. Pectiniform element. Table 7. Diagnosis: see Plate 6.2.
Figured specimen: upper view ×40. Chokierian, Stage, *Homoceras beyrichianum* Zone, loc. ED3 of Higgins (1975).

Paragnathodus nodosus (Bischoff 1957)
Plate 6.3, Fig. 9. Pectiniform element. Table 7. Diagnosis: as *L. mononodosa* except that each half of the cup has a node or nodes originating from its highest point. The species is assigned to *Lochreia* in Chapter 5.
Figured specimen: upper view ×40. Pendleian Stage, *Cravenoceras leion* Zone, loc. CH3 of Higgins (1975).

Lochriea commutata (Branson and Mehl 1941)
Plate 6.3, Fig. 10. Pectiniform element. Table 7. Diagnosis: cup oval to semicircular, extending posterior of the carina, upper surface convex and smooth. Carina slightly thickened, denticles discrete, continued anteriorly as a slightly longer blade.
Figured specimen: upper view, ×40. Pendleian Stage, *Cravenoceras leion* Zone, locality CH3 of Higgins (1975).

Pl. 6.3]   The Carboniferous System: Part 2   223

Plate 6.3

PLATE 6.4

Idiognathoides corrugatus–sinuatus (Harris and Hollingsworth 1933)
Plate 6.4, Figs. 1, 2, 3 and 5. Pectiniform element. Table 7. Diagnosis: left-sided asymmetric unit, platform having two transversely ridged parapets with ridges continuing across a median sulcus. Outer parapet higher than inner. Blade continues from outer side of platform anteriorly. Right sided asymmetric platform consists of two finely ridged parapets of approximately equal height separated by a narrow sulcus. Blade originates from outer side of the platform. Left-sided forms are referred to *I. sinuatus,* right-sided forms to *I. corrugatus* but they may belong to one species which had an unequal pair of elements.
Figured specimens: upper views, ×40. Marsdenian Stage, *Reticuloceras gracile* Zone, loc. CH2 of Higgins (1975).

Idiognathodus primulus Higgins 1975
Plate 6.4, Fig.4. Pectiniform element. Table 7. Diagnosis: unit symmetrical, platform consists of finely ridged, slightly convex plate without a sulcus. Blade continued onto platform for about one third of its length as a carina. Accessory lobes poorly developed smooth ridges flanking the carina.
Figured specimen: upper view, ×40. Marsdenian Stage, *Reticuloceras gracile* Zone, loc. CH2 of Higgins (1975).

Idiognathoides sulcatus parva Higgins and Bouckaert 1968
Plate 6.4, Figs. 6, 7 and 8. Pectiniform element. Table 7. Diagnosis: unit asymmetric, platform consists of two parapets. Outer one noded usually with a sharp edged upper surface. Inner one barely reaching posterior end, usually noded but may be transversely ridged at anterior end, lower than outer parapet. Deep sulcus separates the parapets. Blade up to twice length of platform. Unit small.
Figured specimens: upper views, ×40. Westphalian A, *Gastrioceras listeri* Zone, loc. SH1 of Higgins (1975).

Idiognathodus delicatus s.l. Gunnell 1933
Plate 6.4, Fig. 9. Pectiniform element. Table 7. Diagnosis: subsymmetric unit with a posteriorly pointed, slightly incurved platform covered by transverse ridges. Blade continued onto platform as a carina extending halfway to posterior. Carina flanked by parallel ridge on either side. Accessory lobes, noded or ridged, not prominent but more so on inner than outer side. Blade median. Cup gnathodid.
Figured specimen: upper view, ×40. Westphalian A, *Gastrioceras listeri* Zone, loc. SH1 of Higgins (1975).

Pl. 6.4]   The Carboniferous System: Part 2   225

Plate 6.4

REFERENCES

Aldridge, R. J., Austin, R. L. and Husri, S. 1968. Viséan conodonts from North Wales and Ireland. *Nature (London)*, 219, 255–258.

Austin, R. L. 1972. Problems of conodont taxonomy with special reference to Upper Carboniferous forms. In: M. Lindström and W. Ziegler (Eds.), *Symp. on Conodont Taxonomy, in Geol. Palaeontol. Sonderb. 1*, 115–126, 2 plates.

Bisat, W. S. 1924. The Carboniferous goniatites of the North of England and their zones. *Proc. Yorks. Geol. Soc.*, 20, 40–124.

Bischoff, G. 1957. Die Conodonten-Stratigraphie des rheno-herzynischen Unterkarbons mit Berücksichtigung der Wocklumeria–Stufe und der Devon/Karbon–Grenze. *Abh. hess. Landesamt Bodenforsch.*, 19, 1–64, 6 plates.

Branson, E. B. and Mehl, M. G. 1941. New and little known Carboniferous genera. *J. Paleontol.*, 15, 97–106, 1 plate.

Calver, M. A. 1969. Westphalian of Britain. *C.R. 6ème Congr. Int. de Stratigraphie et de Géologique du Carbonifère, Sheffield, 1967*, 1, 232–254.

Clarke, W. J. 1960. Scottish Carboniferous conodonts. *Trans. Edinburgh Geol Soc.*, 18, 1–31, 5 plates.

Crookall, R. 1955. Fossil plants of the Carboniferous rocks of Great Britain. *Mem. Geol. Surv. Gt. Br.*

Currie, E. D., Duncan, C. and Muir-Wood, H. M. 1937. The fauna of Skipsey's Marine Band. *Trans. Geol. Soc. Glasgow*, 19, 413–451.

Dix, E. 1934. The sequence of floras in the Upper Carboniferous with special reference to South Wales. *Trans. R. Soc. Edinburgh*, 57, 789–821.

Dunham, K. C. and Stubblefield, C. J. 1945. The stratigraphy, structure and mineralisation of the Greenhow mining area, Yorkshire. *Q. J. Geol. Soc. London*, 100, 209–268.

Earp, J. R. and Magraw, D. 1955. Tonge's Marine Band in Lancashire. *Bull. Geol. Surv. Gt. Br.*, 5, 22–32.

Eden, R. A. 1954. The coal measures of *Anthraconnaia lenisulcata* Zone in the East Midlands Coalfield. *Bull. Geol. Surv. Gt. Br.*, 5, 82–106.

Edwards, W. 1954. The Yorkshire–Nottinghamshire Coalfield. In: A. Trueman (Ed.) *The Coalfields of Great Britain.* Edward Arnold, London, 1–187

Edwards, W. and Stubblefield, C. J. 1948. Marine bands and other faunal marker horizons in relation to the sedimentary cycles of the middle coal measures of Nottinghamshire and Derbyshire. *Q. J. Geol. Soc. London*, 103, 219–223.

Ellison, S. P. and Graves, R. W., jnr. 1941. Lower Pennsylvanian (Dimple Limestone) conodonts of the Marathon region, Texas. *Univ. Missouri School Mines Metallurgy Bull., Techn. Ser.*, 14 (3), 1–21, 3 plates.

Gunnell, F. H. 1933. Conodonts and fish remains from the Cherokee, Kansas City, and Wabaunsee Groups of Missouri and Kansas. *J. Paleontol.*, 7 (3), 261–297, 3 plates.

Harris, R. W. and Hollingsworth, R. V. 1933. New Pennsylvanian conodonts from Oklahoma. *Amer. J. Sci.*, 25, 193–204, 1 plate.

Hass, W. M. 1963. Conodonts of the Barnett Formation of Texas. *U.S. Geol. Surv. Prof. Pap.* 286, 1–47, 3 plates.

Higgins, A. C. 1961. Some Namurian conodonts from North Staffordshire. *Geol. Mag.*, 98, 210–224, 3 plates.

Higgins, A. C. 1962. An investigation of the distribution of conodont faunas in the Namurian of the South Pennines. *Unpublished Ph.D. Thesis*, University of Sheffield.

Higgins, A. C. 1967. The significance of conodonts in the Carboniferous of Europe. *Proc. Subcommission on Carboniferous Stratigraphy, Sheffield, 1965*, reissued 1980, 40–43.

Higgins, A. C. 1975. Conodont zonation of the late Viséan–early Westphalian strata of the South and Central Pennines of Northern England. *Bull. Geol. Surv. Gr. Br.*, 53, 1–90 pp., 18 plates.

Higgins, A. C. 1981a. Coprolitic conodont assemblages from the Lower Westphalian of North Staffordshire. *Palaeontology.* 24, 437–441.

Higgins, A. C. 1981b. The distribution of conodonts in relation to the palaeogeography of late Viséan–Namurian time. In: J. W. Neale and M. D. Brasier (Eds.) *Microfossils from Recent and Fossil Shelf Seas*, Ellis Horwood Ltd., Chichester, 37–51.

Higgins, A. C. 1982. A Mid-Carboniferous boundary in the Western Europe conodont sequence. 13, 14. In: W. H. C. Ramsbottom, W. B. Saunders and B. Owens, (Eds.) *Biostratigraphic Data for a Mid-Carboniferous Boundary, Proc. Subcommission on Carboniferous Stratigraphy Leeds, 1982.*

Higgins, A. C. and Bouckaert, J. 1968. Conodont stratigraphy and palaeontology of the Namurian of Belgium. *Mem. Expl. Cartes Géol. Min. Belg.*, 10, 1–64.

Hinde, G. J. 1900. Notes and descriptions of new species of Scotch Carboniferous conodonts. *Trans. Nat. Hist. Soc. Glasgow*, 5, 338–346, 2 plates.

Igo, H. and Koike, T. 1964. Carboniferous conodonts from the Omi Limestone, Niigata Prefecture, central Japan. *Trans. Proc. Paleont. Soc. Japan, N.S.*, 53: 179–193, 2 plates.

Lane, H. R., Bouckaert, J., Brenkle, O. L., Einor, V., Havlena, V., Higgins, A. C., Yang Jing-zhi, Manger, W., Nassichuk, W. W., Nemirovskaya, T., Owens, B., Ramsbottom, W. H. C., Reitlinger, E. A. and Weyant, M. In press. Proposal for an international Mid-Carboniferous boundary. *C.R. 10ème Congr. Int. de Stratigraphie et de Géologique du Carbonifère, Madrid, 1983.*

Magraw, D. 1957. New boreholes into the lower coal measures below the Arley mine of Lancashire and adjacent areas. *Bull Geol. Surv. Gt. Br.*, 13, 14–38.

Manson, W. 1957. On the occurrence of a marine band in the *Anthraconaia modiolaris* Zone of the Scottish coal measures with notes on certain marine fossils. *Bull. Geol Surv. Gt. Br.*, 12, 66–86.

Matthews, S. C. and Moore, L. J., 1967. A conodont fauna from the Westphalian of North Devon. *Proc. Ussher Soc.*, 280–281.

Metcalfe, I. 1981. Conodont zonation and correlation of the Dinantian and early Namurian strata of the Craven Lowlands of Northern England. *Inst. Geol. Sci. Rep.,* **80/10,** 1−70, 19 plates.

Mitchell, G. H. 1954. The Whittington Heath Borehole. *Bull. Geol. Surv. Gt. Br.,* **5,** 1−60.

Mitchell, G. H. and Crookall, R. 1942. The geology of the Warwickshire Coalfield. *Mem. Geol. Surv. Gt. Br., Wartime Pamphl.,* **25,** 1−40.

Mitchell, G. H. and Crookall, R. 1945. The geology of the northern part of the South Staffordshire Coalfield (Cannock Chase region). *Mem. Geol. Surv. Gt. Br., Wartime Pamphl.* **43,** 1−47.

Mitchell, G. H. and Stubblefield, C. J. 1941. The geology of the Leicestershire and South Derbyshire Coalfield. *Mem. Geol Surv. Gt. Br., Wartime Pamphlet,* **22.**

Owens, B., Neves, R., Gueinn, K. J., Mishell, D. R. F., Sabry, H. S. M. Z. and Williams, J. E. 1977. Palynological division of the Namurian of Northern England and Scotland. *Proc. Yorks. Geol. Soc.,* **41,** 381−398.

Ramsbottom, W. C. H. 1952. The fauna of the Cefn Coed Marine Band in the coal measures of Aberbaiden near Tondu, Glamorgan. *Bull. Geol. Surv. Gt. Br.,* **4,** 8−32.

Ramsbottom, W. C. H. 1969. The Namurian of Britain. *C.R. 6ème Congr. Int. de Stratigraphie et de Géologique du Carbonifère, Sheffield, 1967,* **1,** 219−232.

Ramsbottom, W. C. H. 1977. Major cycles of transgression and regression (mesothems) in the Namurian. *Proc. Yorks. Geol. Soc.,* **41** (3), 261−291.

Ramsbottom, W. H. C. (Ed.) 1981. *Field Guide to the Boundary Stratotypes of the Carboniferous Stages in Britain, Proc. Subcommission on Carboniferous Stratigraphy, Leeds,* 1−146.

Ramsbottom, W. H. C., Calver, M. A., Eager, R. M. C., Hodson, F., Holliday, D. W., Stubblefield, C. J. and Wilson, R. B. 1978. A correlation of Silesian rocks in the British Isles. *Geol. Soc. London Spec. Rep.,* **10,** 1−81.

Ramsbottom, W. H. C., Higgins, A. C. and Owens, B. 1979. Palaeontological characterisation of the Namurian of the stratotype area (a report of the Namurian Working Group). *C.R. 8ème Congr. Int. de Stratigraphie et de Géologique du Carbonifère Moscow, 1975,* 85−99.

Ramsbottom, W. H. C., Higgins, A. C. and Owens, B. 1983. Recognition of a Mid-Carboniferous boundary in the Pennine Province, England. *Newsl. Carboniferous Stratigr., IUGS Subcommission on Carboniferous Stratigraphy,* 12.

Rexroad, C. B. 1957. Conodonts from the Chester Series in the type area of Southwestern Illinois. *Illinois Geol. Surv. Rept. Invest.,* **199,** 1−43, 4 plates.

Reynolds, M. J. 1968. *Annu. Rep. Inst. Geol. Sci.,* 97.

Reynolds, M. J. 1977. Conodont faunas from the Duffield Borehole. In *The Institute of Geological Sciences Borehole at Duffield, Derbyshire, Bull. Geol. Surv. Gt. Br.,* **59,** 28−30.

Rhodes, F. H. T. and Austin, R. L. 1971. Carboniferous conodont faunas of Europe. In: W. C. Sweet and S. M. Bergström (Eds.), *Symp. on Conodont Biostratigraphy, Mem. Geol. Soc. Am.,* **127,** 317−352.

Rhodes, F. H. T., Austin, R. L. and Druce, E. C. 1969. British Avonian (Carboniferous) conodont faunas and their value in local and intercontinental correlation. *Bull. Br. Mus. (Nat. Hist.), Geol., Suppl.,* **5,** 313, 31 plates.

Roundy, P. V. 1926. Part II. The Micro-fauna, in Mississippian formations of San Saba County, Texas *U.S. Geol. Surv. Prof. Pap.* 146. 5−23, 4 plates.

Smith, J. 1907. Conodonts in coal measure strata. *Geol. Mag.,* **4,** 239.

Stevenson, I. P. and Mitchell, G. H. 1955. Geology of the country between Burton, Trent, Rugeley and Uttoxeter. *Mem. Geol. Surv. Gt. Br.,* 11−12.

Stubblefield, C. J. and Calver, M. A. 1955. Palaeontology of the coal measures in I. P. Stevenson and G. H. Mitchell and others. Geology of the country between Burton, Trent, Rugeley and Uttoxeter. *Mem. Geol. Surv. Gt. Br.,* 20−30.

Trueman, A. E. 1954. Fossils of the coal measures and their use. In: E. Trueman (Ed.) *The Coalfields of Great Britain,* Edward Arnold, London, 1−187.

Trueman, A. E. and Weir, J. 1946−58. *Weir 1960−68. A Monograph on British Carboniferous Non-marine Lamellibranchia. Palaeontographical Society.*

Varker, W. J. 1964. The conodont faunas and stratigraphy of the Yoredale Series in the Askrigg and Alston regions. *Unpublished Ph.D. Thesis,* University of Sheffield.

Varker, W. J. 1967. Conodonts of the genus *Apatognathus* Branson and Mehl from the Yoredale Series of England. *Palaeontology,* **10,** 124−141.

Varker, W. J. 1968. Conodont distribution in Yoredale Limestones (D_2−E_1) of the North of England. *Trans. Leeds Geol Assoc.,* **7,** 275−290.

Varker, W. J. and Austin, R. L. 1974. The significance of *Adetognathus unicornis* (Rexroad and Burton) in the Mirk Fell Beds (E_{2a}) of the North of England. *Trans. Leeds Geol. Assoc.,* **8,** 399−408, 2 plates.

Woodland, A. W., Archer, A. A., Evans, W. B. and Calver, M. A. 1957. Recent boreholes into the lower coal measures below the Gellideg−Lower Pumpquart coal horizon in South Wales. *Bull. Geol. Surv. Gt. Br.,* **13,** 39−60.

7

Conodonts of the Permian System from Great Britain

A. Swift and **R. J. Aldridge**

7.1 HISTORY OF CONODONT STUDIES

Conodonts have only recently been recognised in the Permian rocks of Britain (Fig. 7.1). The first record (Pattison, 1978) was of a single indeterminate fragment from the Cadeby Formation of the Aiskew Bank Farm Borehole, drilled in North Yorkshire by the British Geological Survey. Subsequent samples from the same core and from another drilled at nearby Sand Hutton yielded the first complete and identifiable elements (Swift and Aldridge, 1982). Further collections from Tyne and Wear and off-shore Northumberland included sufficiently abundant specimens to allow a taxonomic evaluation of *Merrillina divergens*, the commonest British Permian species (Swift, in press).

With the exception of a single collection from strata of uncertain stratigraphic horizon, all conodont elements recovered to date are from Zechstein 1 deposits of Upper Permian age. Several collections are reported here for the first time, and we record a newly discovered suite of elements from the earliest marine rocks of the Zechstein transgression. These include *Neogondolella* aff. *idahoensis,* which has not so far been found in association with elements of *M. divergens.*

7.2 DEPOSITORY OF COLLECTIONS OF IMPORTANCE

All known British Permian material is currently in the collections of the Micropalaeontology Unit in the Department of Geology at the University of Nottingham. Specimens from British Geological Survey boreholes are held on loan.

7.3 DEFINITION OF BOUNDARIES AND INTERNAL DIVISIONS

International agreement on Permian chronostratigraphy has yet to be achieved, but Smith *et al.*

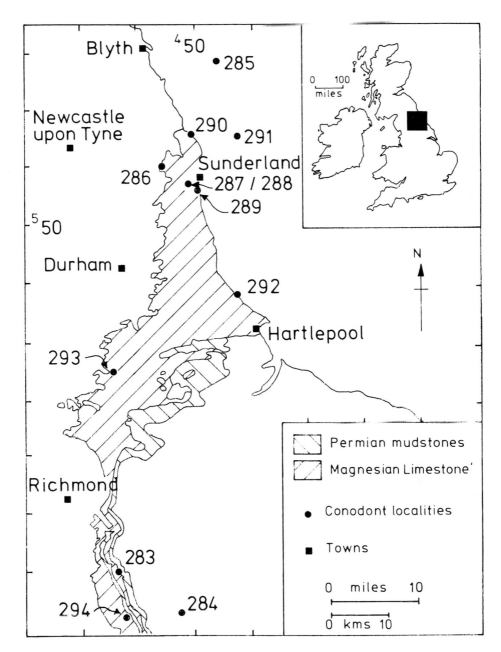

Fig. 7.1 – Upper Permian outcrop and conodont localities in North and North-east England. After *Geological Map of the UK,* 3rd edn., 1979, British Geological Survey.

(1974) proposed temporary adoption of the divisions recognized in Russia by Likharev (1966). In this scheme, the Permian is divided into two series, the Lower and Upper Permian, and seven stages. The British sequence is accommodated within the Ufimian, Kazanian and Tatarian stages of the Upper Permian. Although there is uncertainty about the position of the boundaries between these stages, even in Russia, the Zechstein 1 cycle appears to encompass the Ufimian and the lowermost Kazanian (Smith *et al.*, 1974).

A revision of English Zechstein lithostratigraphy was proposed in the field excursion guide

of the EZ82 conference (Harwood *et al.*, 1982); the scheme was subsequently used in papers in the conference volume (Harwood and Smith, in press) and is adopted here (Fig. 7.2).

Conodont collections recovered to date from

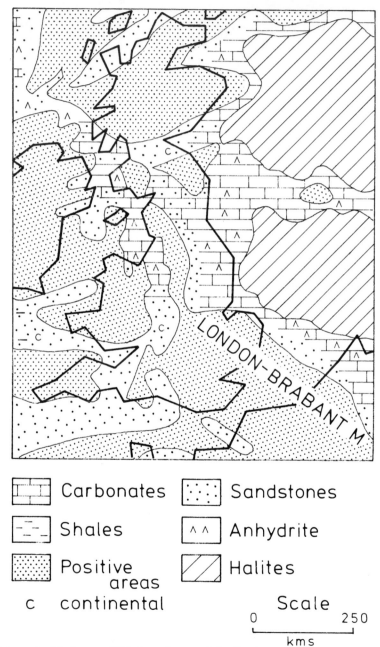

Carbonates   Sandstones

Shales   Anhydrite

Positive areas   Halites

c   continental

Scale

0   250

kms

Fig. 7.2 – Palaeogeographical map of Britain and parts of the North Sea and North-west Europe during the late Permian. After Ziegler (1982), with modifications.

reliably dated sequences are from a relatively short interval in the Zechstein 1 cycle: from the Marl Slate to Ford Formation in the Durham Province, and from the Cadeby Formation in the Yorkshire Province.

American Permian subdivisions referred to in Section 7.5(c) are those of Furnish (1973).

7.4 LOCALITIES

All British Permian localities from which conodonts have been recovered are listed here. Locality numbers accord with the system in use in the Micropalaeontology Unit of the Geology Department at the University of Nottingham. Details of some have been published previously (Swift and Aldridge, 1982; Swift, in press), but several of the following localities are reported for the first time.

283. Cadeby Formation. The Aiskew Bank Farm borehole drilled by the British Geological Survey near Bedale, North Yorkshire (SE 26678888) (Pattison, 1978; Swift and Aldridge, 1982). Permian base in borehole at 96.45 m.
284. Cadeby Formation. The Sand Hutton borehole drilled by the National Coal Board near Thirsk, North Yorkshire (SE 37898157) (Swift and Aldridge, 1982).
285. Raisby Formation. Bates Colliery B2 borehole drilled by the National Coal Board off Blyth, Northumberland (NZ 43917858) (Magraw, 1978; Swift, in press). Top of Marl Slate at depth 164.77 m.
286. Marl Slate and Ford Formation. Downhill Quarry, West Boldon, near Sunderland (NZ 348601) (Swift, in press).
287. Raisby and Ford Formations. Claxheugh Rock, Sunderland (NZ 362575) (Swift, in press).
288. Ford Formation. Ford Quarry, Sunderland (NZ 362572).
289. Ford Formation. Tunstall Hills, Sunderland. Several sampling points at two localities; Tunstall Hills (south) (NZ 396538) and Maiden Paps (NZ 392545).

290. Raisby Formation. Frenchman's Bay, South Shields (NZ 389662).
291. Raisby Formation. The W5A borehole drilled by the National Coal Board off South Shields (NZ 4757065559).
292. Ford Formation or younger. Blackhalls Rocks, N of Hartlepool (NZ 475384).
293. Marl Slate. Middridge Quarry, near Shildon (NZ 249252) (Bell *et al.*, 1979).
294. Cadeby Formation. Bedale Quarry, Well, North Yorkshire (SE 275812).

7.5 CONODONT ZONATION

There is no conodont zonation currently applicable to the British faunas; however, within the interval in which conodonts are known, two distinct associations can be recognized.

(a) Association A

So far found in significant numbers only at Downhill Quarry (loc. 286), this contains Pa elements provisionally assigned to *Neogondolella* aff. *idahoensis*. An associated suite of ramiform elements may or may not represent the rest of the apparatus; these are referred to by locational notation and no multielement reconstruction has been attempted. Small numbers of elements from the association have been recovered from locs. 283, 287, 291 and 293.

Association A has been found in the Marl Slate and earliest Raisby and Cadeby Formations. It has not been seen to overlap with Association B and is the earlier of the two associations where both are found in the same section, as at locs. 283, 286, 287 and 291.

(i) *Distribution*

Depth 89.0–92.2 m in the Cadeby Formation at loc. 283; in Marl Slate immediately above the marine reworked top of the Yellow Sands at loc. 286; in the Raisby Formation 1 m above the top of the Marl Slate at loc. 287; 2.02 m above the top of the Marl Slate in the Raisby Formation at loc. 291; 1.5 m above the top of the Coal Measures in Marl Slate at loc. 293.

(b) Association B

This consists entirely of elements of *Merrillina divergens*. The species appears first in Zechstein I carbonates in the Raisby and Cadeby Formations and is last seen in the complex at Blackhalls Rocks (loc. 292), which consists of foundered deposits of reef-flat cover and may be referable to the Ford Formation or may be younger (Smith, 1980).

Well-preserved collections have been recovered from both the Durham and the Yorkshire Provinces.

(i) *Distribution*

Between depths of 69 and 89 m in the Cadeby Formation at loc. 283; from 17.47 to 37.17 m above the base of the Permian sequence in the Cadeby Formation at loc. 284; depth 154.23–154.53 m in the Raisby Formation at loc. 285; basal reef facies of the Ford Formation at loc. 286; top of the atypically thin Raisby Formation and base of the unconformably overlying reefal Ford Formation at loc. 287; main reefal body at the type locality of the Ford Formation at loc. 288; several points in the Ford Formation reef complex at loc. 289; top of the atypically thin Raisby Formation at loc. 290; from 6.82 to 18.22 m above the top of the Marl Slate in the Raisby Formation at loc. 291; foundered reef-flat cover rocks of uncertain age at loc. 292; 11 m above base of abandoned quarry face in the Cadeby Formation at loc. 294.

(c) Correlation with areas outside the Zechstein basin

Permian conodonts from Britain may ultimately prove to be useful for correlation with sequences elsewhere, but at present only provisional observations may be offered.

Both *M. divergens* and *N. idahoensis* have been used biostratigraphically in other areas. In North America a *'Neospathodus divergens* fauna' (Clark and Behnken, 1971), a *'Neogondolella rosenkrantzi–Neospathodus divergens* Assemblage Zone' (Behnken, 1975a) and a *'Merrillina divergens* Zone' (Wardlaw and Collinson, 1979, after Clark and Behnken, 1971) have been recognized

in the lower part of the Guadalupian series (Upper Permian) of the Great Basin and Rocky Mountain regions. Some doubt, however, attends the assignment of these forms to *M. divergens* (Kozur and Mostler, 1976, p. 11). In a proposed standard chronostratigraphy for the Permian System, Kozur (1978) introduced a *'Gondolella bitteri–Stepanovites inflatus–Merrillina divergens* Assemblage Zone' in the Abadehian Stage at the top of the Middle Permian; Kozur's scheme draws on widespread sources and has not been demonstrated in one area.

N. idahoensis is found in North America in the Leonardian and Roadian stages at the top of the Lower Permian and has been used biostratigraphically at this level (Clark and Behnken, 1971; Behnken, 1975b). The British specimens show affinity with this species, but there are several similar neogondolellid species in the Permian, with careful study of large populations sometimes necessary for identification (Clark and Behnken, 1979). Pending a full taxonomic revision of Permian neogondolellids it is not possible to identify and interpret British collections more precisely.

7.6 FACIES AND ITS CONTROL UPON CONODONT FAUNAS

The initial Zechstein transgression created an inland sea thought to exceed 200 m at basinal depths (Smith, 1980). Deposits included the Marl Slate of the Durham Province, in which *N.* aff. *idahoensis* and associated elements occur. The succeeding sequence records a shallowing of the sea as the rate of basin infill outstripped differential subsidence (Smith, 1980, p. 9), and *N.* aff. *idahoensis* becomes rarer; it has not been found in strata higher than the lower parts of the Raisby and Cadeby Formations.

Monospecific collections of *M. divergens* are found in the succeeding shallower facies of the first Zechstein 1 subcycle, but no conodonts have been recovered from the highest beds, which record diminished depth and probable increased salinity (Smith, 1980, pp. 13, 14). *M. divergens* reappears in the Ford Formation of the second Zechstein 1 subcycle, where a diverse microfauna and macrofauna is associated with the development of a reefal facies.

PLATE 7.1

Merrillina divergens (Bender and Stoppel 1965)

Plate 7.1, Figs. 1, 2, 3, 4, 5, 6, 7, 8 and 9. Diagnosis: apparatus seximembrate. Pa element short, slightly laterally bowed, three to seven diverging denticles. Sa element with prominent posterior bar. S elements with conspicuously large denticles distally on longer process, often associated with a tendency for geniculation at that point. Basal cavity broad and deep on Pa, Pb and M elements, varying from narrow slit to broad slash on S elements; anterior tip unexcavated on all elements. White matter commonly present in denticles, variably distributed. Microstriae invariably present on denticles of Pa elements, irregularly on others.

Figured specimens: Fig. 1, Pa element, inner lateral view, 4315/29A, length 0.335 m, ×80; Fig. 2, Pa element, inner lateral view, 5445/44, length 0.30 mm, ×80; Fig. 3, Pb element, inner lateral view, 4512/28A, length 0.55 mm, ×80; Fig. 4, Pb element, inner lateral view, 4510/15A, length 0.65 mm, ×80; Fig. 5, M element, inner lateral view, 4508/4A, length 0.70 mm, ×80; Fig. 8, Sa element, posterior view, 5448/58, length 0.325 mm, ×80; Fig. 9, Sa element, lateral view, 4513/31A, length 0.675 mm, ×80; Fig. 6, Sb element, inner lateral view, 5148/64, length 0.75 mm, ×80; Fig. 7, Sc element, inner lateral view, 4509/9A, length 0.95 mm, ×80. Figs. 1, 3 and 9, Ford Formation, loc. 286; Figs. 2 and 8, Raisby Formation, loc. 291; Fig. 4, Raisby Formation, loc. 287; Figs. 5 and 7, Raisby Formation, loc. 285; Fig. 6, Ford Formation, loc. 289.

Neogondolella aff. *idahoensis* (Youngquist, Hawley and Miller 1951)

Plate 7.1, Figs. 10, 11, 12, 13 and 14. Pa element.

Figured specimens: Fig. 10, lower view, 5441/21, length 0.465 mm, ×80; Fig. 11, upper lateral view, 5427/98, length 0.85 mm, ×80; Fig. 12, fused partial cluster of opposed Pa elements, 5432/22, length 0.50 mm, ×80; Fig. 13, upper lateral view, 5435/11, length 0.40 mm, ×80; Fig. 14, upper view, 5440/16, length 0.80 mm, ×80. Figs. 10, 11, 12 and 14, Marl Slate, loc. 286; Fig. 13, Raisby Formation, loc. 291.

Remarks: this form is variable in the British collections, but the presence of elongate anterior denticles, moderately expanded 'escutcheon', and gently arched and bowed outline agrees in principle with the original description given by Youngquist *et al.* (1951, p. 361) of a 'rather generalised type of *Gondolella*'. Further differentiating features of this species listed by Behnken (1975a, p. 306), including a long narrow platform tapering only in anteriormost position, suberect cusp and micro-ornamentation on upper platform surface, also apply to the British specimens. A few specimens show a tendency towards serrate anterior margins of the type that characterize the *N. serrata* complex of the North American Upper Permian.

Unassigned ramiform elements

Plate 7.1, Figs. 15, 16, 17, 18 and 19.

Figured specimens: Fig. 15, Pb element, inner lateral view, 5440/15, length 0.375 mm, ×80; Fig. 16, M element, inner lateral view, 5428/4, length 0.25 mm, ×80; Fig. 17, Sa element, inner lateral view, 4509/11A, length 0.175 mm, ×80; Fig. 18, Sb? element, inner lateral view, 5182/26, length 0.15 mm, ×80; Fig. 19, Sb–Sc? element, lateral view, 4509/13A, length 0.525 mm, ×80. Figs. 15 and 16. Marl Slate, loc. 286; Figs. 17 and 19, Raisby Formation, loc. 287. Fig. 18 Raisby Formation, loc. 291.

Remarks: the forms illustrated here are very similar to ramiforms figured by Clark and Ethington (1962, Plate 1, Figs. 4, 7, 13, 16, 17, 20 and 21, and Plate 2, Fig. 2) from the late Lower Permian of Western North America, where they are found with *N. idahoensis* and/or '*Gondolella serrata*' Clark and Ethington 1962. From a similar horizon, Behnken (1975a, Plate 2, Figs. 2, 3, 4 and 6) figured three of the same elements as part of the apparatus of *Ellisonia tribulosa* (Clark and Ethington 1962); *N. idahoensis* and/or neogondolellids of the *serrata* complex were again found in association.

Repository of the specimens in Plate 7.1 is the Conodont Reference Collection, Department of Geology, University of Nottingham.

Pl. 7.1]　　　　Conodonts of the Permian System from Great Britain　　　　235

Plate 7.1

7.7 REFERENCES

Behnken, F. H. 1975a. Leonardian and Guadalupian (Permian) conodont biostratigraphy in Western and Southwestern United States. *J. Paleontol.*, **49**, 284–315, 2 plates.

Behnken, F. H. 1975b. Conodonts as Permian biostratigraphic indices. In *Permian Exploration, Boundaries, and Stratigraphy, Symp. and field trip*, co-sponsored by West Texas Geological Society and Permian Basin Section, *Soc. Econ. Paleontol. Min. Publ.*, **75–65**, 84–90.

Bell, J., Holden, J., Pettigrew, T. H. and Sedman, K. W. 1979. A new exposure of the Marl Slate and basal Permian Breccia at Middridge, County Durham. *Proc. Yorks. Geol. Soc.*, **42**, 439–460, 3 plates.

Bender, H. and Stoppel, D. 1965. Perm-Conodonten. *Geol. Jb.*, **82**, 331–364, 3 plates.

Clark, D. L. and Behnken, F. H. 1971. Conodonts and biostratigraphy of the Permian. In: W. C. Sweet and S. M. Bergström (Eds.), *Symp. on Conodont Biostratigraphy, Mem. Geol. Soc. Am.*, **127**, 415–439, 2 plates.

Clark, D. L. 1979. Evolution and taxonomy of the North American Upper Permian *Neogondolella serrata* complex. *J. Paleontol.*, **53**, 262–275, 2 plates.

Clark, D. L. and Ethington, R. L. 1962. Survey of Permian conodonts in Western North America. *Geol. Stud. Brigham Young Univ.*, **9**, 102–114, 2 plates.

Furnish, W. M. 1973. Permian Stage names. In A. Logan and L. V. Hills (Eds.), *The Permian and Triassic Systems and their Mutual Boundary, Can. Soc. Pet. Geol. Mem.*, **2**, 522–548.

Harwood, G. M. and Smith, D. B. (Eds.) In press. The English Zechstein and related topics. *Geol. Soc. London Spec. Publ.*

Harwood, G. M., Smith, D. B., Pattison, J. and Pettigrew, T. M. 1982. *EZ82. Guide to the Excursions*, 1–53.

Kozur, H. 1978. Beiträge zur Stratigraphie des Perms. Teil I. Die Conodontenchronologie des Perms. *Frieberger Forschungsh.*, **334**, 85–161, 8 plates.

Kozur, H. and Mostler, W. 1976. Neue conodonten aus dem Jungäpläozoikum und der Trias. *Geol. Paläontol. Mitt. Innsbruck* **6** (3), 1–41, 4 plates.

Likharev, B. K. (Ed.) 1966. *The Permian System. Stratigraphy of the USSR*, Vol. 4, Akademii Nauk SSSR, Min. Geol., Moscow.

Magraw, D. 1978. New boreholes into Permian beds off Northumberland and Durham. *Proc. Yorks. Geol. Soc.*, **42**, 157–183, 2 plates.

Pattison, J. 1978. Upper Permian palaeontology of the Aiskew Bank Farm Borehole, North Yorkshire. *Annu. Rep. Inst. Geol. Sci.*, **78/14**, 1–6.

Smith, D. B. 1980. The evolution of the English Zechstein basin. *Contrib. Sedimentol.*, **9**, 7–34.

Smith, D. B., Brunstrom, R. G. W., Manning, P. I., Simpson, S. and Shotton, F. W. 1974. A correlation of Permian rocks in the British Isles. *Geol. Soc. London Spec. Rep.*, **5**, 1–45.

Swift, A. In press. The conodont *Merrillina divergens* (Bender and Stoppel) from the Upper Permian of England. In: G. M. Harwood and D. B. Smith (Eds.), *The English Zechstein and related topics. Geol. Soc. London Spec. Publ.*

Swift, A. and Aldridge, R. J. 1982. Conodonts from Upper Permian strata of Nottinghamshire and North Yorkshire. *Palaeontology*, **25**, 845–856, 2 plates.

Wardlaw, B. R. and Collinson, J. W. 1979. Youngest Permian conodont faunas from the Great Basin and Rocky Mountain regions. In: C. A. Sandberg and D. L. Clark (Eds.), *Conodont Biostratigraphy of the Great Basin and Rocky Mountains, Geol. Stud. Brigham Young Univ.*, **26**, 151–159, 2 plates.

Youngquist, W., Hawley, R. W. and Miller, A. K. 1951. Phosphoria conodonts from Southeastern Idaho. *J. Paleontol.*, **25**, 356–364, 1 plate.

Ziegler, P. A. 1982. Geological Atlas of Western and Central Europe. Shell International Petroleum Maatschappij, B.V., Distributed by Elsevier. 1–130, 40 enclosures.

Tables

Table 1 — THE CAMBRIAN AND ORDOVICIAN SYSTEMS Chart showing the range of selec

SERIES	CONODONT ZONE/ SUBZONE		TAXA

Taxa (columns):
Paro. proteus, Parac. gracilis, Dr. forceps, Paro. parallelus, Sto. stola, Pri. elegans, Oe. evae, Pe. flabellum, Pro. rectus, Paro. originalis, Mi. flabellum, Ba. triangularis, Dr. basiovalis, Ba. navis, Scan. brevibasis, Pro. cf. varicostatus, Ba. prevariabilis norrlandicus, Sco. cornuformis, Eo.? variabilis, Ba. prevariabilis medius, Scal. gracilis, Hi. altifrons, Po. spp., Mi. ozarkodella, Pe. aculeatus, Str. parvus

SERIES	ZONE	SUBZONE
ASHGILL		ordovicicus
CARADOC		superbus
CARADOC	tvaerensis	alobatus
CARADOC	tvaerensis	gerdae
CARADOC	tvaerensis	variabilis
LLANDEILO	anserinus	inaequalis
?	anserinus	kielcensis
LLANVIRN	serra	lindstroemi
LLANVIRN	serra	robustus
LLANVIRN	serra	reclinatus
LLANVIRN	serra	foliaceus
LLANVIRN	suecicus	sulcatus
LLANVIRN	suecicus	gracilis
LLANVIRN	variabilis	ozarkodella
LLANVIRN	variabilis	flabellum
ARENIG		flabellum parva
ARENIG		originalis
ARENIG		navis-triangularis
ARENIG		evae
ARENIG		elegans
ARENIG		proteus

ish and Irish conodont species diagnostic of the Cambrian and Ordovician Systems.

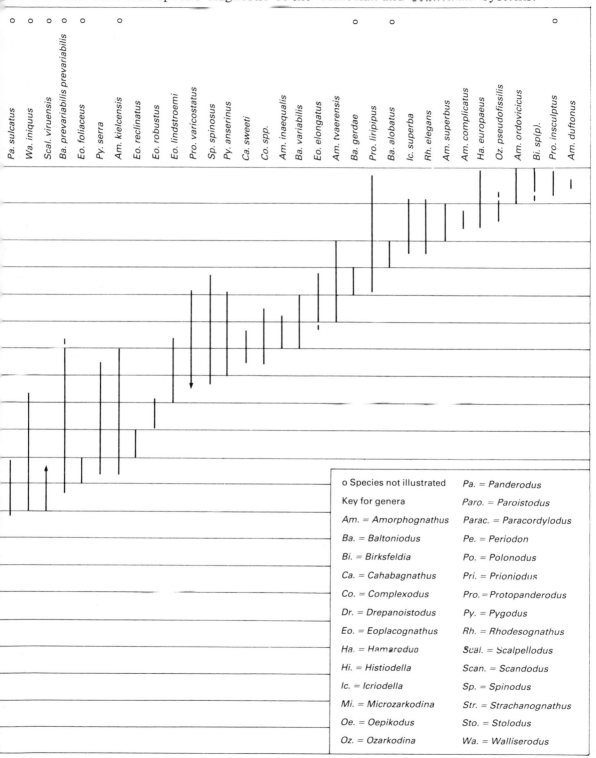

o Species not illustrated

Key for genera

Am. = Amorphognathus
Ba. = Baltoniodus
Bi. = Birksfeldia
Ca. = Cahabagnathus
Co. = Complexodus
Dr. = Drepanoistodus
Eo. = Eoplacognathus
Ha. = Hamarodus
Hi. = Histiodella
Ic. = Icriodella
Mi. = Microzarkodina
Oe. = Oepikodus
Oz. = Ozarkodina

Pa. = Panderodus
Paro. = Paroistodus
Parac. = Paracordylodus
Pe. = Periodon
Po. = Polonodus
Pri. = Prioniodus
Pro. = Protopanderodus
Py. = Pygodus
Rh. = Rhodesognathus
Scal. = Scalpellodus
Scan. = Scandodus
Sp. = Spinodus
Str. = Strachanognathus
Sto. = Stolodus
Wa. = Walliserodus

Table 2 — THE SILURIAN SYSTEM
Chart showing the range of selected British and Irish conodont species diagnostic of the Silurian System.

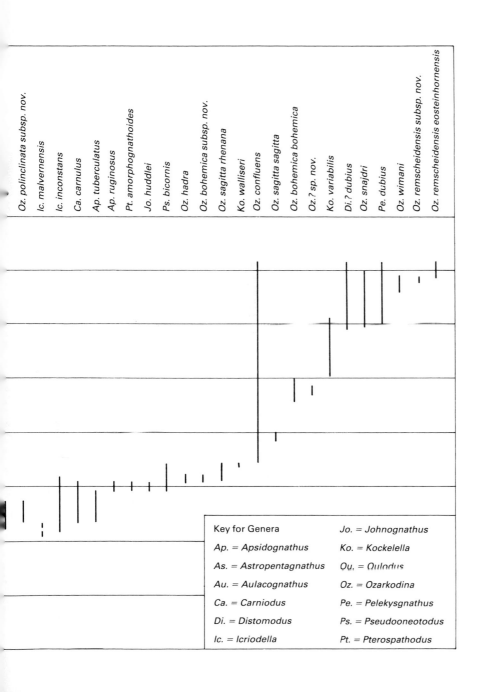

Key for Genera

Ap. = Apsidognathus
As. = Astropentagnathus
Au. = Aulacognathus
Ca. = Carniodus
Di. = Distomodus
Ic. = Icriodella

Jo. = Johnognathus
Ko. = Kockelella
Ou. = Oulodus
Oz. = Ozarkodina
Pe. = Pelekysgnathus
Ps. = Pseudooneotodus
Pt. = Pterospathodus

Table 3 – THE LOWER DEVONIAN SERIES

Chart showing the range of selected British conodont species diagnostic of the Lower Devonian Series. For comparison the ranges are given also with reference to the zones proposed by Ziegler (1971) and Klapper and Ziegler (1979).

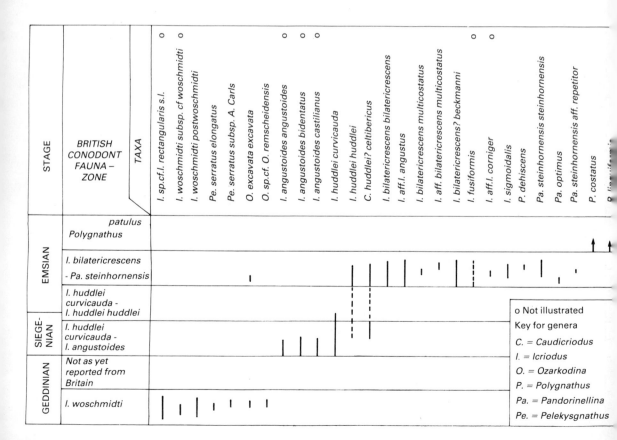

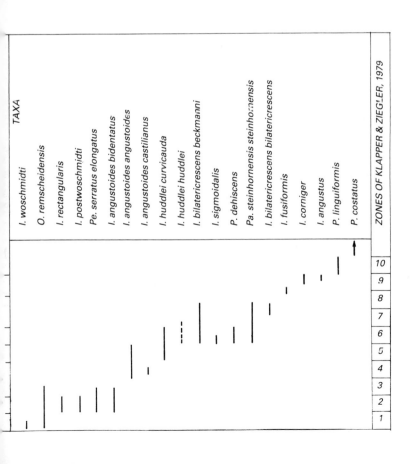

TAXA

- I. woschmidti
- O. remscheidensis
- I. rectangularis
- I. postwoschmidti
- Pe. serratus elongatus
- I. angustoides bidentatus
- I. angustoides angustoides
- I. angustoides castilianus
- I. huddlei curvicauda
- I. huddlei huddlei
- I. bilatericrescens beckmanni
- I. sigmoidalis
- P. dehiscens
- Pa. steinhornensis steinhornensis
- I. bilatericrescens bilatericrescens
- I. fusiformis
- I. corniger
- I. angustus
- P. linguiformis
- P. costatus

ZONES OF KLAPPER & ZIEGLER, 1979

| 10 | 9 | 8 | 7 | 6 | 5 | 4 | 3 | 2 | 1 |

Table 4

Table 4 — THE MIDDLE DEVONIAN SERIES

Chart showing the range of selected British conodont species diagnostic of the Middle Devonian Series.

STAGE	CONODONT ZONE	TAXA		*P. serotinus*	*P. linguiformis bultyncki*	*P. costatus patulus*	*I. retrodepressus*	*I. corniger corniger*	*P. angusticostatus*	*P. costatus partitus*	*P. costatus costatus*	*P. robusticostatus*	*P. linguiformis linguiformis*	*E. bipennatus*	*I. regularicrescens*	*O. bidentata*	*I. struvei*	*P. angustipennatus*	*T. kockelianus australis*	*P. trigonicus*	*P. pseudofoliatus*	*T. kockelianus kockelianus*	*P. eiflius*	*P. xylus ensensis*	*I. arkonensis*
				×				o	×										×						
GIVETIAN	Lowermost asymmetricus																								
	disparilis																								
	hermanni	U																							
	cristatus	L																							
	varcus	U																							
		M																							
		L																							
EIFELIAN	ensensis																								
	kockelianus																								
	australis																								
	c. costatus																								
	c. partitus																								

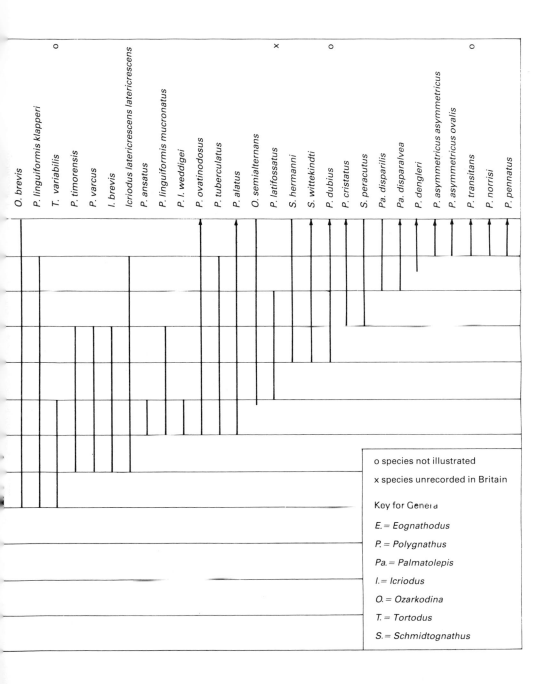

o species not illustrated

x species unrecorded in Britain

Key for Genera

E. = Eognathodus

P. = Polygnathus

Pa. = Palmatolepis

I. = Icriodus

O. = Ozarkodina

T. = Tortodus

S. = Schmidtognathus

Table 5 – THE UPPER DEVONIAN SERIES

Chart showing the range of selected British Conodont species diagnostic of the Upper Devonian Series.

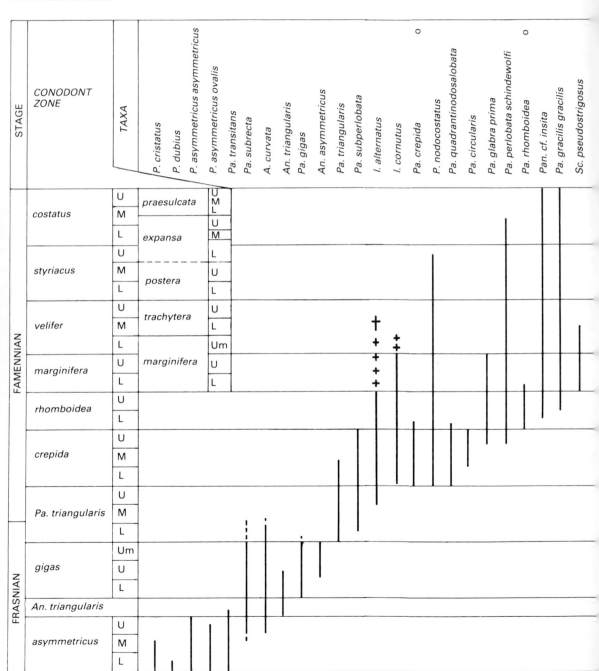

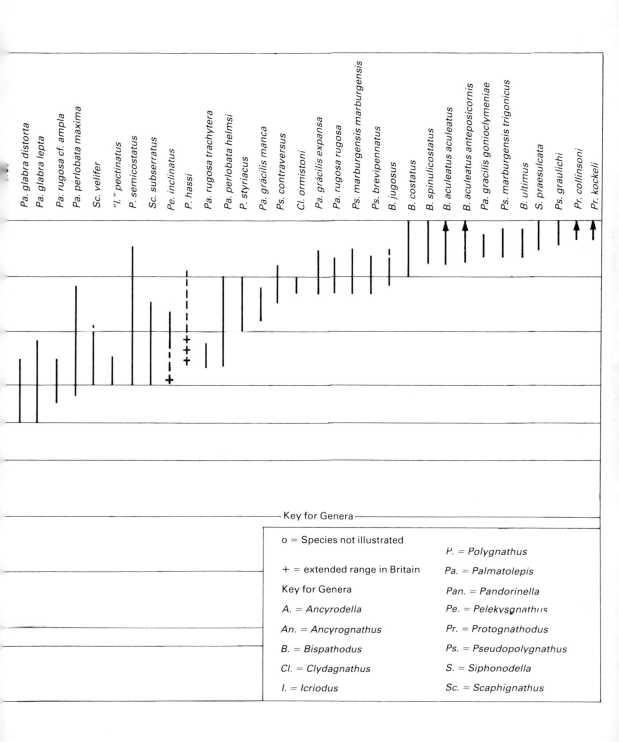

Key for Genera

o = Species not illustrated

+ = extended range in Britain

Key for Genera

A. = Ancyrodella

An. = Ancyrognathus

B. = Bispathodus

Cl. = Clydagnathus

I. = Icriodus

P. = Polygnathus

Pa. = Palmatolepis

Pan. = Pandorinella

Pe. = Pelekysgnathus

Pr. = Protognathodus

Ps. = Pseudopolygnathus

S. = Siphonodella

Sc. = Scaphignathus

248   **Table 5a**

Table 5a – THE UPPER DEVONIAN SERIES

Chart showing the range of selected British conodont species associated with the diagnostic species in the Upper Devonian Series.

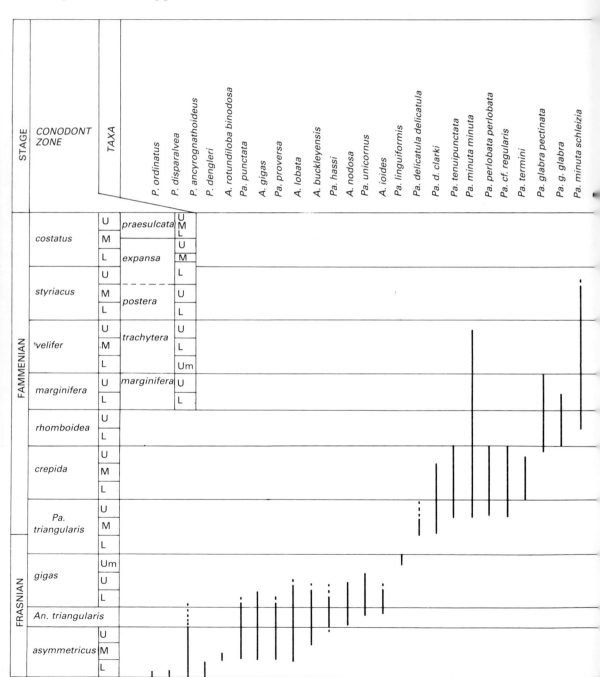

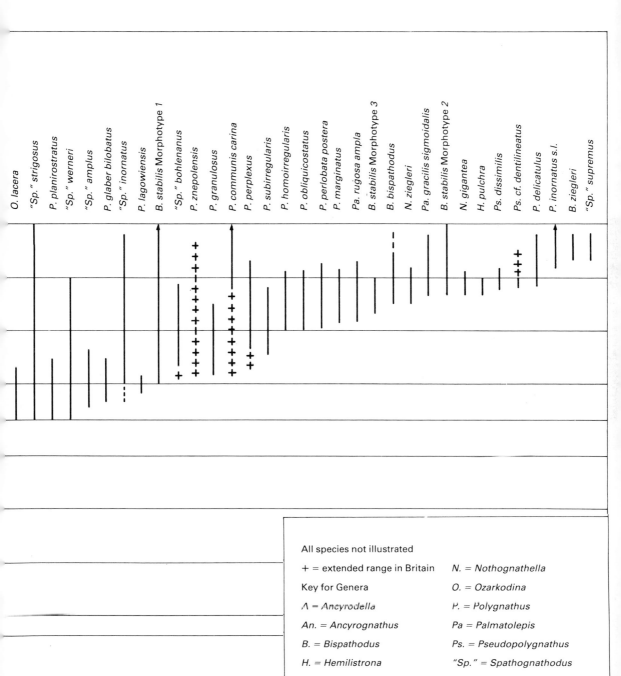

All species not illustrated

+ = extended range in Britain   N. = Nothognathella

Key for Genera   O. = Ozarkodina

A = Ancyrodella   P. = Polygnathus

An. = Ancyrognathus   Pa = Palmatolepis

B. = Bispathodus   Ps. = Pseudopolygnathus

H. = Hemilistrona   "Sp." = Spathognathodus

Table 6 – THE DINANTIAN SUBSYSTEM

Chart showing the range of selected British and Irish species diagnostic of the Dinantian Subsystem and correlation between the zonal scheme presented in this book and that of the Belgian Dinantian Subsystem.

Taxa (columns, left to right): P. spicatus, Pa. variabilis, Ps. dentilineatus, P. inornatus, B. aculeatus aculeatus, B. aculeatus plumulus, Cl. unicornis, P. communis communis, S. isosticha, E. laceratus, G. punctatus, G. delicatus, P. communis carina, G. cuneiformis, Pr. oweni, H. ? cf. cristulus, D. hassi, B. spinulicostatus, Ps. multistriatus, Ps. pinnatus, M. groessensi, Ps. minutus, P. mehli latus, Eo. bultyncki, P. mehli mehli, D. bouckaerti, "A." petilus, "A." scalenus

IN BELGIUM			SHELF MARGIN AND BASIN FACIES
SERIES	STAGE		BELGIAN CONODONT ZONES USEFUL IN SOUTH-WEST ENGLAND AND SOUTH-WEST IRELAND
VISEAN	WARNANTIAN	beckmanni	G. bilineatus
	LIVIAN		Informal unit with Taphrognathus
	MOLINA CEAN		L. commutata
			G. homopunctatus
TOURNAISIAN	IVORIAN	anchoralis	S. anchoralis- P. bischoffi
			E. burlingtonensis
			Do. latus
		carina	D. bouckaerti
			Eo. bultyncki
			E. cf. bultyncki
			D. hassi
	HASTARIAN		Siphonodella

Key for Genera

"A." = Apatognathus	H. = Hindeodus?
B. = Bispathodus	Hi. = Hindeodella
C. = Cavusgnathus	L. = Lochriea
Cl. = Clydagnathus	M. = Mestognathus
Clo. = Cloghergnathus	N. = Neoprioniodus
D. = Dollymae	P. = Polygnathus
Do. = Doliognathus	Pa. = Patrognathus
E. = Elictognathus	Pr. = Prioniodina
Eo. = Eotaphrus	Ps. = Pseudopolygnathus
Em. = Embsaygnathus	Si. = Siphonodella
G. = Gnathodus	T. = Taphrognathus

Table 7 – THE SILESIAN SUBSYSTEM Chart showing the range of selected British and Iri

SERIES	STAGES	CONODONT ZONES AND SUBZONES		TAXA	C. regularis	G. symmutatus	G. girtyi collinsoni	G. girtyi rhodesi	G. homopunctatus	K. macrodentatus	M. bipluti	G. girtyi intermedius
WEST-PHALIAN	LOWER WESTPHALIAN A	Id. sulcatus parva										
NAMURIAN	YEADONIAN G₁	Id. sinuatus — I. primulus										
NAMURIAN	MARSDENIAN R₂											
NAMURIAN	KINDERSCOUTIAN R₁	Id. corrugatus — Id. sulcatus										
NAMURIAN	ALPORTIAN H₂	D. noduliferus										
NAMURIAN	CHOKIERIAN H₁											
NAMURIAN	ARNSBERGIAN E₂	G. bilineatus bollandensis	upper / lower									‖
NAMURIAN	PENDLEIAN E₁	Kladognathus — G. girtyi simplex									‖	‖
VISÉAN	BRIGANTIAN (upper)	G. girtyi collinsoni			‖	‖	‖	‖	‖	‖	‖	‖

...nodont species diagnostic of the Silesian Subsystem.

G. bilineatus bilineatus
L. commutata
P. nodosus
L. mononodosa
G. girtyi soniae
G. girtyi simplex
G. bilineatus bollandensis
R. minutus
A. gigantus
D. noduliferus inaequalis
N. bassleri
D. lateralis
D. noduliferus noduliferus
Neognathodus sp
Id. sinuatus
Id. corrugatus
Id. macer
Id. sulcatus
I. primulus
Id. attenuatus
I. delicatus s.l.
S. nodosus
Id. sulcatus parva

Key for Genera	
A. = Adetognathus	K. = Kladognathus
C. = Cavusgnathus	L. = Lochreia
D. = Declinognathus	M. = Mestognathus
G. = Gnathodus	N. = Noognathodus
I. = Idiognathodus	P. = Paragnathodus
Id. = Idiognathoides	R. = Rhachistognathus
	S. = Streptognathus

Taxonomic Index

General Index